THE KING'S GAME

GAME OF GODS

BOOK ONE

NICOLE SANCHEZ

First paperback edition October 2022

Edited by Tashya Wilson

Proofread by Amanda Iles

Cover Art by Karen Dimmick / ArcaneCovers.com

Header and Page Break art by Leigh Cover Designs

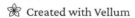 Created with Vellum

For my husband, Mike, the king of my heart. Thank you for taking a chance on me.

AUTHOR'S NOTE

As an author, I want all my readers to feel safe when reading my books. Some elements of this story may be upsetting to some readers. If you're not interested in learning more, please feel free to turn the page. If you have concerns, please see the list below:

Murder
Implication of rape
Manipulation
Death

I

The sorority road trip from hell has just begun, and I am stuck on this adventure. Beside me, my best friend, Catalina Mason, is slouched low with her knees pressed against the graffitied green leather of the seat in front of us. She's been fast asleep since we embarked on this journey a few hours ago, leaving me trapped against the window, watching the sky slowly grow more vibrant.

I know that today will be a good day, even a great one, if I just open myself up to the possibility. With our senior year of college on the horizon, there is so much more I want to do. I haven't told Cat yet, but I'm considering rushing her sorority, Epsilon Lambda Delta, in the fall. I already spend so much time with them, I might as well make it official, even if the idea of being judged by the sisters is what caused me to pull out of the rush process when Cat first went out for it.

Right now, though, I'm tired and cranky, and I think that Zara Rizvi is intentionally digging her knees into my back. I'll give her the benefit of the doubt this time—buses like the one we're on are meant for short trips, like bringing kids to school, not long-haul road trips with twenty women riding for hours to watch their school compete in a beach volleyball tournament. A few of the girls on this trip, like Tiffany Adames and Becca Marsh, have boyfriends on the team, but most of us are just along for the ride.

My eyes slide shut, and I try to return to my happy place. I'm in a blank space that I'm filling with flowers, creating pathways with different trees and plants. Mentally, I'm lounging under a magnolia tree in full bloom, with petals falling on me as I try to sleep. Only, my adoptive mother's text from last night is blaring in my mind: *What are you doing for an internship this summer?*

The peace I've found shatters with that thought, and I open my phone to look at her text. The same one I ignored even though it came with a photo of my ginger cat, Waffles. I plan to explain my delayed response with the excuse that I went to bed early for this trip instead of the truth—Cat and I were at a frat party doing body shots off each other in the hopes that Tommy Baker might realize what a catch Cat is and ask her to their formal.

The text is just one of a long thread reminding me that I'm a disappointment to my adoptive parents. Not that they would ever say it straight out. They love me, I know they do. Thanks to my psych class, I understand that I'm the one keeping them at arm's length. But getting rid of the qualifier *adoptive* would make me feel like I'm erasing my birth parents, even though I never knew them. It's easier to keep pushing my adoptive parents away, the way I have since I was fifteen. Going home with Cat for holidays means that I can stop disappointing the only parents I've known. It's unfair, but maybe after more extensive therapy, I'll be able to quit being so stubborn and say *I'm sorry* and *thank you.*

"You think *so loud,* Daphne," Cat murmurs. She lifts her head and glares at me, then gingerly sits up straight and stretches out her back, rubbing at what I have to assume is a kink in her neck from the way she was sleeping.

"I do not."

"Every night, I hear you thinking about internships and classes. I think your brain is actually a hamster on a wheel running all night long." Her blue eyes find mine. "What's got you going this morning?"

"The text," I confess, shaking my phone at her.

"The internship text?"

"The same."

Cat sighs and twists to face me before pulling her blonde hair from its ponytail and yanking it up into a bun.

"Where does Phil want you to intern?"

It always makes me giggle when Catalina calls my parents by their first names like they're old college friends.

"He's offered to have me join him at his congressional office in DC, but I think he only offered because he knows you're going to be there."

"Daphne Marie Hale, then just say yes. What does Melinda have to say?"

"She wants me to stay home. I think she's starting to stress about what I'm going to do after graduation."

"She's your mom, of course she is. Doesn't her law firm let her work from the East Coast anyway? Just take the summer—you can laze around Congressman Hale's office, and then you and I can party and see what DC has to offer by way of the male specimen."

I sigh and throw myself back in my seat, forgetting about Zara's knees until they dig into my back and she grumbles something behind me.

"It just doesn't feel *right*. Like...I feel like I'm waiting for some sort of sign to point me toward the thing I'm meant to do to become the person I'm meant to be."

Cat grabs my face so I'm looking her dead in the eye. "You're looking for the type of career that's a calling. Anna had that moment when she was lifeguarding and saved a kid from drowning. Bam, she knew she wanted to be a doctor. I know I'm destined to be president of this country. I know the real world is big and scary, but sometimes you just have to take a leap of faith."

I snort. "Me? Leap of faith?"

"You, leap of faith. Let's come up with some sort of a plan. Maybe the universe will send you a sign during this trip. Maybe you'll have your moment this weekend."

This idea of a divine sign is appealing, but what it comes down to is I have to pick something and go with it. With a major in English, I can pivot so many places, but maybe I'll get a master's just to buy myself some time. My parents want me to be more ambitious, try for law school or something equally high stress, but it's not what I want.

I open my mouth to say as much, but my response is cut off by a loud *pop*. My brain grasps to identify the sound, but I can't hold on to a single thought. Burnt rubber permeates the air, and I don't think I'll ever get the smell out of my nose. All around me, screams drown out the grinding of the flat tire on the asphalt.

The bus veers sideways, fishtailing into the oncoming lane of traffic. I find myself sending up a prayer to any god that will listen to help the driver get through this. Through the screaming, I hear the driver call out for us to remain calm, but his voice is shaking and doesn't inspire confidence. Lights from an oncoming car blaze on the palisade beside me, and the bus weaves onto the shoulder. I'm thankful I'm not on the side with a view of the ocean, because as it is, I'm imagining the worst—which is us plunging to our death.

Cat is thrown onto the floor. Gasping, I reach out to her, wanting to keep her close to me, wanting to keep her out of danger, as bags spill over us. With muscles straining, she holds tight to the legs of the seats as she fights to get back up beside me.

The bus rides the guardrail, pushing the limits of its strength before the driver is able to jerk it back. The screech of metal on metal reverberates through my bones and sets my teeth on edge. The swerve is too forceful, and my head smashes against the glass. I see stars, and then pain lances through my temple. Around me, the other women are being tossed around like dolls.

Their cries are drowned out by the horns of passing cars, as if we aren't already doing what we can to correct course. I reach out to try to grab Cat and pull her back into the seat, but instead, I miss and grab a bag. The window I just hit shatters as the bus grinds against the palisade. A dangerous rain of glass confetti is now added to the mix of bags. One of the girls in front of me starts praying.

We're still in the wrong lane as the bus tries to move away from the face of the cliffs. Through the windshield, I catch a glimpse of another car headed for us dead on. My heart slams in my chest. The bus driver jerks the wheel again so we're in the correct lane of traffic, but it's too fast and we continue sideways. A *crunch* sounds as the bus collides with the guardrail. The screaming begins anew. I'm thrown out of my seat onto the floor, landing on top of Cat...and then we're in freefall.

The moment freezes. The fear in her blue eyes mirrors my own. Around me, shards of glass float in the air like out-of-place snowflakes. Abigail, a quiet girl who was in my Government 101 class freshman year, has lipstick smeared across her face. A girl who was sitting in the back whose name I can't recall is staring ahead, her eyes vacant, her neck at an odd angle. Her golden hair is loose, creating a halo around her face.

They say in moments like this, your life flashes before your eyes, but what I see is something different. I see the sun rising and setting, waves crashing on a beach. My heart is full of what I was missing.

I hear the screams around me. I feel weightless. I feel a calling to come home.

2

I'm lying on my stomach, resting on my elbows as I devour the book in my hands. I gently gnaw on my lower lip as the narrator describes in vivid detail what her lover is doing as he goes down on her. I'm so engrossed in my book that I barely hear the bedroom door open. Desire burns through me as I shift my hips, eager for some sort of friction. I'm not at all surprised when someone climbs onto the bed and straddles me.

"Get off!" I object, not looking away from my book. Strong hands start to rub at a knot that's formed in my shoulder from how I'm positioned. I close my eyes, nearly melting into the touch.

"I would much rather get you off." His breath on my neck sends a thrill up my spine, and I fight the temptation to roll over. Even whispering, his voice is deep, with an English accent and so familiar. If the massage I'm getting wasn't already enough to get me hot, his accent certainly would be. I let my head drop down onto my book, giving this mystery man better access to my back.

"Later! I was just getting to the good part!" I say, my voice muffled by the pages. It's a half-hearted objection, and I groan as he works the knot. I slide in my bookmark and set the book aside. "Princess Lorelei is

6

having the best orgasm of her life as the scoundrel Captain Giancarlo goes down on her while Prince Demetrious is stuck in a privy council meeting. They could get caught at any moment," I explain, as the hands work farther down my spine.

"Are they in the same meeting? Because you're giving me ideas for the next time we have to meet with the Council."

"You rake, they are not in the same meeting—obviously Giancarlo is doing this in her bedchamber so he can better protect her from any outside threat, but really the threat is inside the house, because she might be pregnant with the captain's baby and her husband has no idea."

The man lets out a deep, full laugh. He brushes my hair aside and presses a gentle kiss to my neck. I inhale deeply and smell vanilla, cinnamon, and sandalwood. A warm feeling infuses my whole body.

"Shall I distract you with the real thing?" he asks, grinding his hips against my back. I feel him harden through my silk nightgown. I bite my lip, excited at the prospect, and start to roll over. Just as I'm about to see his face—

"OH GOD, THAT WAS TERRIFYING."

I'm startled awake by Cat gripping my arm. The dream is already fading as I try to remember what was going on.

"Are you okay? You're bleeding!" she exclaims as I turn to look at her.

The horror on her face makes me wonder how bad it looks. Her already pale skin seems bloodless. I try to remember my last thought, and the chaos of the bus swerving over the highway assaults me. I look around, confused. At first, I wonder if the bus losing control was just a bad dream, but everyone is injured and in varying stages of distress. We're still on board, but everything around me feels off. It looks as if the world has been painted over with a watercolor blue.

Cat reaches out and touches my forehead, and I hiss, wincing away from her. She glances around and starts pawing through the jumble of bags.

I consider that I might have a concussion, and maybe that's why everything looks off. A head injury is the most reasonable explanation for the strange color wash. Catalina's blue eyes are full of concern as she grabs my chin and gets me to look at her. My vision is still blurry as I try to get an understanding of my environment.

"What the hell happened?" I ask, reaching up to touch my own face gingerly. My brow feels swollen and bruised. My fingers come away red, coated in my blood. I rub the thick liquid between my forefinger and thumb, surprised by how it feels on my skin. I remember hitting my head, but I thought it was more of a glance off the window, not enough to draw blood. I consider that I might have short-term memory loss in addition to a concussion. I'm too squeamish to be pre-med, but I watch enough medical dramas to know just enough to be dangerous.

My thoughts start to order themselves, various realizations hitting me as I come to my senses and my vision clears. I realize that we aren't moving, and I look out the window. The bus is stopped at an overlook.

Cat seems to sense my confusion, and she fills in the blanks. "We had a blowout. Thankfully the driver was able to pull over. Some girls are cut pretty bad, but for the most part, we're all lucky to be alive."

I nod, but this doesn't match what I remember.

The hazy memory of falling must have been me falling off the seat.

"GIRLS!" the bus driver shouts, getting our attention. "Is everyone all right?" he asks, visibly shaken. His kind eyes are full of concern, and he seems to have aged ten years. I am so thankful that my memory of the accident isn't real. He glances around, and

I follow his gaze and see for myself that we're all pretty shaken but otherwise okay. When I lock gazes with a pretty blonde, I see a flash of vacant eyes and her head at an awkward angle. I blink, and she's moved her attention elsewhere. I remember that her name is Madison.

The driver removes his baseball cap and runs a hand over his balding head, then makes his way down the steps and exits the bus.

Out the window over Catalina's shoulder, I see a sleek black car idling. A tall pale-skinned figure, who I assume is the car's owner, is talking with the bus driver. The person places a hand on his arm, and his entire body seems to relax.

The driver quickly returns to the bus with a serene smile on his face as if we weren't all *just* facing certain death. "You ladies are in luck. This bystander saw the whole thing. They're going to let me use their phone to call dispatch since I can't get a signal." He hurries back off, likely to make that very call. The person with the phone walks onto the bus with an air of authority about them, and I hope that they're going to help us get going again. Even dazed, I manage to pick up that the bus driver referred to them as "they." I shiver, chilled to the bone, and rub my arms, but no one else seems cold. I wonder if I'm going into shock.

"Is everyone all right? I saw what happened and wanted to make sure you were all okay." They echo the driver's concern. Their dark brown eyes are scanning everyone as each girl confirms that she's okay. I appreciate their concern, but if the damage is as minor as Cat said, I wonder why they're so worried. The accident must have looked worse from the vantage of a smaller car. They're wearing a long sleeve floor-length dark dress with an equally long vest over it. It's out of style and seems heavy for the seasonable warmth, but I would kill to have something with sleeves right now. Their long brown hair, hanging in a braid down their back, has threads of silver-grey running through it. "You ladies sit tight

—your driver is making a call to his dispatcher. It looks like it's just a flat tire." They sound like an OnStar agent.

Their dark eyes linger on me for a moment before they climb off the bus.

"Does anyone have cell service?" one of the girls from the front of the bus calls out. It takes my brain a sluggish minute to recognize Tiffany; her black braids, once contained, are loose as her wild eyes scan her phone, lifting it up to the ceiling in the universal move to look for a signal. Everyone takes out their phones to check, but the disappointed murmurs give it away. I see my phone on the bus floor and pick it up. Immediately, I know that it's useless. At some point in the chaos, it got smashed, and the screen will no longer light up. Annoyance surges through me, because now I'll have to explain to my parents that I broke my phone in a near accident and that's why I haven't responded. When we get to San Diego, the beach will need to wait so I can get a new phone, even if it's temporary.

I turn to Cat and check her over. There's a tear in her jacket, but she seems otherwise fine. She's holding her similarly damaged phone in her hand while the other rubs her elbow.

"Are you okay?" I ask, putting a hand on her arm. Her hands are shaking, and her usual cool demeanor is shattered.

"You know me! I'm just a little shaken-not-stirred right now. Besides..." Her voice is frantic and high, so out of character. Cat turns her focus to me, getting a better look at my temple. "You're the one with a gushing head wound." She seems glad to have something specific to worry about. My injury helps her come to her senses. She resumes shuffling through bags and pulls out her purse, then digs through it. Always prepared, she rescues a crumpled packet of tissues before leaning forward and gently pressing a few to where I'm bleeding.

"It's hardly gushing," I say, taking over holding the tissue. But when I pull it back to look at it, the red-soaked fabric tells a different story. I shrug off my worry. "Head wounds are notorious for bleeding, and these are cheap tissues. Besides, I'm just cold." I don't mention that it's hard to open my left eye—she can probably see that from looking at me.

"Where did you learn that? *Grey's Anatomy*? You're probably going into shock. We all are." She looks around for something else to staunch the bleeding.

I fold the tissues together and press the clean side to my head harder than before. I can believe that I'm going into shock—my abs are starting to ache from how tense I'm holding my body. I make a conscious effort to relax, but the tension rachets right back up as a chill rattles me.

"Where did *you* learn that? *Grey's Anatomy*?" I parrot at her.

The bus driver comes back, interrupting my train of thought. "Girls. The bad news is we have a flat and I have no way to put a donut on it. I'm also not having a lot of luck reaching dispatch about getting you ladies a new bus." He takes off his hat and rubs his head again. "Good news is, that bystander said their boss lives just off the next exit and has offered to host you guys while I use their landline to call for help. Much as I hate driving on a flat, I don't see much of a choice. Too dangerous to leave you ladies waiting on the side of the road for who knows how long. I'm sorry, I know you girls had plans for the beach today, but maybe he has a beach you can visit while we wait."

He sits and starts the bus, leaving us to contemplate going to this strange place. Around me, conversations start, with questions and speculation about where we're headed. A few of the girls make inhuman noises, startled by the noise as the flat tire grinds against the pavement.

The sound makes my hackles rise. I need to get off this bus.

We travel for another few minutes, but it feels like an eternity. At last, we take an exit, and I focus on the road, leaning my forehead against my window. I half expect there to be no glass, but of course, there is. I must have hit my head harder than I thought.

Along the road are thick, tall hedges blocking any view but the one ahead, until they finally give way to palm trees. It's a seemingly endless private road that twists and turns, leading us closer and closer to the coast until we pull up in a half-circle driveway before a grand house. The entire bus falls silent. I pull on my sweatshirt but still fail to find the warmth I'm looking for.

The concerned bystander gets back on the bus.

"As I'm sure Kenny—" they pat the bus driver's shoulder "—explained to you, my boss lives here. He was gracious enough to offer you a space to relax while you wait. Please gather your belongings and exit the bus. We'll make sure that any medical needs are tended to." For a moment, no one moves.

Before they can walk away, Tiffany shoots out of her seat. "Can I call my boyfriend from inside? I need to let him know we're going to be late."

They pause before turning to look at Tiffany. With a sad smile and a nod, they walk off the bus.

"So, was that a yes?" Tiffany asks, looking around as if any of us can answer. She gathers her things and is the first to get off. Slowly we all move, each of us with a bruise of some sort from today, be it physical or emotional. I'm the last of twenty to get off, and before doing so, I give the inside of the bus another glance. As I look around, I get a flash of all the seats ripped up and water-damaged. I suck in a pained breath, but then I blink, and the vision is gone.

I hoped that by stepping into the California sun, I would feel warmer, but instead I feel colder, as if I've walked into Alaska instead. We all line up outside the bus, and I notice that Kenny is no longer with us. The outside of the bus has no evidence of the trauma that we each bear on our skin. Echoes of metal on metal have me searching the sides for some proof of that noise—a scratch, a dent—but I can't find it. Before I think better of it, I reach out and touch the bus to confirm, but my hand only comes away dirty.

I look at the mystery person. "Where's the driver?" I ask before they can say anything. Their eyes flash to me, and they plaster on a serene but fake-looking smile.

I trust them a little less.

"He's inside using the house phone to call for a replacement bus. If you would all follow me, please." They turn and walk toward the house, and it's only then that I take in the opulence before me.

The house looks more like a castle than a home. I half expect to cross a drawbridge to get to the front door, which has a giant entryway covered in windows and ornate wrought iron that twists and turns. My gaze catches on the subtle pattern of flowers in the iron, something easily missed, but everywhere I look, I see them entwined with an image of the sun.

The front door opens before our guide gets there, as if it has a motion sensor, and we all trickle in. I feel like the number one rule of childhood—stranger danger—has been quickly forgotten in favor of this kindness we are being shown. Even if the danger isn't overt, there's always an element of give and take. This is an awful lot of give; I wonder what the cost will be.

As I gaze around, I wonder just how much land this estate covers. Branching out on either side of the house are impressively tall hedges, the kind used to block the view of celebrity homes, only we're already at the end of a long private driveway, so I wonder what they hide.

My flip-flops slap against the floor, which looks like marble. I hear one of the girls whisper that the boss must be a billionaire, because not only is the house grand, but the pillars inside almost look like gold. There is rampant speculation about who the owner of the home might be.

Three dogs—pit bulls—come running over and sniff around us, nails tapping against the floor. I've always been a cat person, but I want to cuddle these three to my chest. The urge to sneak them bacon or some other treat is overwhelming, but then again, what puppy doesn't deserve a treat?

Many of the girls who were shaken earlier seem relaxed and worry-free as the dogs circle. Even Marta, who I know is afraid of dogs, doesn't step away. Instead, she reaches down to pet them, flipping her long red curls to one side. The movement exposes a nasty cut on her cheek from the accident, if the dried blood is any indicator.

The grey dog comes over to me, and I hold my hand out so it can better sniff, which earns me a lick. I smile, holding on to this normal moment, because this day has been anything but.

"He likes you," a posh voice says, and we all glance up. There is something strange about the voice, something familiar, and my brain tries to rationalize it—he must do voice work for commercials or something. The tone is smooth and comforting in a way I never expected a voice to be. I want to wrap myself in it and have him read me the dictionary just so I can hear it.

Out of the shadows steps a tall tan-skinned man with a slender frame. He's easily six feet tall, if not more, and I see hints that he's muscular under his three-piece suit. I drink in the sight of him, from his black leather wing-tipped shoes, up the narrow slant of his hips, to the solid set of his shoulders. His presence is like a magnet, drawing me to him, and I want to step into his orbit and feel the strength of the pull. He has a young, narrow face with prominent cheekbones and a faint layer of scruff on his strong jaw. His gaze remains stuck on me, unmoving, as he slides his hands into his pockets, almost like he's trying to stop himself from reaching out.

If I had to guess his age, I would have said late twenties, or maybe early thirties at a stretch, but when I meet his electric blue eyes, they seem sad and older than his years. There is a certain weariness to his face. I want to reach out and smooth the wrinkle between his eyes, and light a lavender candle to soothe him. Something in my soul tells me he would like that scent.

His eyes catch mine and linger, and my heart stumbles over itself. I think for a moment that I hear ballroom music, but it's faint, and I assume I'm hearing things. The sadness in his eyes seems to lessen as he studies me closely. His lips twist into a small, closed-mouth smile meant only for me, before he turns his attention to everyone else.

"Welcome ladies," he says, and I startle, trying again to place his voice. Maybe it's one of those medical infomercials? "I heard of your misfortunes this morning. My assistant, Sybil, was behind you in their car and saw the whole thing. Please, come in and make yourselves at home." He gestures toward the large room before us. It's wide open and would be better suited as a ballroom than a living room. On closer inspection, I think it might be just that, dressed up with couches against the walls and the large bay windows. Outside the back wall of windows, I can see an infinity pool, water glistening in the morning sun, and beyond that, the beach. This man must be filthy rich. I study the large marble fireplace, and my gaze follows the stunning architecture up to the ceiling, where three large, ornate chandeliers hang. In the corner is a black grand piano, because, of course. Lifestyles of the rich and famous are exactly like I imagined.

"Can I please use your phone to call my boyfriend?" Tiffany asks. She steps toward him, her long legs nearly clearing the distance between them in one step, her hands clasped together to plead. The gorgeous stranger gives her a dazzling smile that doesn't meet his clear blue eyes.

"Of course. Your driver is currently using it, but once he's done, you're welcome to it. Shall I have some snacks brought out to you?" When no one moves, he walks into the living room, as if we all need to be led.

"Can we get some, like, band-aids and ice?" Cat asks. "My friend's eye is swelling shut, and I want to get it cleaned up." I take her hand gratefully and give it a little squeeze.

"Of course." He sounds almost frustrated as he looks at me and then the cut on my eye before surveying the sorry state of us all. He turns to his assistant, who I now know is named Sybil, and murmurs something in their ear. I feel his gaze on me again as he gives them instructions, and it makes me want to stand up a little straighter and fix my hair. The thought is ridiculous, given what we've just been through.

"Please excuse me. I'll get you all some medical supplies and food," they say reassuringly, and with what looks like a quick bow, slip away. The man smiles at us again, and I see almost everyone smile back. Cat and I sink onto the nearest couch. Although we've been sitting all morning, I feel exhausted. The effort of remaining upright is taking everything out of me.

"Thank you," I call to the man, wondering if he's not telling us his name because he's too famous or rich to want us to know who he is. His blue eyes meet mine again, even as a chorus of thank you's follow mine. I rub my arms, unable to shake the chill I've had since waking up on the bus.

He smiles at me, and this time it reaches his eyes. "Ladies, my name is Essos. Please let me know if you need anything at all. My staff is available to you. Once we have news about your replacement bus, we'll let you know." With that, he turns and leaves down the same hallway from which he came, his footsteps not making a sound.

Sybil returns with a first aid kit and a trio of people dressed in what I assume are staff uniforms who start attending to the more serious cuts. Cat tries to wave them over to me, but I push her arm down.

"I'm really okay; let them take care of the others first. I think I heard someone say Ginny's arm was dislocated." I glance around for the tall captain of the basketball team. She's across the room, curled up in a chair and cradling her arm.

Cat ignores me and sets off in the direction of the medical supplies.

Around me, I hear snippets of conversations about who Essos might be. His posh accent acts as fodder, and I hear a number of ideas thrown around, some of the most popular being that he's a tech mogul, a finance wiz, an A-list director, or British aristocracy. Almost everyone's focus has drifted from getting on the road as soon as possible to trying to figure out Essos's identity. Even the girls who have boyfriends on the volleyball team no longer seem worried about getting back on the road. Only Tiffany is resolutely looking around the room for someone to bring her to the phone. Beside her, Zara is trying to scroll through her phone, and I'm jealous that she still has access to it. Both Zara and Tiffany seem to have escaped the accident with nary a scratch. Zara's shiny black hair doesn't even look frizzy; meanwhile, I feel like I've been dropped down a garbage chute.

The group settles in as more people filter into the room with food and drinks. The surprises never stop, including the number of people tending to us. Although, given the size of the estate, it makes sense that the house has such a large staff.

Cat returns with some wipes and gauze, along with an ice pack. She winces while balancing a second tray of food for the two of us. I let her fuss over me and clean the cut, wincing when the antiseptic touches the open wound.

"Quit being a baby. It's actually not as bad as I thought, but I still want it looked at." When she tries to put the ice pack on my head, I push her hand away. Cat glares at me. "Quit being a martyr."

"I'm really okay," I hedge.

"Daphne, please, you need to bring the swelling down." I take the ice pack from Cat's hand and place it on the tray.

"I'm cold enough already—I don't want to make my head cold too."

The pit bulls continue to sniff around the girls. The three dogs look well loved and tended to, each one proving that pit bulls have a needlessly bad reputation. The black one circles Sybil as they move from girl to girl to apply dressings. They start with a girl named Anna, who has a long but not deep cut on her forearm.

The white pit bull has jumped onto a couch, trying to sneak snacks, and the grey one keeps licking hands and bare legs. They get underfoot and sniff everyone's bags, perhaps for any additional snacks they might have. Eventually, they scamper off in the direction their master went.

Cat's frown deepens, but before she can say anything, the dogs rush into the room again, alerting us to Essos's return. Cat takes advantage of my distraction and places the ice pack on my cut, worsening the chill I feel that no one else seems bothered by. Cat is fortunate enough to not have any cuts, only bruises, so I let her fuss over me.

"I've heard from the driver that the bus company estimates it will be about 6 hours before the replacement bus is available, and then it will need to make its way here. So rather than lose a beautiful day like this, why don't you ladies enjoy the pool and beach? Sybil can show you each to a restroom or guest room so you can change, if you would like." I frown and wonder why the driver didn't tell us this himself. Then again, I wouldn't blame the man if he needed some time away from the group to have a stiff drink. I look back out the large windows and take in the sight of the pool and the beach again.

Essos smiles at us all, and I shiver and rub my arms, smiling back. Maybe lounging in the sun will help my chill. Essos catches sight of my attempt to warm myself, and a small frown appears on his face. With his hands at his side, he rolls one wrist, and I feel warmth spread from my insides out to my fingers, the way liquor warms a body. I relax as the warmth trickles out to my limbs. For a moment, my brain tries to make a connection between Essos's movement and my sudden comfort, but there is no way. Still, I catch the slight easing of tension around his eyes as my body loosens. He must just be very invested in his guests' comfort. That's the only reasonable explanation.

Though I assume Essos must have something more important to do, he takes the time to talk with some of the girls and ask after their welfare. He never comes to me and Cat, but I feel him watching me.

Sybil comes to me next, and Cat gives up her seat so that Sybil can get a better look at my face. Since Cat already cleaned the wound, Sybil focuses on dressing it. My eye feels puffy, and I wish I had gotten a look at it to see just how bad it is. Sybil dabs at my skin, cleaning off the blood around it.

"This isn't too bad. Just a little swollen," Sybil says as they place a fresh ice pack in my hand and press it against the swelling. I figure the ice must be working, because I can open my eye a little wider now, so I hold it in place. My insides are still warm, and I barely notice the cold anymore.

I glance around the room. "Is everyone else all right?" I ask as Sybil gathers the soiled wipes into a little garbage bag.

Sybil's dark eyes study me closely. "Yes. Minor bumps and bruises, a few cuts, a sore neck. You ladies were lucky. It could have been a lot worse." Their words ring hollow to me for some reason, and in the back of my mind, I can hear the screech of metal being torn apart as it grinds against rock. I shake my head to clear the noise.

The group seems to come to the consensus that, while this was not our intended pit stop of San Luis Obispo, a beach is a beach, and we shouldn't lose the whole day—not that we have any choice in the matter without the bus. Cat, who was on edge before, seems more relaxed after spending an hour here. I'm less worried about getting on the road, or even where the bus driver is. Still, the driver's absence is nagging at me. Perhaps Essos has a study he's resting in.

"You're a good friend," Sybil says as they rise, bringing me back to the moment. Gingerly, Sybil takes Cat's hand and wraps it tight with an ace bandage before placing a fresh ice pack over it. Then they continue their rounds with the remaining girls.

By the time I decide to ask after the driver, Essos is walking away with Sybil. Having seen the hallway they turned down, I follow them, catching their whispers as I slip in behind them. The grey dog who is with them swings his head toward me but doesn't alert them to my presence.

"Tonight, over dinner, we can tell them. I want them to enjoy today. Their existence here seems to be soothing their frayed nerves, but I can hardly imagine they will be pleased once they find out. Their whole world is different now." Essos sounds matter-of-fact. The words are turning over in my head, and I wonder what they could mean.

"And that one girl? She keeps asking to call her boyfriend."

Essos sighs deeply at the mention of Tiffany, who has asked every single person for a phone so she can call Steve. Although, she does seem less worried about it the longer that we're here.

The more I think about it, the less concerned everyone seems. Conversations about getting back on the bus to get to Santa Monica have stopped and instead the focus is on how gorgeous the house is and where Essos's money might have come from. Everyone's posture is relaxed, and the emotional stress from the near-accident has melted away. It's as if we didn't almost crash— as if this was our intended destination all along.

"Send it to voicemail. In the meantime, please keep them all entertained as best you can. The longer we can go without questions, or anyone trying to use their phone, the better." He seems to have a lightbulb moment. "Actually, I take it back—I'll allow it to seem like their Wi-Fi is on. That should satisfy their need to 'gram' everything—just ensure that any outgoing calls go to voicemail."

I'm holding my breath, desperate not to alert them to my presence, but I'm sure they can hear my heart thrumming in my chest. Keep us entertained? So far, they haven't done anything to make me think that their motives are different than what they say, but this conversation makes me wonder if things aren't as they appear.

Slowly, I release my breath. I've been listening to too many true crime podcasts with Cat. As soon as we get home, those are coming off our queue, because they have me looking at everyone and everything with skepticism and concern.

I exhale and unclench my hands, which had formed into fists. I need someone rational to talk this out with, and while it might be her idea to watch all the murder shows, Cat has a level head on her shoulders.

"Yes, my lord." Sybil bows, and Essos waves a hand dismissively before striding down the hall into the darkness.

3

I hurry back to the group, the words I just heard replaying in my head. My heart slams wildly in my chest at the risk of getting caught, even as I flee. Regardless of how I try to rationalize the conversation, it was weird, and I have no idea what to make of it.

Cat is now sitting with Tiffany and Zara on a couch in the grand room. Most of the girls are all clustered with their usual subset of friends. A few stand around chatting, while others admire the grandiose room and decorations. The sisters of Epsilon Lambda Delta are all calm as they mingle and take selfies, and I wonder if it was all in my head—the conversation, the severity of the accident, my worries.

A phantom pressure grips my chest, and it's like I'm drowning. Could I be having a panic attack?

No. I'm overreacting to some nonsense and the scare of an almost crash. Talking to Cat will bring me back to earth. She's talked me down before, when I've been preparing for a big test and freaking out. This is just like that.

"I just think it's so nice of him to give us the run of his

mansion," Zara says, digging through her bag and pulling out her lip gloss. Her long, dark, wavy hair hangs loose over her shoulder. Zara has spent her life looking like she should be on the catwalks of Paris without any effort needed. Her good looks often lead people to underestimate her, but after she tutored me in statistics, I never made that mistake again. Her hair doesn't even look ruffled, and her curtain bangs are still perfectly parted just above her eyebrows. Without needing to check a mirror, she applies the gloss to her full lips. I've always admired her ability to turn people's expectations on their heads, but she can be such an asshole about it that I've never said as much to her.

Though she and Cat are pledge sisters, Zara and I have never seen eye to eye. I went out with some guy she was interested in, and while it was only one date that didn't evolve into more, in Zara's mind, I should have known she was interested and stayed away. Personally, I think I did her a favor—he spent the whole time talking about himself, and he kissed like a fish.

"I want to call Steve and tell him that we're going to be late. Otherwise, he'll be distracted during his match looking for us." Tiffany holds up her phone trying to find a signal, only to continue to be disappointed.

"Since there doesn't seem to be a Mrs. Essos, I think I'll make sure our host sees the goods. I would be plenty happy to play house here," Zara says with an eyebrow wiggle before running off to take advantage of a bathroom to primp in.

The mental image of Essos and Zara entwined causes my stomach to drop. I lock eyes with Cat, and she rolls hers.

I need to get her alone to tell her what I heard. I know I can trust Cat to see sense.

Sybil comes over to us, offering to show Tiffany to a room where she can make her call, and slowly everyone moves off to change and get outside.

Cat gets up as well, and I grab her wrist. "I'll come with you." I grab my bag and follow her to one of the bathrooms. We both slip into the room, and I lock the door behind me. Catalina opens her mouth, and I clamp my hand over it as I turn on the faucet, hoping the water will drown out my words if someone is listening. I lean close to her and tell her about the conversation I overheard.

"I went to ask after the driver, but then I overheard Essos and Sybil talking. He said that they should make sure we're happy. The two of them are going to break some news to us over dinner, and they're somehow turning on fake Wi-Fi and sending Tiffany's call to voicemail. None of this makes sense. Why does he think we're going to be here till dinner? Shouldn't the bus be here well before then?" The words rush out like I can't get them out fast enough. "What time is it even?" With my phone out of commission, I have no idea.

I watch as she digests what I've said. Her lips purse as she starts to take off her clothes and root around in her bag before pulling out her carefully curated one-piece swimsuit with a cut-out side.

I sit on the counter, and my back gets splashed by the water while I wait for her to respond. "What are you doing? Didn't you hear what I just said?"

She tosses her top and bra to the floor, and I see bruises on her ribs from where she must have hit the seat. She must see my wince, and she looks in the mirror.

Cat turns in profile to get a better look. "Well, we can't just come in here and not get changed. I know you hit your head, but you're not dense," she whispers back at me, pulling on her bathing suit.

I hop off the counter and start to get changed too, waiting to hear what she has to say about the situation.

Once she's done getting dressed, she sits on the closed toilet seat, gnawing on her upper lip and twisting her hair back into a haphazard bun, both tics she has when she's deep in thought. "Look, maybe you heard things out of context. They have been super nice to us, and you might be reading into it a bit too much."

I frown at her, surprised that she would take this stance. I expected her to jump out of her skin and want to flee as quickly as possible. She moves on to fuss with her ace bandage, unwrapping it to look at her wrist.

"How badly does it hurt?" I ask, reaching for her hand to finish unwrapping it. Cat rolls her wrist around, testing it for pain, before shrugging.

"I banged it and babied it a little. It's not like I was actively bleeding like *some people*."

I stick out my tongue. "Rude."

"I honestly think you might have misheard them. That said, maybe we don't eat anything in case the food's laced with narcotics or something." She nods, liking this idea.

There's a knock at the door, and we both turn to look at it. I nearly jump out of my skin as worst-case scenarios run through my head.

"I don't know. Saying that our world looks different now? Sounds like they're going to lock us all up as sex slaves forever."

"You've been watching too much *Criminal Minds*, but we can't do anything rash, even if you're right. Who knows how many people he has on staff?" Cat's still looking at the door. Her eyes get wide. "Oh, duh—he has so many people that work here, there's no way some serial rapist would have so many prying eyes around. Even if they all had to sign NDAs, I'm pretty sure a mass kidnapping would get a lot of press, and in the case of harm, they could break said NDA. People would be missing us—the bus driver called his dispatch and told them where we are and where the accident was. I think you're just a little traumatized by the near miss, and your brain is working overtime."

I narrow my eyes at her, knowing full well that any knowledge

I have of serial killers and their behavior is from what *she* watches.

"Catalina? Daphne? Are you two in there? We're about the head out to the pool," Zara calls through the door.

"Just a second!" Cat calls out. "Listen, we have a plan. We're not flying blind. We'll just stay cautious. We have to eat something so they don't know we're suspicious, but we can make it small, like fruit—nothing that was made. If we give it an hour, and we notice that no one else is dropping, we can eat a little more to keep up our strength. We know they plan to keep us till dinner, which sounds like something they want us conscious for, so let's act like nothing is wrong but stay on guard. We don't know where we are, and we have no cell service. Maybe we can ask Tiffany where the phone that she used is so we can call for help. Act. Casual. Constant vigilance."

I hug her tight, and we both groan in pain. I have serious doubts about this plan of action. "I love you. I don't know what I would do without you. Should we at least tell Zara and Tiffany?" I ask.

She pauses to consider. "I don't think we should, and hear me out—Zara will totally spill the beans, and Tiffany will have a meltdown of epic proportions that would be counterproductive. Like I said, I don't think they're going to do anything with us until dinner, so we should be fine until then. Besides, there's no reason to turn this into something it's not."

"Cat! Daphne! Let's *go!*" Zara calls again.

Cat turns off the water, and I get a look at myself in the mirror. My suntanned face looks like it's been leeched of all color. The blood has long since been cleaned off my face, but the swelling is still there, and bruises are blossoming on my head and shoulder. I stare into my brown eyes, glad that I can see them clearly. My eye looks better than I expected, given how hard it was to open earlier, and I am no longer cold. I think back to Essos and wonder if he has some sort of motion-activated heating system. Or maybe my paranoia has sunk too deep, or my shock is wearing off. So many unknowns make my head swim.

We follow Zara outside, where everyone is sitting by the pool, enjoying the sun. With all of us in bathing suits, it's easy to see the damage from the accident in the bandages and the darkening bruises. Even so, the mood around me is buoyant, not at all reflecting the trauma evident on our bodies. Some girls are so relaxed that I'm not sure if it's from alcohol or something more, like what Essos said about easing our worries. I would have thought drugs, but no one seems out of control—just vivaciously enjoying the sun.

All the talk about being on alert seems to fly out the window as Cat approaches me and offers a small plate of fruit. Her shoulders are relaxed as she pops a grape into her mouth and accepts a champagne flute from a passing waiter. She passes me one, and even I slip and take a sip before remembering to stay wary. I do accept some of the fruit and eat some pomegranate seeds, realizing that all I've had today is a few sips of coffee. I regret agreeing to minimal food and consider that I might need to see if there's anything I can eat that wouldn't be potentially compromising. One hour—that's how long Catalina thought we would need to watch out.

My skin feels hot all over, and I glance up, my gaze drawn to one of the windows on the second floor. I see Essos in the frame watching us, and my heart catches. Even from this distance I can make out the vivid blue of his eyes, and I'm certain that color is flooding his cheeks. Our eyes hold for only a few seconds before he quickly closes the curtains.

Sybil seems to be more our assistant than his, keeping an eagle eye on us all day, getting any food or drink that anyone wants. They still wear that long dress, despite the sun bearing down on us.

I look away from them and try to clue back into the conversation next to me.

"I couldn't reach Steve. I could only leave a message to let him know that we're okay. I guess he's already in practice. I just hope that he gets it and it doesn't distract him. He has dreams for the Olympics, and I'm sure that losing here could set him back."

Another of the girls, Alex, whose boyfriend is Steve's partner, nods sympathetically. I share a look with Cat behind Tiffany's back, but we say nothing.

"I'm sure they also know that traffic can be a nightmare getting into LA, so hopefully they aren't too worried. With any luck, a new bus gets here tonight, and then we can get on the road."

"I personally wouldn't mind staying here for the rest of the weekend," Zara says and sips from the margarita she was able to get her hands on. She's lounging on her side with an oversized straw hat on her head. "Essos is a thirst trap, and I am *here* for it."

It is a physical effort for me to keep my face from twisting into a scowl. "What does that even mean?" I say from my lounge chair.

Zara tosses her dark hair over her shoulder in a practiced flip. Whenever I spend time with Cat and Zara, Zara is always sure to mention that being pledge sisters created a special bond between them. Her intentional exclusion with comments like that has made it hard for me to connect with her the way I did with some of their other pledge sisters, like Tiffany.

"That means that I wish he was down here with us, so I could make the right kind of impression. Maybe build a friendship from this kindness that he's shown us." She winks at *friendship*, and I scoff, as a few of the girls murmur their mutual appreciation of our host. I fear they wouldn't believe me about what I heard, so I keep quiet.

"I wonder what he's really like. I mean, look at this house and the fact that he has staff just milling around. He must be crazy stupid rich." Cat pulls her long blond hair into a messy bun. She slides into the pool and treads water while still watching the group.

I take a bite of a strawberry and study the façade of the house, envisioning the beginning of the building process and how it looked when it was nothing but frames and studs providing a small glimpse into the future of the home. A house this size is easily worth millions, and who knows how much land it's sitting on. The main room is large, with windows two stories high. Spanning from the center of the building where the ballroom-like space is, I can see two different wings to the north and the south. I noticed only one main stairway, which must connect the two wings of the house.

By the time someone finishes cleaning this place, they must have to start again.

Sybil is talking to each group of girls, making sure that everyone has everything they need before explaining something. I'm studying the faces of the others as they listen. They look enthusiastic as they nod along. Out of twenty women, surely I can't be the only one to have reservations, but as each woman smiles at Sybil, I start to think I am overreacting.

Sybil approaches our group, and I sit up straighter, ready to hear what they have to say. Their tone is as kind as ever. "Ladies, since we're still waiting on a replacement bus, Essos has offered to host you all for dinner this evening. While he prefers formal dining, he is aware that you're not prepared for a formal event. Please don whatever you have brought with you, and we will meet in the formal dining room at five p.m. We have showers available—please coordinate through me, and I will direct you. Before you ask, the time is now 3:30."

My hackles rise. Another delay? I talked myself down, but

with this news, I'm on edge again. "I'm confused—is the bus going to be late?" I ask, my eyes narrowing. We've already been here longer than the six hours we were promised. I didn't realize how much time passed.

Sybil looks at me sympathetically. "Yes. The driver advised that his company is short on buses, so they had to wait for another bus to come back and then drive from the origin to this destination. The new estimated time for a bus is nine p.m., and we want to make sure that you are well fed before getting back to your travels."

I have to remind myself to breathe as dots connect in my head. How could they have known hours ago that we would need to stay for dinner?

A strangled noise escapes Tiffany.

"I have to ask, are you and Essos, like, a thing? I mean, it's weird that he's your boss and you call him by his first name. Shouldn't he be, like, Mr. Essos or something?" Zara asks, looking up at Sybil. It's like Zara is mentally calculating her competition for his affection.

I cross my leg and "accidentally" kick water at Zara, who gives me a sharp look. I tell myself that now is not the time to be thinking about hooking up with Essos, and my action has nothing to do with how I felt when he had his eyes on me earlier.

Sybil flushes before answering very firmly, "No, we are not. We just work closely together. If you have any further needs, let me know." They move along, shaking their head.

Sybil chats with the remaining cluster of girls before resuming their post by the door. I survey the groups as they chatter animatedly, and I don't see a shred of concern, apart from Tiffany. None of the others with boyfriends on the team seem worried about getting to the event. In fact, none of the conversations I hear around us even mention missing them.

All at once, girls start to get up and ask Sybil about having a shower and preparing for dinner. Cat and I share a look, a silent vow to stick together.

This trip is starting to feel like some sort of Lifetime movie where only one of us is going to live to tell the tale. That's not going to happen if I have anything to say about it.

4

Cat and I share a bathroom again to get ready for dinner. Rather than wait for Cat to take her usual hour-long shower, I jump in ahead of her. Then, while she sings in the shower, I braid my hair before unbraiding it, uncertain about how best to style it. I give up, allowing my dark brown curls to drop at will. At some point, I started to care what I look like for dinner with Essos, and I'm mad at myself for it.

For all I know, he could be a serial rapist. If TV has taught me anything, it's that we should be wary of a guy in his late twenties to early thirties, a loner type with a secluded spot where he can take his victims. Usually, an unsub like this will be charismatic, putting his victims at ease. Essos fits that bill, and while I've yet to have a direct conversation with him, he's been attentive to everyone's needs. And yes, I would have to be a moron not to admit how good-looking the man is. If all things were made equal, I wouldn't say no if he asked me out.

Cat steps out of the shower with a towel wrapped tight around her body. She looks at my outfit, a grin brightening her face. "Isn't that my dress?"

"No, it's mine, you just borrowed it freshman year and never returned it."

She shrugs, her way of acknowledging that I'm right. "It's strange, isn't it?" she asks, her blue eyes locking with mine in the mirror.

"What is?"

"That we're both pretty sure we're going to dinner with a serial killer, but we still want to look our best." She lets out a sharp laugh, and the thought sinks in for both of us. I regret not telling the other girls and rallying them against this possible psycho. I place my hands on her shoulders, a sad smile on both our faces. As if craving touch, she pulls me into a tight hug.

"You know I love you like a sister, right, Daphne?" She stands and looks at me head-on. She towers over me, even in the sensible flats we're both so thankful we packed. We grabbed them assuming we'd need them for wandering around Santa Monica, not so that we'd be ready to run for our lives.

"Stop, we're going to be fine. I probably misunderstood—I could have brain damage or at least a concussion," I say, trying to reason with myself, but there is no belief behind these words. While we were outside, I looked around to see how we could get out if we needed to. I failed to come up with a workable plan. Essos has security cameras everywhere and endless staff milling around, and I remember coming through a large gate before driving down the mountainside to his house.

"No, *you* stop. In any case, today was terrifying, and I just want to make sure you know that." Cat hugs me. I'm careful to not hug her as tightly as I did earlier, more aware of her bruises.

"Of course, I know that. You're closer to me than my family is. We're going to be fine. I promise we'll make it out of this alive." I try to reassure her, but I have no way of keeping that promise, and we both know it.

All the other girls are in the dining room by the time we

emerge, and we're lucky to find two seats side by side at the far end of the table. The other girls already jockeyed to get as close to Essos as possible, which is fine by me. Silently, I map the exits. There aren't many; the door we entered through leads back into the main living area and foyer. Across the room from that door is what must be a servants' door that leads to the kitchen, if the people emerging with plates are any indication. Essos is seated closest to the main entrance while I'm directly across from him, a bare wall at my back. He meets my gaze and gives me a tentative smile, and it feels like the room dims a little, the lighting becoming more romantic. When I look around, no one else seems bothered by a change in the lighting...because there was no change.

The food is served as if we're in some sort of period drama, with people slowly moving around the table and allowing us to put the food on our own plates. We're all pulling from the same platters, family style. The food starts to the left of Essos and circles around the table so that he is always the last one served. A few of the girls fumble, as if unsure what to do when presented with white-glove service. I probably wouldn't have known either, if not for watching *Downton Abbey*.

I take very little of the food, since nerves are keeping my hunger at bay, but it all smells delicious. I keep watching to see if Essos is taking food and eating it, and I'm glad to see that he is. Sybil is standing at the back of the room, just watching. I want to think that it's creepy, but their manner feels almost protective. Their behavior makes me doubt what I heard even more—I don't sense any intent to harm anyone. They seem concerned for our safety.

Once everyone has been served, Essos stands, setting his napkin to the side of his plate. "This conversation is always a difficult one to have, I find." He's not looking at any of us. Instead, he glances at Sybil, who seems to encourage him with a sympathetic nod. Cat and I exchange glances, glad that we didn't eat any of our food. I slide my knife off the table and keep it in my hand on my lap. Cat does the same thing, and Zara spots the movement and gives her a confused glance. Essos locks eyes with me, an odd look on his face—a mixture of excitement and dread. I wonder if he knows I know—if he saw me slip the knife away.

"This is something that many of you will have a hard time hearing, but I believe for some of you, it won't come as a shock. Earlier this morning, your bus got a flat tire. However, your bus driver was never able to control the vehicle afterward, and the bus plunged over the guardrail and into the Pacific Ocean." Essos pauses to let this sink in. He glances from face to face.

I feel cold all over. A flash of flying through the cab of the bus comes to mind before I remember hitting the water. I remember how cold the water was, and trying to wake Cat so we could get out of the bus. I remember kicking at the window, but it didn't budge, my body weak from the anxiety crashing through it. Where was that superhuman strength of women who lifted cars off their children? I remember choking, trying to breathe in, only to find water instead of air. I remember the water flooding into my lungs before everything went black. Farther up the table, a sob escapes, someone probably having their own memories of the accident.

"I know this is very, very difficult to hear, and I am so very sorry to have to be the one to tell you, but each of you perished in that accident. You're in a different plane of existence."

There is silence in the room as we all let the news sink in. The stages of grief surround me; I can see denial, depression, and anger on everyone's faces. I glance at Cat and see sorrow, her dreams gone in a blink. I snap out of my trance as someone—Madison—stands abruptly, knocking her chair to the ground.

"This is bullshit, and totally fake. I'm getting the hell out of here," Madison shouts.

One of the servants sets the chair straight as she stalks toward the door. Essos raises a hand, and the doors all slam shut. I look at Cat, who is wringing her hands under the table. This is so much worse than we could have imagined. I was wrong not to tell the other girls, but even if I had, I'm not sure what difference it would have made.

"I sincerely do not mean this as a threat, but please, take your seat again so I can finish explaining." Essos waits, as if he has all the time in the world for Madison to decide what to do. His voice is as soothing, as if he is practiced in needing this patience. I wonder how many times he has delivered this speech. Realizing that there's nowhere for her to go, and no other options, Madison retakes her seat.

"Thank you," Essos says with a slight nod of his head. He looks pained as he goes on. "I am in a position of power within my realm. You're currently existing in the Realm of the Gods, in my home. You all have fallen under my rule. I am King of the Under-world, God of the Dead. My position requires that I not perform my duties alone, the details of which will be covered at a later time. It is that same position that makes it difficult to find someone willing to share the burden. The accident today happened under a specific set of circumstances. When a tragedy like the one that befell you today happens, an archaic process known as the Calling begins, in which I hope to choose a wife. It's horrifically anti-feminist, however, the rules for the Calling were created by another group. It's been named such because becoming my queen truly is a calling." He pauses as he studies our responses. I am fighting every urge in my body to react, biting down so hard on my cheek that I taste blood.

"If you do not wish to take part in the Calling, you have the option to leave. If you elect to leave, it will not be to return to the life you had. You will be crossing over into your afterlife. Should you choose to stay here and proceed, you will have the chance to become so much more. Being my bride means becoming the Queen of the Underworld and accepting powers fit for the role. It is not a job for just anyone. I wish I could give you more time to consider your choice, but the Calling will begin tomorrow. You can opt out at any time." It might be my imagination, but it feels like he's speaking only to me.

I catch Cat's eye, but there is too much for us to communicate with just one look. I look away from her and meet Essos's gaze. There is a glassy sheen to his eyes, and my heart stumbles, wanting to reach out and comfort him. Essos braces his hands on the table, still holding my gaze while a storm brews in them. He looks like he would rather be anywhere but in this room full of tears.

"What about the driver?" I ask, thinking about the kind man who helped us with our bags. Essos stares into my eyes, and that feeling of familiarity fills me. That warmth from earlier that I chalked up to some super fancy heating system floods my body again. Looking at Essos now, I'm not even close to cold, and I don't think it's because of his powers, either.

His tone is soft when he answers me. "He has passed into his afterlife. If it makes you feel better, he was greeted warmly by loved ones whom he missed dearly. I personally saw him off. Know that you will all have such a fate, should you decide not to take part in the Calling or not be chosen."

Tiffany cries silently in her chair, her future with Steve gone in a flash. Essos walks over and places a hand on her shoulder. She sniffles a few more times before her tears stop, and then her whole body seems to relax, all the tension draining from it.

Cat jumps up as if ready to spring across the table at him. I follow suit, prepared to back her up without hesitation.

"What are you doing to her?" she shouts at him. Girls around us hiccup and gasp as they try to remain composed.

"I'm giving her peace. She's grieving for a love that's been lost." He withdraws his hand from Tiffany's shoulder and holds both palms up in the universal symbol of not intending harm. My muscles relax, and I tug Cat back down to our chairs. "I know that this won't be easy for any of you, and it will take a few days to come to terms with your new situation. It will take time, and I understand a decision will not easily be made." He walks back to the head of the table. "I will leave you all to eat and discuss the situation amongst yourselves. While I wish I could afford you the time you need, you will have 24 hours to decide whether you want to proceed. Sybil will be taking care of you for the duration of your time here and will answer any questions that you may have to help guide you through your decision. If you should opt to leave, do so of your own free will, and know that there is no pressure from anyone here for you to stay or go. Should you decide to stay, you will each have your own room and will be appropriately provided for in the months to come.

"With that, I bid you goodnight." Essos gives a small bow to us before exiting the room with Sybil close on his heels. The warmth that infused my body minutes earlier dissipates, as if Essos has taken it with him. I clear my throat, trying to find something to say, to put something into words, but I can't.

Once they have left the room, I place the knife I was holding on the table. We sit in stunned silence before erupting all at once.

"Be careful what you wish for, Zara," Cat yells at her from across the table.

"This is so fucked up. Like, I'm out of here," Olivia says, standing to pace the room. This is her senior year, and I know she was going to Dartmouth in the fall to get a graduate degree in engineering.

"What is this guy smoking, and where can I get some?" Anna laughs, tossing her vibrant pink, purple and blue hair over her shoulder. I have to hand it to her for leaning into the denial phase. Not that I can really blame her; she's only a freshman.

"Are we seriously locked in here with a crazy person?" says Penny, a short girl with russet hair who is looking at her food like it's been poisoned.

My brain is trying to sort through the information Essos gave us, but instead of processing it, my thoughts are stuck on drowning. The memory is overwhelming my ability to handle anything else. I look at Cat and, instead of seeing her face, I see her unconscious as I try to keep her head above the rapidly rising water. I looked to see if there was any way out, trying the emergency door in the back and before I started kicking the windows. I remember thinking that I was glad Cat was not awake for this as I watched her body try to breathe in the water only to choke. I remember wishing that I was unconscious, and that I didn't have to watch my best friend die. I shudder, suppressing the urge to throw up the water my body expects to still be in my lungs.

A few girls start crying harder as they settle into their own traumatic memories. I take a bite of food, since I now know Essos is not trying to kill us, but it tastes like ash in my mouth.

Cat calls my name, and I look at her again. "What are we going to do, Daphne?" She sits back down, looking so lost. For once, I have no idea what to even say to her. Tears are welling in her big blue eyes. "I'm never going to be President."

I reach out and squeeze her hand. Around the room, I can see everyone's hopes and dreams dying right in front of me. "Never say never." I stand up and lead her to one of the servants posted against the wall. Beside him is a doorway that I don't remember seeing earlier, but now that we're dealing with fucking magic, mapping the exits feels futile. He seems to be the youngest and therefore the most approachable. He's all long limbs and boyish good looks, with his dark black hair slicked away from his face. He stares forward as I approach him, and I sense he's trying not to look at me. "Can you please have someone show us to our rooms?" I ask softly, still holding Cat's hand.

39

"Straight away, ma'am." He nods but doesn't move. I wonder if in a past life he was a member of the Royal Guard at Buckingham Palace. I wonder if all the people who work here were once people, or if they're some other sort of creature.

Cat and I are sharing a look, unsure what to do next, when Sybil walks in and glides over to the two of us. "If you will follow me, I will show you to your rooms." They walk away, skirting the other girls in the room as they lead us out. We walk in the opposite direction of the rooms where we all got ready for dinner, to the grand stairwell. The two of us follow Sybil up the curved stairs, and I notice they never touch the banister. I, on the other hand, am holding on to it and to Cat's hand for dear life.

On the second floor, they lead us down a long hallway before stopping in front of two opposing doors.

"These are your rooms." Sybil gestures at the door on one side for me and then motions across the hall for Cat. "As Essos mentioned, you will be provided with everything you need. Inside each room is a full wardrobe with clothes in your size, along with your old belongings. Should you choose to stay with us, there will be requirements both in dress and behavior that we will cover tomorrow morning." With a small bow, they turn and disappear down the hall.

I open the door and step into the space that is to be my room for the foreseeable future. In another life, this would be my dream bedroom. The space is breathtaking, like the rest of the house, and is immaculately laid out, including a queen-size, four-poster bed with a beautiful lavender comforter. I hear Cat gasp as she steps into my room as well. The windows overlook the beach, and I can hear the waves crashing against the shore. I step to the window and pull back the curtain to get a closer look, and I might be crazy, but I think this might be the same window I caught Essos watching us from. The pool and the exact spot where I was sitting are in view below. Between the two large windows is a beautiful white vanity, which, at a glance, has all the brands of toiletries that I love.

"Sweet baby Jesus." I turn to see that Cat has opened the double doors opposite the bed. I follow her to find a walk-in closet stuffed to the gills with gorgeous gowns and shoes. In the center are two dressers pushed together with a large, see-through jewelry chest on top, beautiful gems glittering from behind the glass. Rings and earrings and bracelets all begging to be worn dazzle me from the case. I gently lift the top and run my fingers over them, feeling the cool metal and stones.

My heart stalls. Nestled among all the shiny new gems are two familiar pieces. My maternal grandmother's wedding band and engagement ring, one a solid gold band, the other a gold band with a diamond solitaire. They weren't worth much monetarily, but Phil and Melinda were keeping them for me in the family safe until I was ready for them, something I was always afraid I would never be. Even now, I'm afraid to run my fingers over them. These rings represent a long love that didn't end with death. To me, they're a priceless reminder of home.

I look at Cat, and the same thought crosses our minds. I replace the top, and we race across the hall to her room, which is equally resplendent in a deep burgundy. The view out her windows is of a vast garden, which I don't recall seeing when we arrived. It's dark out now, but I make a note to check it out and see if I can put my green thumb to use.

Cat, too, has a closet full of dresses and shoes and gems, all not only fitting her personal style but also in colors that will complement her hair and eyes. While she looks through her closet, I step into her bathroom to take a moment for myself.

The truth of what is happening is settling on me like a weighted blanket, and I want to let it drag me down. With the lock engaged, I lean against the door and cover my mouth to stifle a sob. I might not have been sure about what I wanted from my life, but I know I wasn't ready to die. I wasn't ready to leave after keeping the only real parents I've known at arms' length. All that time I expected to have to fix my stubbornness is gone. If I had known, I would have texted my mom back. I would have told her I loved her. I died leaving her on read. My only comfort is knowing that they'll take care of Waffles. They got me the cat as a bribe when I moved in with them; he was meant to be proof that they would love me and give me whatever I wanted. Instead of running to them with open arms, I squandered those years.

Bracing my hands on the bathroom counter, I look at myself in the mirror. It hurts to force a smile onto my face, but I need to shake off this despair because, as much as I kept my family at arms' length, Cat was close with hers. Tonight, I need to be the rock. I can find another time to break down.

Emerging from the bathroom, I catch Cat digging through her vanity.

"I suppose this could be better than being President." Her laughter echoes in the room, but it sounds flatter than usual, and I know she's trying to bolster both our spirits. I laugh along with her, if only to fake a calm that I don't yet have.

"Do you think you'll stay?" I ask, not meaning to bring us both down, but we're pretty low anyway.

"Do you?" She's deflecting, feeling me out.

"I think so." I nod, slowly at first, then more vigorously. "I mean, what do we have to lose? We're already dead. We already have nothing but our afterlives. I doubt I'll be chosen—my resume isn't exactly fit for a queen. Future president of her sorority and our country, however..."

Cat falls back on the bed, frowning.

I wince at my own carelessness. My thoughts are coming in an awkward way—in the same breath that I'm talking about possibly becoming Queen of the Underworld, I'm also mentioning the future Cat was supposed to have as if it could still happen.

"Don't you want to see your parents?" She's treading lightly, not wanting to make me uncomfortable, which I deserve after my comment. I fall back on the bed as well and turn my head to look at her.

"Honestly? Not right now, no. I guess I always thought I would see them through the pearly gates or whatever, and I would have this mountain of accomplishments to point out. Like, look at this awesome thing I did, I was able to cure cancer or be chief of staff to the first female president. Right now, all I can say is, what? I can hold a keg stand for 27 seconds? That I once chugged an entire bottle of champagne through a beer bong without vomiting? I wanted them to be proud of what I accomplished, and I don't have anything to show for my life. I would also like to point out that all of those things do not a queen make."

Cat squeezes my hand. "I really hope it doesn't take another 24 years to elect the first woman president—that would be fucking sad. Kidding aside, I think you're well adjusted for the level of trauma you've survived, and that alone is an accomplishment. Look, if you want to pass on, I think they will be proud of you, not just your parents, but your grandparents too."

"You didn't answer me," I point out, trying to bring us back to where we started.

"You're right. That's because...I don't know. It's not like I can go back to my old life. But I miss my parents and my brother. I was looking forward to the end of the semester and going home to see them, and that can't happen. I just wish my last goodbye hadn't been muffled by a bagel as I ran out the door. I want to hug them one last time, and I can't. Staying or going isn't going to change that. If you stay, I stay. For what it's worth, I think you would make an awesome queen—doing a keg stand for 27 seconds shows a level of dedication any king would be lucky to have. Real talk, you do this all the time—convince yourself you're not good enough, and at the last minute, stop because you're afraid of what you'll hear. You did it with rush, and you did it when we ran for government in our freshman dorm."

"I only withdrew because you wanted it so much more."

"And I love you for that, but it doesn't make me wrong. You've been living with Phil and Melinda for ten years, and I swear, sometimes it's like you're still waiting for them to return you to sender. You're a smokeshow, you're ridiculously smart, and anyone would be lucky to be loved by you, because you're fierce when you love someone."

"Ride or die," I whisper, hooking my pinky with hers.

"Ride or die." She gives my pinky a squeeze, sealing our fates.

5

That night, my dreams are haunted by a man.

We are lounging in a park, under a tree, with a blanket spread out beneath us. The man with me is dressed in a three-piece suit, with a hat pulled low over his face, blocking the brilliant sun above. Only his plump lips are exposed, practically begging for me to kiss them. He is seated with his long legs extended before him, while I am lying on the blanket in a long-sleeve blouse and a full-bodied long skirt, a black fascinator perched on my head.

He leans over me, brushing a stray curl of hair away before cupping my face. I squint, trying to look at him clearly, but the sun is so bright it hurts. It doesn't matter, I trust this man, so I close my eyes, letting him hold me. His lips meet mine as he kisses me with abandon. I return his kiss with equal passion and press my body against his, the fascinator knocked askew. I place my hand on his chest and feel the beating of his heart through his suit. He rolls on top of me, his weight a delight as he settles between my legs as best he can, given my voluminous skirts. His hand moves from my face to my breasts, his fingertips skimming the tops as they peek out over my corset. He groans a name that feels like mine before his hand slides down the length of my body, fighting to reach the ends of my skirt.

"Must there be so many layers?" the familiar voice huffs.

I laugh. "But, sir, how else am I supposed to keep my virtue safe?"

"It just means a rake like me has to be completely devoted to the destination." His responding kiss is deep as he lifts my body so I'm sitting pressed against him. "You are the only destination in my life, and I'll burn this dress to the ground when we get home to show you how wonderful the journey can be."

I SHOOT UP IN BED, my body flushed and hot.

Cat is sprawled beside me, hugging the stuffed bear, aptly named Honey Bear, that she's had since childhood. She left it behind for the weekend but found it sitting on her bed, another pleasant surprise provided by Essos and Sybil. Evidence like the bear and my grandmother's rings helped the two of us start to come to terms with this.

After thoroughly inspecting her room, we went back to mine to look deeper, mostly in the closet to see how they outfitted us both. Surprisingly, all the clothes were things I would have grabbed for myself, but maybe it's not surprising. It's clear Essos and Sybil did their research. We stayed in my room for the rest of the night, even after hearing the other girls start to trickle upstairs to their own. Neither of us wanted to talk it out with anyone else.

We struggled to fall asleep last night, both of us trying to put on a brave face for the other. Still, Cat's sobs shook the bed until she cried herself to sleep and I wound around her like the big spoon.

I ease out of bed and slide on a pair of slippers, then grab the robe that's hanging behind the door before sneaking down the stairs. My steps are silent as I walk down the grand staircase, and I try to imagine doing so in one of the dresses from the dream closet upstairs. I pinch myself, something I've been doing periodically to make sure this isn't all a strange dream. The memories of dying are there, the feeling of the water in my lungs. The despair, the pain, lingers in my mind. I could barely stand to wash my face before going to sleep.

I walk through the foyer and into the ballroom before going out the back door to go to the pool, and I come to an abrupt stop. A dark figure stands on the deck facing away from me, but the silhouette is a dead giveaway of who it is. My pulse skyrockets at the idea of having alone time with him.

I study his back for a moment, undetected. His dark hair is slicked back, but I can see curls at the nape of his neck. Somehow, with the knowledge of who he truly is, he seems larger than before.

"Well, do come on. I don't bite, I promise," Essos turns toward me, a coffee cup in his hand. When he smiles at me, he gets little crow's feet beside his eyes, but I can see the weight of the world resting on his broad shoulders. The impulse to reach out and run my hand along his strong back, as if I could unburden him with this action, is almost overwhelming. Instinctively, I know that if I did that, I would feel the raw power in his body. I step closer to him, wanting to do something to make him smile again. He doesn't do it enough.

"And if I wanted you to?" I say. I have no idea where the words came from, but they're out there and, rather than be ashamed, I stand up taller.

Essos, on the other hand, was mid-sip of coffee, and he coughs, raising his eyebrows at me over the brim of his mug. "Then just say when."

I blush and walk to stand beside him. I stop at the railing and look at the beach, admiring the view. "How does it work? Are we actually here? Are we in California, or is this all fake and magic or whatever it is that you do?"

"Ah, it wouldn't be any fun to give all my secrets away on the first day, would it?" He gives me a wink before leaning against the railing and studying me.

"I would consider this the second day, wouldn't you?" I lock eyes with him, daring him to look away, but he doesn't. Instead, he reaches toward the violent purple bruise on my face, stopping just short of contact. He takes a step closer, and I feel like a flower opening to the sun. While the swelling on my face is mostly gone, this bruise is something I will carry for days as a reminder. Of course, I'm making an assumption that I'll heal the way I did in the mortal realm.

Essos's hold over me releases when he clears his throat, but he doesn't step away, and neither do I. "It's a boring combination of both. My world exists beside yours. My power allows the world to be more condensed, more concise than your world. In the land of the dead, people crave what they know—it helps them to transition. You don't know this house, but you know California; you know the beach." He pauses, thoughtful eyes studying my face. "Would you like me to do something about your bruises?"

I reach up to where he is gesturing, and my fingers brush his before I touch the bruise around my eye. I contemplate his offer. I'm not entirely convinced that the way the swelling rapidly resolved wasn't Sybil's doing. "It's not going to heal on its own?"

"It will. You are dead, but because you haven't passed into your afterlife, you still maintain the damage you sustained before you died." He takes a deep breath before continuing, as if it causes him actual pain to say, "You...you drowned, so I imagine there have been a few moments where it's felt like you're drowning again. It won't feel like that again, but it's your body's way of trying to reconcile your death."

"Is that why I've been so cold?" My words are low, barely a whisper. I can feel the heat radiating off his body, and I don't know if it's due to the chill from the morning air or something else, but I'm gravitating toward him as if I'm seeking him out.

"Yes, but you shouldn't still feel that way. I can't say from experience, but usually once you're aware of your death, your body compensates. Think of it like a pressure chamber for divers." This time when he lifts his hand to my cheek, I can feel the featherlight brush of his knuckles on my skin. "You never answered my question—would you like me to heal you?"

I lift my hand again, not to touch the bruise, but to touch where he's touched me. His blue eyes are studying my face so intently that if a dinosaur in a tutu danced by, I don't think either of us would look at it. "No. It's the only thing that feels real right now."

My hand lingers there before I bring it back down and pull the robe tighter around me. The chill is back, sending a shiver down my spine. Essos lifts his hand once more, but this time, he gently drags the back of his knuckles down my arm, warmth spreading from the point of contact. It's so light that if I hadn't watched him do it, I could have convinced myself I imagined it.

"That was you, yesterday? Warming me?" I ask, already knowing the answer.

Essos winks, looking young and boyish when he does. "Don't tell Sybil. I'm not supposed to give any preferential treatment." I stare at him, looking at his face, finally able to see him up close. His features seem unreal, like something Michelangelo created from marble and chiseled to perfection. His blue eyes are light, almost like thick ice over water. His stubble from yesterday is gone; instead, his skin is smooth, as if freshly shaved with a sharp razor. He has a distinct face, and I'm sure I would recognize him if

I had seen him before. All the same, he feels comfortable, familiar, as if I *have* been here before, standing on this very deck as we sipped coffee and got ready to face the day together.

"Your secret's safe with me." I promise.

"Honestly, talking to you now, unchaperoned, is also against procedure," Essos warns me with an eyeroll.

"Procedure?" I ask, curious about who set all these rules.

Before he can respond, the dogs appear, their tails wagging happily. The same grey dog that licked me yesterday nuzzles my hand for petting. Essos must be prepared for the onslaught, because he perches his coffee precariously on the banister.

"What are their names?" I ask, scratching behind the dog's ears.

Essos pinches and pulls up the legs of his pants before he squats down to their level. Two of the dogs rush him, nearly knocking him to the ground in their attempts to lick him. The grey pit bull settles down at my side. "Well, Spot is the white one and Shadow is the black one, and at your side is Dave."

I laugh. "Dave? Who named him Dave?" I squat down too, to get closer to Dave and give him more pets, and the other two come bounding over to me as well. The three of them nearly knock me over, but when I look at Essos to hear his response, he looks as if my question knocked the wind out of him. For a second, he has a hard time meeting my eye, and I wonder if I've pressed on a tender bruise.

"Someone very dear to me. Dave is much more human than the other two, so it suits him."

I laugh as Spot knocks me over and licks my face while Shadow and Dave fight over trying to get a piece of me too. "And my other question?"

"You'll learn about it eventually." My displeasure must show on my face, because Essos laughs softly. "There is a council of nine. When there are conflicts between the three realms, we defer to the Council. It was the Council that determined that, after five hundred years on the throne alone, I should have someone else by my side." He swallows hard, his Adam's apple bobbing from the effort.

The door behind me opens, and Sybil walks outside. "My lord —" They stop abruptly when they see me on the ground.

"Yes, Sybil?" Essos asks, looking away from me and standing up.

"The girls are starting to rise. I wanted to inquire if you had outfit specifications for the informational breakfast this morning."

Essos's chuckle sounds nervous as he sticks his hands in his pockets, looking sheepish. Sybil gives him an admonishing look. I stand up and dust myself off, although the dogs are not done seeking my attention.

"Heel," Essos commands, using a different tone than I've heard so far.

The force of his voice and the power threaded in the order make me want to drop to my knees before him and heel as well. Even the thought of being on my knees in front of him makes my insides clench at the desire that thrums through me. I fight the very strong urge to look at his crotch and wonder how he would taste. Does he enjoy letting his partner take control, or does he need power in all things by face-fucking whoever is lucky enough to be with him? My cheeks warm as these thoughts invade my mind.

The dogs all stop immediately and trot to sit by their master's side. "Sybil, please bring Ms. Hale back to her room. Allow the girls to wear pajamas or whatever they want to breakfast, and for the afternoon, they should dress for interviews."

"Understood. Ms. Hale, if you would follow me."

Surprised by the formality, I start to follow Sybil, but turn to look at Essos one last time. The Essos before me seems a different man from the one I was just talking with. I want to bring that Essos back, hear the deep gruffness of his laugh. It sounded so weary from disuse, but his back is already turned, both of us dismissed.

Sybil leads me back up the stairs and stops before my room. I reach for the doorknob, but they grab my wrist. My breath catches, and I pull back my hand as I turn to face them.

They don't look angry so much as concerned, their brows furrowed as they study my face. "Heed my warning, girl. There is much more at stake here than you realize. You *must* follow the rules—your life may depend on it." In a flash, they're gone, as if they were never there to begin with.

I'm left alone in the hallway with my thoughts.

Inside my room, Cat is still sleeping, and I leave her to it and shower in my private bathroom. Sybil's odd warning echoes in my mind. What life are they talking about? The life I could have as queen? I mentioned my doubts to Cat about my ability to be a good queen, but I'm willing to see this through, willing to try with Cat by my side. Essos is, in a word, intriguing. He seems to run hot and cold, but what do I even know about him? We've had all of two conversations, but the way he looks at me makes me feel like I'm missing something. Already, I've seen so many sides to him— the doting dog dad, the careful, controlled king and that softer, lighter side he showed me this morning.

I turn on the water and run my hands under it until it turns hot. A flash of frantic memory where I bang my hands uselessly on a window streaks through my mind. I shake my head, as if that can shake the memory away, before I get into the shower. It's jarring, the feel of the water against my skin, now that I have these memories. I try to focus on the fact that I'm still here, still... alive? Undead? I'm not drowning, in either case. I'm in between, somewhere that I get to try to earn the affection of a gorgeous ruler.

I recall my dream, remembering the feel of Essos's hands in my hair and the weight of his body pressing on mine. I want to finish the dream, want to feel him reach for me. Instead, I slip my own fingers between my legs. My eyes flutter shut at the slickness of my sex, as I imagine Essos's fingers touching me. I let my head fall to the side, calling to mind the feel of his mouth on my neck. My breaths come faster, and I'm panting at the phantom sensation of his body against mine.

Before I can find release, there is a banging on the door, and I jerk my hand away. I stagger back and lean against the cool tile while the lust-filled fog in my head dissipates.

"I'm going back to my room!" Cat shouts, and soon I hear my bedroom door close.

Once I'm thinking clearly, I step back under the spray and reach for the temperature controls. Ice-cold water sluices over my body in a liquid rush. It's a shock to my system and clears my head completely. My favorite brand of shampoo and conditioner and all my usual shower accessories were already in here, down to my brand of razor. I find it hard to believe that any of this is real, unless Essos is a professional stalker who learned the sizes and preferences of twenty girls in order to...what? Buy us nice dresses? Slaughter us one by one?

I can hardly imagine, and it doesn't answer the question about how he managed to warm me up from the inside out.

Maybe it's time to let go of the fantasy that this isn't real. I should lean in and accept what Cat said the night before—that this is something I can do. I'm not ready to leave Cat and go on to my afterlife, whatever that might look like.

These are the lies I tell myself as I get dressed.

Putting off the chance to meet my birth parents because of a guy is shitty, even if there is a magnetism to him that makes me wonder what it would feel like to see him in those raw, unguarded moments where he isn't a king or a god, just a man in love with a woman. To see if this fantasy I have of him is anything like the real deal.

I dress simply for the morning, not in the matching set of silk pajamas he gave me but in a deep red circle skirt with a white button-up blouse. Maybe someday I will dare to wear one of the beautiful necklaces and other jewelry he placed in my room, but that day is not today. I'd feel like I was playing dress-up in my mom's closet. Once I get my bearings, I'll go all in. I finger my grandmother's rings in the ring drawer, comforted to have them close, but I leave them where they are.

When I step out of the closet, I take a moment to study the room. From my window, I can see the pool and the deck where Essos and I just were. The thought floats through my mind that we could have been seen together. It makes my heart race at the illicitness of this, but, ultimately, we weren't doing anything wrong, so what does it matter? My gaze snags on the spot where we stood, and then I look beyond at the rolling waves of the ocean. I'm lucky to have a view of the water, but I'm also jealous of Cat's view of the gardens. What little I was able to see of them in the dark last night makes me wonder about their size.

For the first time, I notice an arrangement of flowers sitting on the vanity, a mixture of lavender and hydrangeas that matches the purple of my room. I study the flowers, thinking back to a class I took freshman year on flower arranging. Hiding within the flowers are little forget-me-nots, which is an unusual choice, and I love how they tie in to the bouquet.

I slip across the hall into Cat's room and wait for her to get out of the shower. I've left my hair down to keep the bruise covered as much as possible. Maybe it was foolish to reject Essos's offer to heal it.

I stand in front of her window, gazing at the gardens below. In the light of day, I can see a mini hedge maze with flowers all around. Someone has taken the time to love and nurture the plants, and I wonder if Essos is the one tending them or if he has a gardener. Would it be too much to ask to work there and get my hands dirty?

Cat emerges from the shower and then dresses for the day in a white blouse, black slacks, and a beautiful emerald statement necklace that drapes around her throat.

I fake a big gasp and clutch my chest. "My god, look at you!" She gives a little spin in the beautiful pumps she's wearing. "It's good I already know we're dead, otherwise I'd think we died and went to heaven."

"Is that where you think we are? Heaven?" she asks, her playfulness rushing out.

"I don't know what to think." I stand up from the bench at the foot of her bed. "I do know that I'm hungry, and I think we should get moving to find out exactly what's going on."

I'm not sure why, but I decide to keep my morning encounter with Essos to myself. I trust Cat with my life, but for however long this process lasts, we're all going to be competing to be with Essos, and I would like to hold on to this one piece for myself. Something about our conversation felt private. I don't think he often lets people see him with his hair down.

As Cat and I descend the wide spiral stairs, other girls are also leaving their rooms. All of the rooms are located in the same long hallway, like a hotel. Some girls are still in their pajamas, discomfort written on their faces as they probably wonder if they should turn back and change. Tiffany is among them, dressed in a beautiful light blue top and shorts set that stands out against her dark skin. The set is similar to my lavender one and Cat's burgundy set. I wonder if we all have unique colors to help differentiate us.

A few of the others are dressed similar to Cat and me, in skirts or slacks or jeans and a simple blouse. Then there are those dressed like Zara, emerging from their rooms as if they're about to walk the red carpet instead of going to breakfast. Zara is adorned in a pale pink long-sleeved dress that stops just above the knee. When she catches Cat and me looking, she does a small spin in her black and white pumps to show us that the dress is backless. Cat gives her a whistle as she struts by. Anna comes down in her swimsuit and cover-up, ready for another day at the pool. Leslie, a petite redhead Anna is close to, is also ready to hit the pool.

We settle into the same seats we had yesterday. Essos remains at the head of the table with Sybil behind him against the wall, hands clasped behind their back. I take this moment to watch how they study each of us. Their brown eyes are critical while the rest of their face remains impassive. Essos might have told us to dress as we please, but someone is passing judgment.

"Good morning, ladies," Essos starts, standing before us all.

"Good morning, Charlie," I whisper to Cat, who laughs behind her orange juice at the *Charlie's Angels* reference. Essos must have heard me too, because he has to hide his laugh behind a cough. His blue eyes flick directly to me with a private smile, and god, if my heart doesn't stumble at the sight of it.

"I hope you were all able to get a good night's sleep. I know yesterday was traumatic, and I dropped a few bombs on you that cannot have been easy to accept." He says this with a practiced cadence, as if he's given this talk hundreds of times. I wonder if he has, and how many girls have lived here throughout the centuries, hoping to be chosen.

While he speaks, our breakfast is served. Normally, I'm not big on breakfast, waiting until the last possible minute to roll out of bed and run to class. Now, I'm presented with what I regularly order at brunch. My plate is full of avocado toast, bacon, and breakfast fruits, including strawberries, blueberries, and pomegranate seeds. We are each served a personalized meal. Tiffany, a vegetarian, gets toast and fruit parfait, while Cat has her own perfect brunch meal—eggs benedict on crab cakes. Across the table, Zara lets out a sigh of pleasure as she bites into a Belgian waffle smothered in fruit.

"Before I begin, I want to give anyone who does not want to stay the chance to go. There is no shame in electing not to continue." He pauses as he glances around the room, stopping on me for a moment longer than anyone else. I think he might be holding his breath as he waits to see if I'll speak up—if I'll walk about the door. When I don't, I watch him release that breath, and I give him a tentative smile. We all look around, wondering which of us will be the first to leave, but it appears that moment will not be now.

"Right then." His voice is somehow stronger, more confident. "Welcome to the Calling, ladies. For lack of a better term, this 'competition' is so much more than that. This is meant to help each of you grow into a potential queen for my realm. Gradually, you will learn about the other gods and goddesses of my world, but to start you will have history and art lessons. It may feel pointless, and you might question why I need you to know the difference between impressionism and baroque, or how the Romans built the viaducts, but you could be questioned on any of this should you make it to the final ball.

"There are traditions and rules associated with the Calling that were created by the Council, and it will be up to you to adhere to them. If you are caught disobeying any of these rules, you will be dismissed. If certain rules are broken, the entire process will end immediately. I beg you to please take this seriously. I am responsible for enforcing the rules, at my own discretion. I will do everything in my power to prevent this experience from ending prematurely. Since you are ignorant of the rules, any prior transgressions will be forgiven at this time, but know that this is a one-time deal." His gaze lingers on me again before moving along.

Goosebumps break out on my skin.

"If you are dismissed, you will be sent on to the Afterlife. Depending on the offense, you may be dismissed immediately. In fairness, I do try to allow you the closure you deserve. I'm not a monster—I recognize the pain of losing someone without a chance to say goodbye, and if I can avoid that, I will." Essos looks down at the table, and I sense deep pain behind his words. I wonder if the person he's thinking of is the same one who named Dave. What must it be like for a god to lose someone he loved?

Composing himself, Essos glances around the room again for understanding, and we all nod.

"Over the next three months, I will get to know each of you. I'll be looking for more than just chemistry—my selection will be as much about finding someone who can prove to me that they have what it takes to reign over the Underworld with grace and kindness as it is about finding someone I connect with. At the end of those three months, you will be able to put those ballgowns in your closets to use for a ball during which you will be mingling with the very gods and goddesses you will soon be learning about. During this time, I may determine that someone is not a good fit, and they will be asked to pass on to their afterlife. There is nothing to be ashamed of in being asked to leave. There *is* shame in breaking the rules. I need a partner I can trust to understand limits and to know when to push them and when not to.

"This afternoon, I will meet with each of you one on one to see if you are compatible with me and this process. Sybil will guide you as far as appropriate attire, but don't worry, I just need to get to know each of you a little better. This will be a long afternoon, so please be prepared. For that I am sorry.

"Sybil will be your guide during this process. They know the rules and will advise you on those as well as answer any questions that you have. Please take this seriously—it is serious for me. I will be expected to choose someone to rule beside me at the end of this Calling."

He turns to leave, then stops. "Sybil will create a calendar for each of you, but there will be no extra time or preferential treatment for *anyone*. Am I clear on this?" He looks at us expectantly, and we respond with nods and yeses across the room. "Then I shall see each of you later. Sybil, you're up."

Essos picks up his coffee mug and walks out. With each step he takes away from us, I see the tension slip from his shoulders as he hangs his head.

Sybil steps forward and clears their throat. They are dressed the same as the day before, in a simple black dress that sweeps the floor as they walk, their brown hair still styled in the same long braid. I wonder if this is some sort of uniform for them.

"As Essos indicated, the most important rule is to keep to your new schedules. You will need to remember that Essos will be developing a relationship with every one of you, and retaliation or retribution against another woman here will not be tolerated. You are also not permitted to wander around the house in the evening after the conclusion of the day. We ask that you remain in your own rooms, although there is no rule forbidding you from spending the night in someone else's room. There *is* a rule forbidding violence against another person—that is one of the rules that is grounds for dismissal. Essos is conscious of how difficult the coming weeks will be.

"Each of you will meet with him one on one today, and some of you may leave. We will, of course, permit you time to say farewell to your friends. You will all be sorted into smaller groups for convenience. This will be done after your one-on-one time this afternoon. This evening, Essos will tell you who will be moving forward in the Calling.

"Please dress smartly for this meeting. I know it sounds formal, but it truly is meant to be a chance for you to get to know him. This is a two-way process. If you don't like him, or don't feel you're compatible after your meeting, you are free to leave. If at

59

any point you no longer want to proceed, you can opt out. Each night, we will dine together, and it is important that you attend every meal. This will provide you with valuable time to get to know Essos as well. His days will otherwise be spent working and not with you. Please use the time you do have with him to your advantage.

"Again, today, you should dress informally but not casually— certainly not like you're going to the beach. Perhaps Anna and Leslie shall go last so they can spend their day as they've so clearly planned." We all give a little laugh, the ice broken.

"Meetings begin at one o'clock sharp, so please be in the ball-room by then. If you would like an example of how to dress— Catalina and Daphne, will you please stand?" Awkwardly, Cat and I stand, a few of the girls shooting daggers at us already. I fight the urge to chew on a nail, self-conscious about the attention. If I want to be a queen, I'll need to get used to scrutiny, so I stand up straight.

This process is certainly not going to make anyone fast friends. We've been here for all of five minutes, and already girls are gunning for Essos like he's the last man alive, which...I guess maybe he is. Or maybe it isn't just the hope of being with Essos that people are deciding to stay behind for—maybe part of it is fear of the unknown.

After breakfast, we're dismissed to get ready for the interviews. Cat and I beeline to my room and are debating whether we should change again when there's a knock on the door.

"It's open!" I call, stepping out of the closet to see who's there.

Tiffany and Zara walk in, ready for the day. Tiffany changed into a power suit in dark red, but her desolate mood dampens the effect. Her heart clearly isn't in this, and I don't blame her at all. Zara didn't change, but she did add a dramatic necklace with a chain that flows down the smooth dark skin of her bare back.

"So, this is weird, right? Like, this isn't just some hallucination or weird fever dream?" Tiffany asks.

"Or shared psychosis? Seems legit," I say, sitting at my vanity. I changed into a tank top for now so I could get a better look at my shoulder bruise. It's gotten worse, turning mottled purple and deep red. The cut on my forehead probably needed stitches, but does that matter once you're dead?

"You should do something for your bruises. I heard Sybil can heal stuff. Ginny dislocated her shoulder, and Sybil popped it back into place and healed it. Of course, we didn't know that it was healed until last night, but it makes sense." Zara wanders around my room touching things. When she picks up my flowers to sniff them, I start to my feet, oddly protective of the blooms. Zara looks at me questioningly, then places the small vase back on the top of my dresser. Playing it cool, I walk past her to grab my robe off the foot of my bed so I can hang it back up. As if catching my hostile undertones, Zara moves toward the bed.

"Does it make sense, Zara?" Cat shoots back. "Because I don't think any part of this makes any fucking sense. We're dead."

"But not really. Like, look at Daphne's bruises—they have literally gotten worse since we 'died,' Pretty sure that's not how death works." Zara gestures at me before checking herself out in the vanity mirror. Her fingertips touch the edges of her bangs, adjusting them slightly.

"Actually, it's called a perimortem bruising, and it will continue to develop," Cat informs her in a haughty tone.

"Oh, stop it, you with the *Criminal Minds* talk. I don't think of it like we're *dead* dead. Like, we're not zombies—we just don't exist on the same plane that we used to. We need to start thinking of it another way, because it honestly hurts my head. It's also depressing as fuck to think that we're dead, so enough. We're on vacation." Zara picks at invisible lint on her dress.

Tiffany stays quiet, and I can guess that she's missing her boyfriend and who knows what else.

Yesterday, Cat and I had pointedly ignored discussing how we died. I can't wrap my mind around the idea of death, of being gone. I might not have known where I wanted my life to go, but there were things I wanted to do—travel the world, get married and, if I was with the right person, maybe have a baby. Getting a cat sibling for Waffles was definitely part of the plan. As great as the dogs are, I want to crush Waffles to my chest one last time.

My head hurts at the existential crisis happening around me, and so I make the vapid choice to play with my hair, attempting to style it out of my face. Time to embrace the bruises that brought me where I am today. As I braid my hair, Cat shows Tiffany and Zara my closet, and I listen to them coo over the dresses and shoes.

"Do you think, like, Sybil got all these outfits for us?" Zara asks, holding up a dress in front of her body.

"I think magic happened." Cat steps out of the closet with another dress on a hanger. She holds it out to me. "You need to wear this." It's a scoop neck, form-fitting grey dress that ends mid-thigh, with ruching on the sides. The long sleeves make it seem more modest, and the material looks smooth and comfortable. Behind her, Tiffany steps out with a pair of black knee-high boots. Zara looks at what they've put together out of the corner of her eye, jealousy flashing, but she buries it quickly.

"I think *this* is magic happening," Tiffany remarks with a broad grin.

Though I doubt they meant to, Sybil made me feel self-conscious about what I was wearing by singling me and Cat out earlier. I'm not comfortable with the idea of being held up as a paragon for attire, so I decide to at least try on this dress.

When I emerge, I ignore how Zara's eyes cut away from me with a fake smile on her face.

"I'm guessing you two are going to stick around and go through with the process?" I ask, checking myself out in the mirror, I turn to see how my ass looks in the dress, and admittedly, it does look good.

"We're dead, Daphne, and this is a chance to become a queen. I know I've always been one, but now others will finally realize all I have to offer." Zara tosses her hair over her shoulder with an easy flip.

"As long as Zara is in, I'm in," Tiffany confirms. She sounds bright and bubbly about it, but the excitement never reaches her eyes.

"Then I guess it's time for us to put our most regal foot forward."

6

Tiffany and Zara go down early in hopes that we're seen in order of arrival. Cat slips back to her own room for a moment alone while I change. By the time I arrive downstairs, everyone has congregated in the living room. I smile nervously at the girls as I make eye contact. Everyone went back to their rooms to change, to try and dress as if they were going to a job interview. Two of them are wearing suits.

I spot Cat, Tiffany, and Zara sitting in a corner, and I hold back an exclamation. Zara went back to her room and managed to find a dress similar to the one I'm wearing but with a deeper scoop in the neckline and a shorter hem. Cat gives a small shake of her head in acknowledgement, but we say nothing.

Sybil sweeps into the room with a clipboard in hand and calls the first name. Despite having been dressed for the pool, both Anna and Leslie are now wearing business casual, except I can see the strings from Anna's bikini sticking out the back of her dress. I manage to catch her eye and signal her about it, and she gives me a wink as she tucks them away. Sybil must have taken pity on them, because Anna and Leslie are the first two to go.

As the afternoon goes on, they move down the list, and I feel the same stress I did at graduation, waiting for my name to be called, waiting for my diploma, except that there is no rhyme or reason to the order. Some people spend more time with Essos than others—the longest session is just short of an hour, while other girls spend 10 minutes with him. When Cat's name is called, we squeeze each other's hands, and she goes off.

Zara watches Cat leave, then hops into her seat. "So, this is weird, right? Like, it's almost like speed dating, but just for him. I wonder what he's like." I watch her, keeping my face neutral, mentally tallying every *like* she uses. Sometimes I think she plays into expectations to get people to lower theirs before wowing them with her intelligence. I would fall for it if I hadn't seen her do the same thing during debates in the classes we've shared. "And also, what does being a queen even entail?"

"Sounds like an excellent question for him. I think a more important question is, why do you want to stay here?" I counter. Zara's dark brown eyes search my face, as if she's trying to read what I'm getting at.

"Because either way, I'm headed for the Afterlife. Might as well try to find some happiness," Zara answers simply but seems to get the picture that I'm not interested in talking to her. We sit in silence, waiting for the next name to be called. When it's Zara's, she pops up and strides to Sybil, and I swear I catch her hiking her skirt up just a little higher. I miss her as soon as she's gone, because even though we're regularly at odds, being in the presence of someone I know was comforting.

Eventually, I'm the only one left. I've sat here for hours, watching the girls leave one after the other, and I wish I had a book or something to distract me from seeing the minute hand make round after round after round until I get dizzy.

When Sybil walks in, they smile at me. "And then there was one. Follow me, Miss Hale."

I stand up and smooth out my dress before following them down the hall that Essos first emerged from when we arrived. At the end, they open a door and gesture for me to enter. The room is large with a fireplace on one side and a desk opposite. Between these two points are a long leather couch and a large comfy chair. The smell of the burning fire combined with vanilla puts me at ease.

Essos is seated at the desk, pouring over paperwork. He glances up at me, glasses perched on his nose, and my pulse jumps. It's like I've pulled away another layer of Essos. I could see myself taking his glasses off and distracting him while he works, taunting and teasing to see how long he can hold his focus while I use my feminine wiles on him. When our eyes meet, something between us tugs on my heart, drawing me to him. He signals to Sybil to close the door before looking back down. With eye contact broken, I'm able to get a better handle on my raging emotions. I've never had such a strong reaction to someone, a bone-deep need to be in their presence, and I don't understand why it's happening now. I study him from just inside the door, unsure what to do. Should I sit? Do I need to be invited to sit?

Essos doesn't seem to notice me watching him, so I take advantage. His glasses are thick, dark frames, giving him a Clark Kent look. The glasses don't distract from how ridiculously good-looking the man is. If anything, they accentuate it, making his eyes bluer and the strong line of his jaw more angular. He didn't have them on yesterday, and I wonder if they're only for reading.

"Please bear with me. I just received some unexpected paper-work. I know I've already made you wait several hours, and I would hate to make you wait too much longer," Essos says finally, looking up at me. "Have a seat, please. I'll be right with you."

Instead of sitting down, I wander to the bookshelves and glance at the titles, unable to read any of them. They appear to be in a different language, a combination of the Greek alphabet and something older. I want to reach out and run my fingers over the spines, but they look old, like my fingertip might break down the precious material. I can't imagine what is held in these tomes.

Although...the longer I look at some of the titles, the more clear they seem to become. I can make out *Antigone* and *The Odyssey* and more that were undecipherable, and I wonder if being in this world is changing my ability to read different languages.

On the floor beside the fireplace, Spot, Shadow, and Dave are resting, watchful eyes glancing from me to their master. Dave looks at me, his tail thumping furiously on his large bed. I walk over and rub his head, and I could swear he smiles at me.

"There we are. So sorry about that. You have my undivided attention." Essos notices me sitting with the dogs. "Although it would seem that I will have your divided attention," he continues with a smirk.

I stand and turn to face him. "No, undivided."

Essos gestures for me to have a seat on the couch, and so I do as he sits in the chair beside me. Dave whines and crawls on the ground toward me before settling at my feet.

"Tell me a little about yourself," Essos starts at the same time that I ask him what he does. He laughs a little and leans back in the chair. "All right. That is a fair question. I am a sort of ferryman and an overseer. I help people into their afterlife. Some people think that makes me a harbinger of death or the grim reaper, but I am not—I simply manage the Afterlife. It's a lot more complicated than that, but those are the broad strokes. Now, tell me about you."

"I'm not sure there's a whole lot to say." I look at the book-shelves. "Do you do a lot of reading in Ancient Greek or whatever language that is?"

"Deflection, nice. Yes, it's the only way I will read the *Iliad*. I find most translations not nearly as poetic. The other books are written in the language of the gods, my people. What was your plan for after college, what was your major?"

"Okay, here's the CliffsNotes version—I was an English major. I wanted to be a florist, but my adoptive parents didn't see it as a financially sound career choice. So, they wanted me to get an advanced degree as a fallback, but I didn't know what was going to come next." My words are rushed. Not wanting to see his expression, I look at the fire.

I can feel his total focus on me, and it draws my eyes back to him.

Essos cants his head, studying me, and I shift uncomfortably under the directness of his gaze.

"Clearly, you're not a fan of talking about yourself. When did your parents pass?" Essos asks delicately, and my eyebrows lift in surprise at his tone. I have to wonder if Essos is just really good at guessing, or if he's able to see the layers of loss someone has faced and all the ways death has touched their lives.

When I do look at him, I don't find what I expected. I find his expression inscrutable. His brow is furrowed slightly, but his face and hands are open, willing me to continue to talk about my life. Tentatively, he reaches a hand out to me, reaching first for my bare knee before he seems to think better of it, sliding his hand into mine with a reassuring squeeze. I expect the calming pressure he exerted the night before when people were in hysterics, but it doesn't come.

"My parents, Ron and Linda, died when I was a baby. You would think that babies would be easy to place, but my cute years were squandered with my maternal grandparents, who died when I was five. I was an absolute terror after that, so even if a family had wanted to foster-to-adopt me, I made myself unlovable. I landed with a really great foster family eventually and they adopted me, but we never got close. I think that was mostly my fault, though. They had high expectations—Phil is a congressman and Melinda's a lawyer. I think I regret that most—that I never got a chance to tell them how much I appreciated them loving me when I didn't think I was worth it. Instead, Cat became my family. It was easier to start over than to admit my mistakes, and if I could do it over, I wouldn't be so fucking stubborn." I force a laugh, and Essos lifts one corner of his mouth. Something about how he's holding my hand makes me want to open up to him and release all my secrets.

It would be easy to curl my feet under me and sit by the fire-place with a glass of wine and just tell him about my day until he put his work away to sit with me. I'm positive he's a scotch man, and he would join me there, on the floor with his tie loosened until we made love in front of the flames.

"Catalina mentioned that you're like a sister to her."

I look away from him and pat Dave, who has, as stealthily as a pit bull can, climbed onto the couch. With his tail still smacking the leather, he rests his head on my lap. "So does being the King of the Underworld come with a uniform?" I deflect again, uncom-fortable with how I've bared myself to him already. In my heart of hearts, I know that I'll bare my soul to him if he keeps me talking.

"I beg your pardon?" He frowns, leaning toward me.

"You and Sybil both wear black all the time. I wasn't sure if there was a reason for it."

"I'll let you in on a little secret, but you have to keep it to your-self. You think you can do that?" I hate that he says that to me like I'm a child, but I never get a chance to rebut. His question was rhetorical, as he is already unbuttoning his shirt. Something low in my stomach turns, and I realize that I want to be the one unbuttoning his shirt. My cheeks flush. His undershirt is a bright blue that matches his eyes. I lean toward him, my gaze catching on something around his neck. I reach out, my fingertips grazing the skin of his neck, and pull it from under his shirt. It's a bold action, but I can't help myself. His hand catches mine, and he holds it for a moment as I look at the pendant in my hand. There is a waning crescent moon wrapped in a vine with flowers on it. There are stars between the moon, and a sun completes the rest of the circle with what appears to be crushed petals in the resin. Gold metalwork binds it all together. It's a delicate piece, and not something I would have expected him to wear.

"Someone I loved very much gave this to me." His voice is unexpectedly gruff, and he clears his throat, pushing the emotion out of it. When he speaks, my fingers are close enough to his mouth that I can feel the brush of his lips against them.

I stare at it, hearing the sound of my laughter and almost seeing the glare of twinkling lights, but it seems far away. Our faces are close as I study the pendant, which has been worn smooth as if it was used as a sort of worry stone for centuries. There might have once been an engraving on the back of it, but it's long gone.

"To bring some light into your dark world." The words feel like the right thing for me to say at this moment. Essos is watching me closely as I let it go and look up at him, blinking away my confusion. His eyes close for a long moment, and I wonder if I've done something wrong, said the wrong thing, and I want to fix it. Very nearly, I reach out to cup his cheek.

"Something like that. You'll keep my secret?" Essos confirms.

I lean away from him, settling back into my spot on the couch. "That you like bright colors and wearing jewelry? I promise not to out the God of Death."

"Not the God of Death, God of the Dead, but thanks for the demotion. The first is a grim reaper, and the other a guardian. I shall hold you to that promise. If you want to be part of the process, I welcome you to stay...but this is your chance to leave." He pauses, waiting for me to speak, but when I open my mouth, his eyes shutter, locking away any thought and emotion on his face.

"I actually wanted to ask a favor." Essos's eyebrows lift. "Can you…" My voice breaks, and I take a breath. His hand is on my knee this time, giving me warmth. "It's stupid and inconsequential, but can you fix my phone? It was broken in the accident. I don't want to send any texts or anything, but I want to be able to look at photos of my parents and my cat."

At the mention of Waffles, Dave lifts his head, then shakes it in the dog approximation of disgust.

"Of course," Essos says, nearly leaping out of his chair. He raises his hand from my leg and holds out my phone to me, conjured from the air. The screen is now glossy and uncracked. I take it gratefully and squeeze it in my hand.

"I'm sure you get a lot of stories about people's regrets when they die." I shrug, not looking at him but staring instead at the dark screen of my phone. "My mom sent me a text asking what I wanted to do for the summer, and I ignored her. I was getting ready for a party and was tired of having the same conversation about what I wanted to do after college. My last text to my mom was to tell her I was going to miss Mother's Day for this volleyball game. It took dying for me to stop adding a qualifier, too. I've always called them my adoptive parents, but they were so much more. They were my parents, but I felt like if I didn't add that, I would somehow be dishonoring my birth parents."

"You're allowed to have complicated feelings about your parents. Relationships of all kinds are complicated, and family probably the most so. Even I have complicated feelings about family." His hand is on my cheek, brushing a tear away with almost reverence.

"Do gods have families like humans do?" I ask, trying to move my focus from how badly I want to cry. Breaking down into tears hardly seems queenly.

Essos leans back with a harsh laugh. "I have a mother and father and siblings like most people. It's possibly more complicated because I have lived for so long and seen so much. You'll learn about my family, but not until the final month before the ball. They can be overwhelming, so we—Sybil and I—keep that information back until it is need-to-know."

"Mommy and Daddy gods?"

Essos snorts but barrels on. "They are the mother and father to this world. They created many minor gods and goddesses and plants and trees together with their magic. Only my siblings and I are their true progeny, however.

"This evening we will have a formal dinner and a small gathering afterward. This will happen regularly so that I have a chance to get to know those of you who stay." Essos tucks his necklace back in and buttons up his shirt carefully. "Do not be surprised if other gods come to the house. I am still conducting business, and, as I mentioned, the Calling requires a specific set of circumstances to begin, so it is rare. We try to limit interference as much as possible to avoid disturbing you, but my sister, well..." He trails off.

I wait patiently for him to gather his thoughts.

"Some people will seek to manipulate you and turn you against me. They will fill your head with falsehoods about me, or worse. I am trying to keep them away at all costs, but I cannot guarantee it. All I ask is that, if you decide you don't want to be here any longer, you tell *me*. You are not my prisoner. But most important, Daphne...." He pauses until I look him in the eye. "I need you to trust me. Things are not always what they appear, and I hate that I can't tell you everything, but it's dangerous if too much is revealed too fast. I promise that, when this is all over, the truth will be revealed, but for now, as I explained, there are rules, and everyone here must follow them. Will you trust me?"

"Why can't you be fully honest with me?" I ask. Trust is a concept that has always been difficult for me to comprehend. I've found that when it's easily given, it's easily broken. When I first started in the foster care system, I was trusting, but that trust was abused time and time again. If I don't trust someone with my heart, they can't break it. And yet, at this moment, I want to believe that I can trust him. Sitting here, looking into his eyes, I can see the depths of how badly he wants me to trust him. So far, though, everything I've experienced here has been a careful manipulation. We were led here under cloak and dagger pretenses and told the truth only when it was convenient for him.

"Because there is only so much information that we can share at any time. Think of this process like an onion—we have to slowly reveal the information. I'm not going to beg you, but I will ask you one last time. Please, trust me."

But did I trust him? I would have to wait and see.

7

I take my time walking back to my room, studying the artwork in the hallways as I go. I catch sight of a Monet and pause before the painting from the *Water Lilies* series. My mind goes over and over what Essos said about being the king or god or manager of the Underworld.

I think about all that I know about death and the Afterlife. I think about the mythos surrounding it—heaven, hell, karma, reincarnation. I think about what I learned in my World Religion class and in life. I wish that I had used my time to ask him more questions about what to expect from the hereafter. Instead, I squandered it admiring how his glasses made his eyes bluer and wondering what it would be like to unbutton his shirt myself.

I should have asked who was right about the Afterlife. I should have asked him why he has been alone for so long. I should have asked so much more, but I was on the defense, too afraid of what it would mean to open my heart to him.

There is so much more to this house, not just Essos's office and the main area. As I climb the stairs to our rooms, I look to the right, toward the other wing of the house, and wonder if that is where Essos's rooms are. Is he only steps away from us every night, able to hear us gossip in our rooms? When he's lying in his bed, what does he dream about?

I hear chatter upstairs along with some tears as everyone speculates about what is to come and what this means. As I walk down the hall, murmurs make their way through the doors, snippets of the conversations the girls had with Essos as they tell their closest friends, their lifelines.

Cat is waiting in my room when I get back. As much as I love her, I wish she wasn't here so I could really think about my conversation with Essos. It feels like a raw nerve, opened to the elements. Can I put my trust in this man? Open myself up to the possible heartache of a rejection? I never had the same social worker for more than a few months, never the same family until I turned ten and was adopted. Him asking me for trust after I've known him only a day is like asking someone to get into a van labeled *Free puppies*.

At the same time, I can't stop thinking about the sun pendant. I believe that, if he never wanted me to see it, I wouldn't have. Was this his way of bridging trust with me? Then there was the matter of our accidental pre-breakfast meeting. Of course, he wouldn't want anyone to know about it, since it could end this entire process, and who knows when the next bus full of coeds will drive off a cliff.

"So that was...strange," Cat starts, pulling Honey Bear closer to her chest and her knees up to her chin. It's not surprising that she chose to bring her comfort animal into my room while she waited for me.

"I think at this point, we need to accept that strange is the new normal." I sit on the bench at the foot of my bed and pull off one boot and then the other. Should I tell Cat about meeting him this morning? I trust her, but something is holding me back, something about keeping it just between Essos and me. Well, and

Sybil, but it seems that he trusts them completely. "How was your fireside chat?"

"Well, we talked about how becoming his partner is akin to becoming president. I wouldn't just be some powerful man's wife. Whoever he chooses will have powers of her own, and he said he wants a true partner, someone to make decisions with jointly." Cat has already changed out of her outfit and into lounge clothes. I envy her, knowing that because my interview was so late, I have only a short amount of time before we need to change for dinner.

"Still plotting world domination, then?" I ask, my brown eyes meeting hers in the mirror.

"I'm still me, aren't I?"

I laugh.

"We're supposed to dress in an evening gown for dinner tonight."

"Jesus. What did we unwittingly sign ourselves up for?" I say, looking at my closet and realizing all those fine gowns make sense. I get the feeling that gone are the days of eating ramen for dinner in bed while wearing leggings and an old T-shirt. Instead, we're trying to become queens and have to look and act the part. "I guess we might as well spend our afterlife playing dress-up."

"What did you two talk about?" Cat asks, watching me from the corner of her eye.

I walk to the wall of shoes so that my back is to her. "The usual getting-to-know-you stuff. Hopes, dreams, how being an orphan has shaped who I am today. What his uniform is. Standard things."

"So, you told him about your parents?"

"I mean, not in detail, just the broad strokes. You'll be proud of me; I opened up more than usual." I'm not yet ready to admit to Cat the regrets I told Essos about. I'm sure she knows and would get it, but her own grief is still so fresh, so tender.

There's a pause as I think about how Cat spent our first night in the house crying herself to sleep. Her family was kind enough to take me in during the summer after freshman year, but forging a parent-child bond was not something that came naturally to me.

Eager to lighten the mood, I turn to face her. Her expression tells me that she knows I probably wasn't totally forthcoming with Essos. I hate that, without even knowing the content of my conversation, she's pointing out with only a look what a hypocrite I am. Essos is asking me to trust him by putting his trust in me. Not with his silly blue shirt, but by revealing the necklace, which is very dear to him.

"I mean, do I really need to divulge all my inner traumas to a man who knows enough about us that you have Honey Bear and my grandmother's rings are in my jewelry box? Unlikely."

Cat shrugs, squeezing Honey Bear tighter. How many times has Essos gone through this? How many times has he been burned in his attempt to find—what, love? At the least, he's trying to find eternal partnership, and I clammed up, unwilling to share anything. While trust might not come easily, I can see that he's also trying to find someone he *wants* to place his trust in. I can't imagine that trying to build relationships with twenty coeds is easy.

I have a sudden idea and start looking through my closet, but don't find what I'm hoping for. "Do you know how we can get in touch with Sybil?" I ask, prompting Cat to give me a funny look, but she graciously allows the subject change.

"I think they're a little like Bloody Mary—you have to say their name three times while turning in a circle with your eyes closed in front of a mirror."

I immediately do so, causing Cat to laugh until there is a knock at the door. My eyes fly open.

Cat beats me to the door and when she pulls it open to find Sybil on the other side of it, she bursts into laughter.

Sybil gives her a strange look and thrusts a sheet of paper into each of our hands. "Your schedules for the week. The times and outfit requirements are listed there for your convenience. Please be downstairs for dinner by 5 p.m." They turn to go, long braid swinging.

"Sybil!" I call out, stopping them. They turn toward me. "Can I speak with you?"

They nod and step back in, and I shoo Cat back to her own room to get ready. She looks almost hurt but seems to accept that I need my space.

Sybil closes the door behind them. "Is there something you need?" they ask, holding their folder to their chest.

"Actually, yes. Would you be able to get me something before tonight?"

Sybil tilts their head, curiosity written all over their features. "Why don't we see if I can?"

And so, I make my request.

8

I shouldn't be surprised that Sybil is able to fulfill my request, but I am. It does set me behind in getting ready, but I hardly mind, since it will help me send the right message tonight. I can't explain it, but I'm a bundle of nerves, anxious to get downstairs and get on with this evening.

I descend the stairs, my heels clicking with each step I take, my hand on the cold metal banister keeping me steady. Everyone is gathered in the ballroom, chatting, including Essos, who stands by the grand piano. I hold my head high as I walk down to meet him in my turquoise blue satin gown, the same color as the undershirt Essos showed me earlier in the day. The full skirt rustles as I make my way into the room.

Time seems to slow as Essos turns to look at me, taking in the full effect. I warm as his gaze sweeps me from top to bottom before coming back to meet my eyes. It's almost too much, like an inferno is burning inside me, and it has nothing to do with his powers and everything to do with how he's looking at me. His lips part as he reads into this exactly what I intended. The urge to run my thumb over his lower lip causes my mind to malfunction, because so easily the image of him nibbling gently on my thumb after the action comes to me. Even though I know that this is what he asked of me, my hands still shake with nerves over his reception.

The neckline is modest, but the dress is backless, which he doesn't yet see. My hair is swept away from my face again, in a simple chignon at the nape of my neck. The bruises on my face are not an exact match to the dress, but I can do only what I can. I wear no jewelry except for drop earrings. At the bottom of one hangs the moon, and on the other, the sun.

Beside Essos, Madison realizes that he's no longer listening to her. She might turn to face me, but I don't know, because I nearly stumble taking the next step. The restraint is obvious on Essos's face, as he takes a step toward me, but I just give him a bright smile and shake my head. If I don't look away from him, I will fall down the stairs and break my neck.

After Essos, I look for Cat in the crowd, and when I see her, I smile. She's dressed in a simple black high-low gown and bright pink heels. Around her throat is the emerald necklace again, and simple pearl studs adorn her ears. I've always admired her sense of style; she's able to take something simple and make it her own. I turn my attention back to Essos when he starts speaking.

"Now that Miss Hale has decided to join us, perhaps we should have our chat," Essos says, finally ripping his gaze from me to look at everyone else.

I make my way to stand beside Cat, Tiffany, and Zara. The girls wear a variety of dresses, from simple tea length to full ballgowns and slinky barely-there numbers. White-gloved servers circulate the room bearing silver trays full of champagne glasses. One with bronze skin and sandy-blond hair offers me a glass, and I have to fight the urge to down it all in one go. I take it with a smile and a demure nod of appreciation. The man oozes boyish charm with a mischievous smile and a wink. The waiter looks like he would be better suited for riding his surfboard on the beaches of California. I'm not complaining; he is yet another beautiful fringe benefit to being here.

"Four of you will be leaving us tonight," Essos continues. "Those of you who are leaving already know this. It is no great secret that this is about finding someone whom I have a connection with, and I'm sad to say those leaving do not feel that connection." If someone were to ask me, he doesn't look all that sad. He looks like a man who's had part of a burden lifted. I suppose when it comes to getting to know twenty—or rather sixteen—different women, every little bit counts. "There will be a chance for goodbyes later. I want to make sure all involved have the best sendoff." He pauses to take a sip from his own glass. His tuxedo gives him a classic, romantic air, and I'm a little surprised that it doesn't have tails. I can envision Essos playing the piano while I sit beside him, my head resting on his shoulder.

"After dinner, we shall practice dancing, but not the dancing you are used to. During the ball, you will be required to entertain my guests. You will have to exhibit grace under pressure as you dance and mingle with the highest-ranked members of my society, as you will be required to do when you are queen. This is one thing that will be expected of my partner at the end of the Calling.

"To assist you tonight, some friends of mine have come to see how much help you will need to learn our dances. These gentlemen have filled this role for numerous Callings before. You will each have a partner available to you during your dance practices for the duration. I will also dance with each of you during the evenings, giving us a chance to get to know each other. The gentlemen will join us after dinner. So, if you ladies will please lead the way..." Essos gestures toward the dining room, and we all file in.

It's the same room but tonight has a more intimate feel, with candles lit in the sconces and on the center of the table. They seem to have replaced the long table we sat at yesterday with a smaller one that seats us closer together. I appreciate that touch.

Dinner is more relaxed this evening. Those who are leaving drop the bomb during the appetizers. Their reasons vary, from wanting to move on to see family to one girl admitting that Essos is simply not her type. There are a lot of tears shared over the news, and while none of the four are anyone I knew very well, I'm still surprised by the wave of sadness I feel. They were sorority sisters and were tied by those bonds. It's like the last vestiges of normal are being left behind as each one leaves.

Tonight, Cat is seated next to Essos. We will be rotating for each meal so that we all get a chance to talk with him.

It's impossible to look at the two of them and not see how regal she looks beside him, her blond locks curled, framing her face. She leans closer to him to tell him something, and he closes the distance to hear her better, their laughter inciting more than a few jealous glances. I imagine her as the Queen of the Underworld, ruling by his side, and a small pang settles into my chest. I hate myself a little bit for it.

I'm seated at the opposite end of the table, the farthest point from my lifeline. Directly across from me are Tiffany and Zara, who are having their own conversation. The same waiter from earlier offers me bread. I manage to catch his eye as he moves about the table, which earns another smirk and a wink. No one else gets the same attention from him, and my curiosity is piqued. Beside me, Anna is talking about her interview today with Essos.

"So, he's telling me that he's the King of the Underworld. And I'm all, 'But what does that *mean?*' And he's all, 'That means that I have to herald souls from their old lives to their afterlives.' And then I say, 'So, like, everyone gets to go to the Afterlife?' and then he asks if I can keep a secret, and I totally nod, and then he just tells me that he can't tell me that yet." She's talking to anyone that will listen, and I'm one of those people, though I'm trying to pretend I'm not as I butter my roll.

During dinner, Sybil announces that we will be split into groups of four for the remainder of the process. I hold my breath, waiting for them to announce who I'm grouped with, and I let go of the breath I'm holding when my name is called with Cat's. Also in our quad are Zara and Tiffany. Being grouped with the people I know best here makes me breathe easier, even though Zara and I haven't always seen eye to eye. Of all the people I would want to be with, those are the three I would pick for myself.

We each smile at each other, but when I meet Tiffany's eyes, her smile doesn't quite reach them. I make a mental note to check in on her after tonight to see how she's coping. She's radiant in a simple strapless yellow gown that complements her ebony skin. She kept her look simple while the rest of us tripped over ourselves to try and stand out.

Tonight, Zara chose a show-stopping red dress with a deep slit and a low neckline. She's always boldly and unapologetically herself. I know she'll have no problem with the dance portion of the night, given her training as a dancer. I, on the other hand, will have to find a way to become a wallflower and hope that Essos doesn't seek me out. It's not that I'm against dancing or anything, but I am tragically uncoordinated, which makes me tragically bad at it.

Unlike breakfast, we're all served the same meal with some differences for vegetarians or vegans. Part of the meal is a pesto pasta, which I'm careful not to get on my dress, knowing that oil-streaked fabric is not the look I'm going for. Madison stops her waiter mid-serve to alert him to her nut allergy. Sybil swiftly moves in to let her and everyone else know that we no longer have any allergies to fear.

It's bizarre to think of the things we once worried about and now don't have to. Madison's delighted reaction to trying something with pine nuts in it makes us all laugh, helping to ease a layer of tension in the room. As a special treat, for dessert Essos brings out macarons for her to try, and I think I might see her shed a tear for how much she enjoys them. I loved them in life and eye the colorful cookies jealously, making a note to ask for some for myself. Watching Essos, I believe he enjoys telling Madison about all the new foods she'll get to experience that she couldn't previously. His excitement over this might be more than Madison's own, and it's infectious.

After dinner, we are led back into the ballroom, where 16 gentlemen in a line wait in full tuxes, hands folded behind their backs. I feel like I'm on my very own episode of *The Bachelorette*. I glance at each of them as I move down the row. Recognition dawns on me as I look at their faces. At one point or another, these men have been flitting around the house as waiters. I've seen two of them talking to Sybil, including a tall, dark-skinned man who was at the pool yesterday and a short white guy who wears his long brown hair in a ponytail at the nape of his neck.

One of them is the sandy-blond waiter with the champagne glass and bread. He manages to catch my eye and gives me another bold wink while Sybil announces who our partners will be. When my name is called, I step forward at the same time as my waiter. He gives me a small bow as all the men before him have done for their partners. I wait for him to approach me and then take his offered hand, and he leads me off to one side while the pairings are completed.

As the rest of the names are called, he leans in close to my ear. "I'm Finn."

I smile, looking up at him. "Sybil said that. Did you enjoy eavesdropping as you passed around the bread?"

He grins like a cat that caught the canary. "You're going to be a tough nut to crack, aren't you?" He lifts our joined hands in invitation as the music begins.

I start to fully face him, but think better of it, instead moving to the nearest wall out of the way of everyone. "I don't think so. I would rather not dance."

His golden eyes twinkle at my refusal. "I don't think you have a choice. I won't step on your feet, I promise," he says sweetly.

I look past him at the dance floor, where everyone is trying to get to know their new partners. "It's not *my* feet I'm worried about," I mutter, but I let him lead me onto the floor.

He holds me a little closer than seems necessary.

"Shouldn't we get to know each other better before starting to dance? This is awkward." I press.

"Nope. Dancing will help us become friendlier because of how intimate it can be. How have you been adjusting?" he asks, trying very hard to hide a wince as I step on his toes.

"Ah, you know, what's not to love? Fine clothes, food; it's practically a vacation. Intimate? You sound like you're here to score someone for yourself." I step on his foot again and mutter an apology.

"Hardly. Trust me, it's not a vacation for much longer. Sybil will be breaking you down in no time. In fact, they are the reason most people leave." He pulls me tighter against him to avoid a rogue dancer behind me. I look up at his face, so very near to mine.

"Have you been through this before?" I ask, my gaze darting to his lips. He loosens his hold.

"A few times, and by that, I mean all of them. Essos is like a brother to me. I'm happy to help out." Before I can ask any more questions, the song changes, and behind me someone clears their throat.

"Might I cut in?" Essos asks, offering me his hand.

Finn instantly releases me and bows. "Absolutely. I need to ice my feet anyway." He winks and disappears into the dresses and tuxes.

I glance around, realizing there is no way for me to get out of this. "I have to warn you, I'm not very good." I take Essos's hand. He rests his other hand on my shoulder blade, his fingers brushing my bare skin. A shiver runs down my spine.

"Cold again?" he asks, his voice velvety soft. I struggle to look at him, remembering the feel of the mystery man's hands in my dream. How they tangled in my hair, and how they lingered on the inside of my thigh. I think about the feel of the man's lips against mine, at first lazy, like we had all the time in the world, before growing more urgent.

"No, not now," I whisper, finally meeting his eye. He leans in, his mouth beside my ear, and I can feel his warm breath on my skin. My thoughts are racing as fast as my heart at the thought of having Essos between my legs. Under my hand, I can feel the strength in his arms and shoulders, and I feel safer than I have in my entire life.

"Is this gown your way of saying you'll trust me?" He pulls back to look me in the eye, a sort of desperation there.

I wonder if he knows about the dream—if he knows that he's taking the place of the mystery man when I close my eyes. Have I lived my whole life just to die and be here with him? Has fate been a cruel mistress just to lead me to this moment?

The insane thought skips around in my brain. "Yes," I whisper.

He nods. "Good. Then stop fighting and let me lead you." His hand slides down, down, down to the small of my back. I nod as he pulls me closer and we find a cadence to our movements. We remain silent as we dance, and I give in to letting him lead me, so consumed by his proximity that I could hardly maintain a conversation if I tried. I wonder if his lips are as soft as those of the man in my dreams, and how it would be to kiss Essos like that.

I desperately want to find out.

Unexpectedly, he spins me away and then returns me to him, closer than before, if that's possible. I hold his hand tightly as he smiles. I don't fight dancing the way I did with Finn. My body wants to follow Essos's lead.

"I think this color looks great on you," he whispers in my ear, his hot breath caressing my neck.

"You should try it sometime," I volley back at him with a smirk. I'm disappointed when the song ends. His eyes betray the same disappointment, but given that this is only the first night, it's his duty to dance with everyone. He releases me then sketches a bow.

"Maybe I will." He smiles and leaves me on the dance floor.

My gaze follows him as he approaches Zara and asks her to dance, and it's almost painful to watch. I regret not talking to him more and want to kick myself.

Finn appears beside me with a glass of champagne in his hand.

"See? He didn't have to hobble off to ice his feet after dancing with me," I remark, taking the drink, just holding it as I watch Zara settle into Essos's arms as close as she can get. She moves with grace, her feet barely touching the ground. He laughs as he tries to change it up with a faster box step, and she matches his moves easily.

Finn's gaze follows mine, and he turns to face me, grabbing my upper arm gently. "Essos is too much of a gentleman to show it, even if he did. Why don't we sit?" He doesn't wait for an answer, leading me to the couches. We settle on one, and I can't tear my eyes away from Zara and Essos. I can see them chatting as he twirls her, and when he laughs, an ugly feeling settles into my soul.

"Let me guess. These bruises you wear proudly are from your accident?" Finn asks, gesturing to my face and shoulder. I pull my shoulders back, adjusting my posture at his scrutiny.

"Yes, and I'll let them heal naturally, thank you very much," I retort.

Finn snorts and sips his whiskey. His golden-brown eyes study me closely. "There is nothing natural about the Calling, sweetheart. Why don't you look at me and not them?"

I turn toward Finn fully so that I can't see Essos in my peripheral vision. My mouth twitches as I try not to look again.

"Daphne, it's going to be a very long three months if you don't get used to this now. Essos has to go through this entire process to make sure he finds the right girl. Just know that it's as tough on him as it is on you, and he has his day job to handle as well as you lot. Cut him some slack."

I let out a breath, considering this. "So, what, you're my stand-in for the next few months?" I take a sip of my drink, trying to pace myself.

Finn's lips quirk, his brown eyes shining as he considers me. "Something like that. I need to get you into dancing shape, because the Calling Ball is no joke. There are going to be nasty people there who don't want to see Essos happy. For them, keeping Essos down keeps them up, and I have no interest in letting this Calling fail."

I look at him sharply, pulling my gaze away from where Cat is laughing so hard that she snorts. "Fail? Why would that happen?"

Finn shrugs, draining his glass as he prepares to answer my question. "There's always one reason or another—none of the girls were a good fit, or occasionally rules get broken and it needs to end. I think one year he just dismissed them all right after they showed up. There was a lot of pushback when he did that. He has his reasons, but know that the ball is only the illusion of the finish line. After the ball, his choice has to contend with his family, and they are truly something else."

I want to ask why he's being so cryptic, but I get distracted watching Essos go outside with Zara. His hand is on the small of her back as they step into the fresh air. I regret sitting next to the windows, because all I can do is watch as she tilts her head up to him and presses her lips to his.

Finn must see something on my face; his gaze follows mine. He curses under his breath and stands abruptly. After removing the champagne from my hand, he places our glasses aside before taking my hand in his and leading me onto the dance floor.

"Sweetheart, please trust the process. It's about Essos finding a partner for life. He's been looking for a very long time, and he's been patient about it, but you have to also... just..." Finn pauses, glancing toward the windows then to me. "Trust him," Finn stresses emphatically.

"You all talk of trust as if it's a piece of gum to be given freely. Trust is something that you earn. I can hardly think of a reason that he's earned it from me." I just told Essos I would trust him, and now I want to stomp back to my room and wash off all the makeup and just sleep for years. Instead, I focus on dancing, not looking up when Essos and Zara re-enter the room.

"Don't be a child, Daphne," Finn says seriously, his voice flat. "You're better than that. This is no different from some dating show, or even just dating around. It's not exclusive—it just sucks because it's in your face that he's with these other girls. He's been looking for literally centuries. You can be patient for three months. Besides, from what I can tell, he's given *you* his trust."

I look up and flash Finn a fake bright smile.

I'm lying to myself if I say I can't pinpoint why I'm acting like a petulant child. I don't want to share Essos. I don't know if I want to be with him, but I am drawn to him in a way that I've never felt before. I want to explore whatever this is or could be in normal circumstances, where I have Cat at the ready with an excuse if the date is shitty. I want to be able to open up to him slowly. I want him to have time to earn my trust instead of me having to give it freely.

I consider the question I posed to Zara earlier. Why do I want to be here? I didn't think it would be like this, having to watch the man I'm interested in make out with other girls, but if I was hoping he would kiss me eventually, why not consider that others would want that too? It was one thing to watch dating contests on TV—I never considered what it would be like to live through one myself. I'm drawn to Essos in a way I never was to anyone in the real world. I want to know what his hair looks like first thing in the morning and whether he has bad habits only his partner would know. I want to give this a chance. I'll figure out what it means to be queen later.

Finn tries to engage me for the rest of the night, doing what he can to make me laugh. I try to ask leading questions about Essos where I can, but Finn doesn't fall into my thinly veiled trap.

"Was there ever a Mrs. Essos? Does he even have a last name?" I ask, five glasses of champagne and two shots of tequila in. I feel bolder as I take another sip of champagne. Finn hesitates before he leans against the banister outside in the same place where I spoke with Essos just that morning. I lean on the banister too and look up at him, realizing that I might have stumbled onto something.

"There was someone in his life before all this, yes. And he does indeed have a last name; he's not Cher." He's choosing his words carefully, clearly not as tipsy as I am.

I RUB OVER MY HEART, trying to soothe this odd pang over Essos having been with someone before the Calling. "Who was she?"

Finn studies me, "She was another goddess, and she—" He cuts off suddenly, like he can't go on. Clearing his throat, Finn tries again. "Then there's also the women during the Callings. His last name is—" Again his voice cuts off. His head drops back in what I think is frustration. He reaches out and grabs an abandoned drink and finishes it instead.

"How are you not hammered right now?" I ask. I kick off my heels and drop three inches. I regret this action almost immediately, knowing that there's no way I'll put them back on. Having to look up at Finn makes me go a little crossed-eyed when I realize just how much taller he is.

"I've had a long time to build up my tolerance." He takes another sip of his whiskey.

"So, what, you're like immortal or a god too?"

Finns lets out a barking laugh. "Something like that. It's a lot more complicated, and I worry that your tiny human brain will explode if I tell you too much. That happened to one of the girls once, and the clean-up was not pretty, so now we try to be careful with how much information you're given. There are also lines I literally cannot cross."

Essos's words from earlier about the dangers of finding out too much too fast come back to me. I know I'm gaping, because my ability to control my facial expressions left me three glasses ago.

Finn fights to stay serious, but eventually, his lips screw up into a grin. "I wish you could see your face right now," he says with a laugh.

I reach out to hit him. "Don't be a shit. That was so far from funny, I'm pretty sure it's on another planet called Opposite of Funny." I pause. "This is actually a pretty scary prospect. I mean, I'm facing down death, literally, like, that's what Essos is, right? The God of Death? Sorry, God of *the* Dead—he said that God of Death was a demotion. Right, and like... It's like, I can follow this bizarre fever dream down this path to god knows where, or I can go to my afterlife, and just be dead, and who even knows what that is?

"I don't really know what I want from this whole thing, if I do even want it. Essos is asking me to trust him, but I have literally trusted only one person in my whole life, and that's Cat. Even right now, if my insubishions...wait, that's not right. Whatever, you know what I mean—they're lowered, and part of me is whispering to stop, but the drunk part of me is just sitting on that part of my mind. Anyway..." I'm drunk-babbling, and I can't stop myself. "So, it's not easy to just lay my trust at someone's feet and then watch him with other girls, which is like, the literal opposite of what trust is supposed to be, right? Is this like speed dating for him? And I'm, what, like, dating a guy who is dating fifteen other women, and are we even dating?

"I don't know what I wanted out of life. I was twenty-one years old. But I do know I wasn't done living." I swipe angrily at the tears that spring to my eyes. I realize the second shot of tequila was a mistake, because it's like a dam inside me has opened up, ready to spill my whole life to Finn. "Fucking tequila," I scold myself, wiping at more tears.

Finn reaches out a hand and rubs my arm. "Is this okay?" he asks, and I nod, letting him envelop me in a hug. This manages to soothe me somehow.

He pulls back, wiping an errant tear. "Gods, this is only night one, and you're already drunk-crying. This is not easy for you. I know. Essos knows. Sybil knows. Everyone knows it, but not everyone will care. For the past millennium, Essos has been alone. For the past five hundred years, he's gone through this process, waiting for the right soul. Each time, there's a large group of women, all scared, all uncertain. But so is Essos, because finding the right person to lead the Underworld and the Afterlife with him is fucking hard, to be frank. He wants a woman with a vagina of steel who won't back down and is strong beyond her years. Every time I think he's found someone, he lets his hope free, and it always comes back to him damaged. There is only one woman for him, no matter how many times he's tried.

"He understands how you feel. He's a really great listener, if you ever decide that you can open up to him. I'm sorry that you don't have more people you can trust, but just like your trust is a bird you nurture inside you, afraid to let it go, so is Essos's hope. He has let that bird go more times than I can even count, and it always comes back battered and bruised. Despite that, he always tries again.

"If there was ever a time to learn to trust, Daphne, it's now."

Before I can respond, Cat pokes her head outside. "There you are, gorgeous! Sybil wants us all in for a final dance before we *retire* for the evening." She grins, a thin sheen of sweat glistening on her forehead. She's been dancing the night away with her sorority sisters who are leaving. She's always fought to include me, but I know tonight is important to them. Mindful of what they all must be going through, I stayed out of the fray as they sang their sorority songs, although I managed to get roped into those two shots.

Finn stands up and adjusts his suit jacket before offering his arm to me. "Come on, Cinderella. You may have already lost your shoes, but you have one more dance before you turn into a pumpkin." I smile and take his arm, letting him lead me inside. I leave my shoes where they fell.

Around me, the sisters of Epsilon Lambda Delta are hugging those who are leaving. Tears run down their faces. I watch them hug and dance as contemporary music plays, a farewell to those who won't be with us in the morning.

Before we begin our final dance, I reach up a hand to pull out the clip that was holding my hair in place, and I shake my dark locks free. Uninhibited, and far less deadly to his feet with no shoes on, I let Finn lead me onto the dance floor once again. He twirls me, and I feel like we're stealing the show when, out of the corner of my eye, I see Essos watching.

Instead of worrying about him, I focus on me.

9

Is it Essos? Or am I just inserting him into my mystery man's place because he's all I can think of?

WE'RE ON A BEACH, *the wind whipping my hair across my face. I stand, alone at first, looking over the water with a shawl pulled tight around my shoulders, cold, trying to find warmth where I can. Hands wrap around me, pulling me against a firm chest.*

"You are always so cold, my love," he says, ducking his head next to mine. He nuzzles my ear and places a gentle kiss below my lobe.

"Only when you're not here to warm me." I turn in his arms so that I'm facing him. The sun is shining in my eyes, so I can't look directly at him. Instead, I rise on my toes to kiss him, only able to reach the spot on his neck just below his ear where he kissed me.

"I want to build our home here. I want to have the beach at my fingertips."

"What else, can I give you, my love?"

"I want a library, and gardens, and stables. I want a vineyard,

because I want to make wine that even Dion will covet. Of course, we will entertain. We need a lot of space, so a lot of bedrooms."

"We'll need to fill those bedrooms," he says, mischief tinging his voice. "I'll give you everything you asked for. But I can't give away my heart."

"No?"

"You've already got it."

He dips his head and kisses me full on the mouth. We stay there for what feels like hours, watching the sun set over the water, kissing occasionally, but mostly just taking in the sky.

INSTEAD OF WAKING in strong arms, I open my eyes to find I am alone in my bed, the sun only just rising. It's almost painful to get up as the weight of lost hopes and dreams layers over me. My first dream, I could have chalked up to being a fantasy—a weird, period-drama fantasy. After all the *Downton Abbey*-esque moments, that wouldn't be surprising, but this feels like more. I'm crushed by the sensation that I've lost something

My head is still in a fog as I go down to breakfast in my pajamas, which is appropriate attire, per Sybil's schedule. I appreciate the detailed schedule, which includes specifics down to the types of shoes one should and shouldn't wear. Zara and Cat have their heads bent together, whispering about something. I'm surprised that I'm not the first one up and am glad not to be the last.

I take my seat beside Cat, curious to know what they're talking about. I don't have to wait long to find out, because Zara gladly tells me all about it.

"Essos and I kissed last night," she says excitedly, and it's like my stomach drops out of my body at the reminder. Somehow, in the haze of the booze and my dream, I had managed to forget this.

My brain starts concocting lies to make myself feel better, my favorite being that she's just trying to intimidate others. From the looks on some of the faces, it's working. I force myself to listen to her.

"And then we spent the remainder of the evening on the beach, waiting for the sun to rise. I just got changed now. Oh, Daphne, we talked all night, about everything from families to history to pop culture. He knows about books and movies and all the things in the mortal world." Zara's story explains why Sybil looks particularly weary this morning. Normally, they stand in the corner with their hands behind their back, alert and watchful, but today they are nursing a coffee.

My breakfast is placed before me, and I give my thanks to the server, but I can barely stomach eating now. If Finn and Essos want me to trust the process, then that is what I have to do, but the whole thing feels absurd, and I wonder if I should ask to move on to the Afterlife.

No. I will never leave Cat, not willingly anyway. If she wants to stick this out, then so will I.

"That sounds *so* special," I choke out, before shoving a forkful of food into my mouth. The eggs have no taste this morning.

The schedule today calls for no time with Essos until dinner. Instead, we're going to learn more about the Calling and the traditions we'll be expected to know for the Calling Ball.

Learning and college feel so long ago, I can't imagine having to do something as mundane as going to class. Maybe, though, learning about Essos and the traditions of his people will give me something to do besides drown in jealousy.

Sybil slips out of the room once everyone is at breakfast. When Essos appears, he smiles and asks what we thought about the dancing and the ball. I keep silent, not wanting to think about Essos kissing Zara, or how dirty this level of jealousy feels.

"What about you, Daphne? You usually have an opinion," Essos says.

"I think Finn was really nice, and I hope I didn't do permanent damage to his feet." I avoid his eyes and take another bite of my breakfast in hopes of avoiding talking further.

"You're a terrific dancer, Essos," Zara says, putting a hand on his arm. An ache in my jaw makes me realize I've been clenching my teeth.

He pats her hand and nods. "All of you were wonderful, and I hope it was a fine enough sendoff for your friends. Although they didn't have their own escorts, I believe all of your escorts did their part to make sure no one felt left out." Everyone murmurs their agreement, but we all fall silent when Sybil rushes in and bends to Essos's ear. His mouth presses into a flat line, and he abruptly excuses himself.

Sybil takes over, ordering us all to get ready for the day to come.

When we come down to the ballroom, it has been reorganized into a classroom of sorts. There are notebooks scattered about on the couches, which are all facing a chalkboard. Sybil stands at the front, writing various dates and names on the board. I recognize a few of the names, such as Aristotle and Helen, and places, like Troy and Sparta. I don't recognize the place at the top of the list —Solarem.

"Ladies, please take your seats. You will note that on your schedules, once a day, you will have two hours with me to learn more about history. As Essos mentioned initially, you will be attending this ball and attempting to impress the citizens of Solarem with your knowledge of history, the arts and philosophy. Many of these gods lived it, and they love nothing more than to talk about their glory days. Your success depends on being able to impress these people, so take these lessons to heart."

"Solarem?" I ask, impatient. They might cover this later, but I think context is important.

"The realm of the gods. Currently, we are in one small part of that realm, however, the main city of Solarem, where most reside, is above us, in the clouds." Their eyes search my face, and as if they realize that I'm not going to let it go, pushes on. "Solarem has its own separate ruler, which we will address later. In an effort to be closer to those he rules, Essos established his home here, closer to the Underworld. Think of Solarem as a three-tiered cake—the top layer is the city, situated in the clouds, and below that is Earth. There is a veil between Solarem and this home and the mortal realm. If someone pulled back that veil, mortals would see a floating city. The final layer is the Underworld, where Essos rules.

"I have heard some of you call him the God of Death or Lord of the Underworld. One of those titles is correct. He is a god, but not of death—he is God or King of the Underworld. He prefers Lord, but will—how do you say it these days? Flex?—he will flex before others and insist he is given his rightful respect as king. All the people we are to discuss are gods or goddesses, major or minor. Remember to show them their rightful respect."

I flip open the notebook and start scribbling furiously, trying to keep track as best I can. The information flies at us faster than we can keep up. I glance over and see that Cat is writing in the shorthand she's been using forever.

Sybil stresses the importance of knowing the difference between Helen of Troy and someone named Helene, and to speak deferentially to the people who will be at the ball. Before I know it, the lesson is over.

Sybil explains that the lessons will get more and more detailed. More than anything else, it sounds like we have to learn the gossip of old. In the Sybil-us that they provided, I see we're going to cover the rise and fall of the Romans and the Greeks. I avoided philosophy in college, but I am going to be learning a lot of it now. Much of our first lesson was a setting of the stage before we learn who the key players are. Sybil promises us that, all in due time, they will teach us about the various gods and goddesses, including Essos's family tree, but we need to learn the boring bits before we can get to the good stuff.

After the lesson, we're led down the hallway toward Essos's office, stopping at each painting in the hall. Sybil confirms that the one I admired is indeed one of Monet's *Water Lilies* series, hanging beside an original Picasso. Each name they list as we walk down the hallway brings me back to my freshman Art History seminar.

"This is Essos's pride and joy," Sybil says as they continue down the hall then stop at a set of double doors across from Essos's office. They push open the doors and lead us into a full gallery. I don't remember seeing these doors when I had my one on one.

"I know that you received a lot of information this morning, so you have the rest of the day to yourselves. Take your time in here, or do what you please." They take up a post in one corner of the room.

Almost everyone wanders around for a few minutes before leaving to sit outside in the sun. I catch sight of Cat pouring over her notebook as she walks out. I opt to stay behind and look at what is before us. Knowing that Essos already has priceless treasures in his hallway, I want to know what he keeps formally in his gallery. I'll admit that my attention during Art History 101 was sporadic at best, but some of the images before me are familiar.

I lose track of time, but I get at least a half hour alone to forget my circumstances, which I need. Everything is a touch overwhelming. I stop when I come upon *The Starry Night* by van Gogh, easily my favorite work of art. Surrounded by some of the most famous pieces of art in the world, I don't understand how they're here, but at the moment, I don't care.

"Beautiful." A voice barely breathes the word. I've grown familiar with that voice, and I'm not surprised when I look up to see Essos standing beside me, watching my expression. A small part of me wants to think he's talking about me and not the painting, but he kills that hope when he gestures at the art. "Isn't it?"

"Breathtaking," I say, nodding. He smiles, gesturing farther down to *Birth of Venus* by Boticelli, and I walk with him.

"I love to see the art admired. Too many mortals stop for a picture to say they've seen it without really enjoying the piece."

"I never went to many art galleries, but I can see that being frustrating—that people don't take a moment to enjoy the beauty." I pause as we move to another piece. "I didn't peg you for an art collector."

"Why not? Running the Underworld has its perks. The painting in the hall was a gift, a continuation by Monet for...uh..." he actually stumbles on his words "...me. It was a gift for me. My realm is surrounded by the most precious resources to mankind. That puts me in a unique position financially. All the world's gemstones come from my realm, and my younger brother, who is in charge of everything else, can't be bothered with such pedestrian problems as finances. It falls on my shoulders to see that precious gemstones and metals are produced for the mortal realms, and as a reward, I'm also in charge of the banking institutions for the citizens of Solarem. So, I acquire beautiful things to brighten my domain." He smiles, clasping his hands behind his back.

I consider what he said about gemstones coming from his domain. All the sparkling gems in each of our rooms make sense. We continue to walk through his gallery, and every so often he pauses before a painting and tells me about it and what it means to him. As we go, I find myself admiring the animation in his face and tone almost more than the artwork.

Eventually, a thought occurs to me, and I take a stuttering step. "Aren't we breaking the alone-time rule?" I ask. I don't want him to stop talking, stop giving me these little nuggets of information I wouldn't otherwise learn until much later, but I also don't want to get kicked out. The thought of that happening nearly makes me stagger.

He pauses to gesture at Sybil, standing in their corner and watching us but trying to pretend they're not. "No. Sybil brought you all to the gallery so I could give you a tour. My meeting ran later than expected, and so I was late. You're the only one still here, and I believe we shouldn't let a good museum outing go to waste. Would you like to see the interior of the Sistine Chapel?"

I nod, too shocked to say anything as he leads me through another doorway at the back of the gallery. The door does indeed lead to the Sistine Chapel, complete with pillars, the altar, and the glorious ceiling.

Essos lets me walk around and take in every bit of it, occasionally dropping an odd fact as he follows me. "Contrary to what many people say, Michelangelo was standing as he painted it, not lying on his back on scaffolding," he says as I study the famous work.

"So, what you're saying is that Spaceship Earth is wrong?" I ask, turning to face him. He's studying me intently, and I feel my cheeks warm. I can imagine what I must have looked like with my head dropped back, gaping at the beauty above me.

"The mouse was wrong," he admits grimly, meeting my eyes. I laugh, earning a smile, and my stomach stumbles for a different reason. Is this what it feels like to fall for someone at nearly first sight? I never thought it possible, but with each glance from him, I find myself flushing with the desire to be around him more. I wish that he would smile all the time, because when he does, it feels like the whole room is more illuminated, and his eyes are clear and bright.

"How is this all possible?" I ask, letting Essos lead me to a bench. His hand is on the small of my back as we sit to just look, and I want him to leave it there forever. I sit for only a moment before standing abruptly and then lying on the ground, so I can stare at the ceiling without straining my neck.

"We are in a different plane of existence. This house exists on earth—on your Earth—but where we are is neither here nor there. I am able to keep things from the mortal realm here without them ever moving there. The doorway to the Sistine Chapel is a portal of sorts to the real thing. It's easier for me to do that than to actually visit the mortal realms."

I nod as if this makes sense.

Essos gets off the bench and stands over me before lying on the floor beside me, our heads very close. I turn to look at him, and I'm close enough to see a freckle or two on his nose. When he turns to face me, our noses nearly brush, his eyes widening at just how close we are. It's hard to miss from this distance how his eyes sweep to my lips then up again before his gaze travels back to the ceiling. His Adam's apple bobs as he swallows. "It's quite a bit outside anyone's grasp. If this were not my own life, I'm not sure I would understand it myself."

Taking his cue, I look back up, trying to see it through the eyes of someone who was there to watch it be built. I reach a hand toward his, unsure what to expect, and he twines his fingers with mine. His hand is smooth and warm as he rubs his thumb over mine.

"Have you always led alone?" I ask, turning to face him. Finn confirmed that there was someone before, but not in what role. I hope that, perhaps foolishly, Essos will open up to me a little about his life. I know there are limits, but surely telling us facts about himself isn't one of them. He turns his head toward me, and all that light I saw just moments earlier dims. I'm sorry for inflicting that on him. I wish I could read his mind and know what's going on as his blue eyes study my face.

"No, not always. But I—I can't elaborate."

I nod.

He lets out a long sigh, looking past me, then back at my face. "There was someone a lifetime ago. I can't say any more than that." He is handing me this piece of trust, and I think a piece of his heart along with it. I give his hand a gentle squeeze. He sounds like he wants to talk about her, or him, but these pointless rules won't let him.

"Who are all the people that we're going to meet at the ball?" I ask, changing the subject. Sybil told us some of it, and it feels like a safe enough topic.

"Ah, many gods and goddesses from Solarem. Nymphs and dryads. My family will be there, but just my siblings—none of their children will be in attendance, nor will my parents. They've taken retirement from building the realms and are off living their lives or whatever it is retired gods do." He sounds wistful. "Sybil will be giving you the ins and outs of who is who as part of your lessons."

"They started to. What happened this morning that dragged you away from breakfast?" I press.

He reaches his free hand toward the bruise on my face. His fingers graze my skin, but I don't look away, settling into the warmth of him touching my face. It's an intimate gesture, one I've seen between my adoptive parents so many times. My father was always looking for some excuse to be touching his wife, brushing a lock of hair away from her face, adjusting her coat so she was warm, holding her hand.

I might not have had the ideal childhood, but I grew up watching my grandparents, who loved each other for fifty years, and watching my adoptive parents, who also loved each other deeply. I've seen what kind of life all-consuming romantic love can bring you, and I want it so badly for myself.

My eyes close, and I catch a whiff of paint and dust. In the distance, I can almost hear the sound of my and my mystery man's laughter. He sounds like Essos. Am I hearing what I want to hear? My voice says something, but it sounds far away.

"You can't be serious that he's going to stand on these scaffolds and keep painting this; my neck aches just thinking about it!"

"My dear, I promise you, this will be a sight to behold when he's done. Just you wait." His voice is barely a whisper on the wind.

"Please?" Essos asks, his voice pleading as his fingers dance over the edges of the bruise. My eyes shoot open at the sound of his voice in the here and now.

My face is no longer swollen, and I'm almost positive that Sybil had something to do with that. While I want to hold on to this tangible evidence that we went through something, I can see that the bruise pains him. For me, it's a reminder that I've died—I can't imagine what sort of reminder it must be for Essos. Perhaps that countless women have to die for him to find a partner. I can find another way to remember that this is real; it doesn't need to be so dramatic, so in his face.

My head moves, nodding. I'm not sure why, but this time I let him heal me, letting go of the life I knew before. I close my eyes again as my face warms, and I'm not sure if it's a blush or from him. I keep them closed until the warmth goes away, thinking about all those I left behind, and all that I've lost. The list is short, just my adoptive parents, Phil and Melinda, who I am sure will land on their feet, and my cat, Waffles. It's time for me to start moving forward instead of holding on to my pain and regret.

My eyes flutter open as Essos withdraws his hand. I'm about to ask him about the odd daydream I had about the Sistine Chapel, and if these dreams are more than just dreams, when he answers my earlier question.

"This morning there was fighting in the mortal realm, and I had to tend to a sudden influx of souls as well as address the reason. The situation is more complicated than that, but again, broad strokes. The events of the Calling mean that business cannot be conducted as usual, so I needed to send an emissary to handle it."

I want to ask him more, but Sybil approaches us and taps their wrist, signaling that time is up. Essos is the first to rise, and he offers me his hand and pulls me to my feet. Maybe he underestimated his own strength, or I pushed off too much, but for a moment, it's like I'm airborne before I collide with Essos's sturdy chest. He catches me, holding me to him, and his scent settles something deep in my soul, giving me a calm that has my shoulders relaxing and my body melting against his. When he's sure I'm stable on my own two feet, Essos loosens his grip on me but doesn't release his hold on my upper arms. Awareness of every spot we touch sings through my body, from my thighs to where our chests are pressed together. Sybil clears their throat, causing us to jerk away from each other like teenagers caught making out. Essos dusts off his clothes and straightens his suit like we've done nothing wrong.

"Duty calls. Please, stay and enjoy the gallery for as long as you want. Know that you are free to enjoy this space whenever you wish." He dips his head to me, then takes a file from Sybil and strides toward the exit.

"Wait!" I call, and before I've even finished the word, he's spinning toward me. Sybil gives me an impatient look, and I know I can't blow this chance. "Who is Dion?" It's a gamble that I'll even get an answer, so I picked something small to confirm if my dreams are rooted in reality.

Essos furrows his brow. "Where did you hear that name?"

"One of the escorts must have mentioned it. I was wondering."

I think I hear Essos swear under his breath, cursing Finn, but he's too far away for me to be sure. "He's the God of Wine and Debauchery. Fortunately, he's preoccupied in the mortal realm, so you won't meet him until after the Calling Ball. I really must be going."

My body stills, like I've been caught doing something I'm not supposed to, and I want to avoid the attention. Sybil has their eyes narrowed suspiciously, and I think they may not believe my lie.

"Are the gods really that scary?" I ask Sybil as we watch him leave. I glance at them as they watch his long legs carry him out the door. I wonder about the two of them again, but the thought passes quickly as they face me, frowning.

"If you have to ask, you weren't paying close enough attention today." With Sybil's words ringing in my head, I follow them from the gallery, wondering if I've somehow earned a mark against myself.

10

That evening, while I'm getting ready, Cat comes into my room and is surprised to see that the bruise on my face is gone.

"Got tired of it finally and let Sybil heal it?" she asks. She's brought her dress to my room and hangs it on a hook outside my closet. She tosses her heels on the floor, then flops onto my bed on her stomach and runs her fingers through her locks, looking eager for the gossip.

"Actually," I say slowly, "after you all left the gallery, I ran into Essos there. I let him heal it for me." I try to say this with as much nonchalance as I can muster, but she sees through me the way only a sister could.

"Doesn't that violate the no-alone-time rule?" she asks, clearly wanting to know more. I'm sitting at my vanity, watching her in the mirror. She hangs her head upside down, her blue eyes watching me as I apply my mascara. How this doesn't give her a headache, I don't know.

"Apparently, it was supposed to be a tour for everyone, but he was late, and everyone had left. Sybil was there the whole time."

Cat grins. She's not mad that she missed it, and I love that about her. "How great that must have been to have him all to yourself without Zara drooling all over him." I think she's genuinely happy for me, and that makes my crushing jealousy so much worse. I can barely muster a smile when she talks about him to me. I've never been good at being the bigger person.

"It actually was really nice not to worry about sharing him with other people," I say, getting up to pull out my own dress.

Cat lays her dress on my bed before coming over and hugging me. "That's because you grew up an only child and then had to go into foster care. You rarely had things to yourself, so you intrinsically hate to share."

I hug her back, glad her ribs are healed so I can squeeze as much as I want. Cat understands me in ways I don't even understand myself. Having someone like her in my life means not having to explain myself when I get touchy about my things. It's why we've been roommates since freshman year. She is my friend-soulmate, my fellow TV-show binger, and I am so glad to have her with me now.

"Is that *Criminal Minds* talking, or psych class?" I tease, prompting her to shrug her shoulders dramatically and turn back to my dresses.

"A little of both," she huffs, moving on to the shoes, cooing over some high-heeled boots.

"How are you handling this so well?" I ask her, knowing that there are broader implications to my question.

She hesitates before speaking. "Because I'm not an only child, I've had to share everything. Besides, it helps to look at this as a job interview and not a relationship. I'm being pragmatic." She tosses the boots at me. "I'm tired of helping—you pick my dress for once!"

I laugh and follow her into her room across the hall, the

clothes she brought with her left behind. "You came into my room! You brought a dress!" I fire back.

She harrumphs and lifts her head higher. She holds the door open for me and shepherds me toward her closet. "I changed my mind about that dress; help me pick another." We leave her door open a crack, but I'm surprised when it's opened farther. The culprit is revealed to be none other than Dave. He jumps onto her bed and makes himself comfortable. As always, his tail is wagging, and Cat crosses to him and starts petting his beautiful blue-grey coat.

I pull out a red dress embroidered with gold flowers. Cat hesitates then ventures closer. Slowly, she grins, seeing my vision. Tonight, I help her get ready. Even though she won't be sitting by Essos's side, I make sure that she looks like a knockout.

As I return to my room, I see a figure walking down the hall and call after her. "Tiffany!"

She spins around to face me and smiles. "Hey, Daphne."

I lean against my doorframe and cross my arms, my attention on her. Dave follows me and sits on the floor at my feet. "I wanted to check in with you to see how you're doing. You seemed a little down last night."

Her head bobs in agreement, and I open the door to my room, letting her know that I'm available. After a moment of hesitation, she comes in and sits on the lounge at the foot of my bed. Dave trots in with her.

"I miss Steve, and it's hard to let go of that. I don't even want to be with Essos. But, like, I just...I'm not ready to move on. I'm not ready to leave Zara." She sniffles, and then the tears start.

I hand her a tissue box then sit next to her, tucking my feet under me. Out of the corner of my eye, I catch Dave licking her leg. "It makes sense. You guys were together since freshman year."

She shakes her head. "We actually started seeing each other

during our senior year of high school. We met at an accepted-students weekend and really hit it off. We were talking about getting married after college, you know? I thought I'd have my whole life with him, and I feel like I've been robbed of that." Tiffany blows her nose and gets up to toss her used tissue in the garbage. She stands there a moment before starting to pace, her long legs carrying her across the room in just a few strides before she turns around.

"I think there's a lot of that feeling going around." My eyes track her as she continues to pace.

"Well, I think it's bullshit. I didn't deserve this, and it's not fair." She stops moving and looks at me. I can't disagree with her.

"Are you thinking about moving on to your afterlife?" I ask delicately. The conversations around the pool and breakfast pointedly ignored this topic, I suspect because we're all uncomfortable with the thought. It's like asking someone if they're going to have a baby after they get married. You never know someone else's life plans, and in this case, you don't know what other implications there might be.

"I mean, I could? But what does it even mean, to enter the Afterlife?" she says, not looking for an answer.

I shake my head. I wish that Essos or Sybil would give us some insight. Is the Afterlife more like *The Good Place,* or are we talking about a more biblical Afterlife?

"I wish I knew. But you're right, you didn't deserve this. None of us did. You deserved to have a long life with Steve and get married and pop out babies, if that was what you wanted. I'm not sure if anyone has said it, but I am so sorry." I stand and walk to her, then lay what I hope is a comforting hand on her upper arm. "We may be the ones who died, but we're also grieving the loss of everyone in our lives. I wanted to make sure you know I'm here for you, if you ever want to talk about it, or just share memories of

Steve or your parents. I think maybe we should talk to Sybil to see if that's something we can do—have a night where we're able to grieve what we lost."

Tiffany throws her arms around me and hugs me close. "I think that's a terrific idea—we should suggest it at dinner tonight. I think, for now, I'll stay, see it through with Zara. She's my best friend, and I just lost Steve—I don't want to lose her too." Tiffany's words are not a surprise to me. It's what I would do for Cat. "I have to get ready for dinner tonight—my hair does not braid itself. But thank you for reaching out, really." She braces herself on my arms, giving me a teary look, and then quietly leaves.

Dave has made himself comfortable on my bed, curled in a tight ball, soulful eyes watching me as I lay down next to him.

I don't want to get up. I want someone to tell me what my dreams mean, and what it really means to be here. Instead, I get non-answers and dodges. I let my eyes close for just a moment, and I'm back on that beach in my dream and this time it's definitely Essos's soft lips pressed against mine, his body firm as he kisses me. While we were dancing, I could feel the muscles in his arms and shoulders, and I want to get to know them up close and personal.

Dave whines, and I turn to face him, letting out a deep sigh. "All right. You win. I'm going."

I don't like the dress I chose for the second night of dancing, so I put it and the boots Cat had admired away and turn to Dave for help. Each new dress I show him, he either huffs at me for *no* or wags his tail emphatically for *yes*, which helps me narrow the choice down to two.

"Which one do you think Essos would prefer?" I ask him, holding up the two dresses. One is a full-length lavender dress that I'm doubtful of, because it feels juvenile with its illusion neckline and lace flower appliques from the shoulders to slightly below the waist. Dave barks. I lower that one and raise up a sexier option, a strapless and form-fitting black dress.

Dave gives a small growl, so I put the offending dress away, still doubtful. I hang the lavender dress on the hook outside my closet.

"He is your master. I suppose you would know best." I jump in the shower, realizing I'm low on time. When I come out in my towel, Dave is where I left him, watching me with his big eyes. I give his head a good scratch, and his tail pounds on the bed. Sliding into the lavender gown, I feel less like a child as I admire the plunging neckline I previously overlooked.

"Since you've proven yourself such a fashionista, which shoes?" In my hands, I have a pair of black flats and some pointy-toed silver heels covered in rhinestones. When Dave barks for the heels, I frown and hold up the flats again.

"Are you sure? These seem much more sensible." He huffs in response. "Heels it is."

Having burned so much time asking for Dave's opinion, I have no choice but to leave my hair down. I hardly have enough time to blow dry it, and as I flip my hair over, I'm positive there are still damp clumps. I pass on all the large statement jewelry again and opt for a long chain with a teardrop gemstone that rests between my breasts. I look at myself in the mirror and adjust my bra, then decide I'm ready.

Desperate to not be late, I slide my shoes on and stride to the stairs. Thankfully, other girls are descending the stairs as well, so I am not last. I join the flow into the dining room, letting out a sigh of relief. When I catch sight of Essos, I'm surprised at the smile that springs to my face. Maybe I want this more than I thought.

It takes just a second for my smile to fade. He's walking with Zara on his arm, and I can just hear them through the chatter as she makes a suggestion.

"Essos, this might be out of the norm, but I think we should have a little ceremony to mark what we each lost. I think it would be a great way for us to begin to heal and move forward from what we went through, in order to really open us up to this process."

I stop walking, shocked to hear my idea come out of her mouth.

"I think that's a wonderful idea," Essos agrees, leading her to the chair beside his.

I want to hit her, but instead, I take my seat and clench my teeth. Through my anger, I make a mental note to thank Dave, since Zara is wearing a black dress that's almost identical to the one I was considering.

Once everyone is seated, Essos stands, and we're all served glasses of wine. "Zara just reminded me that you are all struggling with this adjustment and grieving the loss of your loved ones, and I'm sorry if I haven't been more sympathetic to this fact." Essos places a hand on Zara's bare shoulder, and I have to look away. Otherwise, my glare might burn a hole through them both, and then I'd have to hear all about their matching holes.

"Her idea is to have a memorial so you can each remember your families and friends and the life you've left behind. I propose we go around the table and have each of you talk a little bit about someone that you lost—or many someones, as the case may be. Zara, why don't you start?"

My ears are red hot, burning with fury. As Zara stands and starts to talk about her parents, Tiffany manages to catch my eye, and she mouths her apology to me. I give her a curt nod while grabbing Cat's hand under the table and squeezing it. My action catches her off guard, and she looks at me quickly. I shift my gaze to shoot daggers at Zara, who has started to talk about her grandparents.

Before I can tell Cat why I am crushing the ever-loving shit out of her hand, Zara's wine glass shatters in hers. I jerk back and stare in disbelief. Everyone is startled, most of all Zara.

Essos looks at me, an odd combination of concern and pride on his face. Before I can figure out what that means, he does a sweep of the room, looking to make sure that no one else is affected.

"Oh god, I must have been holding it too tightly while talking about grandpabby. Oh no, I'm bleeding." Zara doesn't seem too put off by the blood as she practically swoons into Essos.

While everyone fusses over Zara, I turn to Cat. "The memorial was my idea. Tiffany and I talked about it earlier," I whisper to her.

"That two-faced bit—" Cat starts.

"Don't. She's not worth it. I'm just... To hear Zara say it was her idea was frustrating."

Our conversation cuts off as soon as they're ready to continue around the table. Tiffany lights up, talking about Steve and her parents, and I dread the moment it's my turn to talk about the people I am grieving. This was meant to give people a chance to talk if they wanted to. I don't want to. I would rather grieve in my own space and let people lean on me.

The people I would grieve all left me behind years ago. My parents died when I was too small to remember them. I miss my maternal grandparents, but my memories of them are too fuzzy to hurt the way others are hurting. I miss my adoptive parents, but I'm not as heartsick as some of the others here.

When it's finally my turn, I have figured out what to say. I stand up and smooth down the tulle of my dress.

"Melinda and Phil were better parents than I deserved. When they adopted me, I was bitter and resentful of my situation, and I laid a lot of my issues at their feet. My only hope is that this doesn't break them. I also really miss my cat, Waffles—he was such a good boy. He loved to beg for food and steal my socks." I raise my glass and sit back down. Wide eyes around the table make me realize that this is probably the most any of them have heard me talk about myself. It makes me want to retreat back into my shell, but I refuse, keeping my back straight.

I glance at Essos, and he offers me a small smile before focusing on Cat, who is talking about her brothers and parents. I reach out to take her hand again and give it a less punishing squeeze, so she knows that she is never alone. I will never not need her in my life.

Following dinner, we meet in the ballroom with our escorts. Finn bows and offers his hand to me then leads me onto the dance floor. I follow him, realizing that I should not have listened to Dave about my shoes. I should have gone with flats.

"This dress is a bold choice." He tries to guide me, but I keep stepping on his toes. Finally, he stops. "I lead. You need to let someone else take charge—you cannot control what is happening on this dance floor any more than you can control being dead or what happens during the Calling. So, let. It. Go." I am taken aback, but he reaches out and takes my hands again. We start moving to the music.

"Someone is in a mood today," I snark at him, put out at being reprimanded.

"Yes, well, I had errands to run, and they were not very fun. You're doing better. You just need someone to bully you into letting them have control." We are gliding more easily, although I stomp on his foot on purpose at that comment. Finn growls at me.

"So, were you the emissary that Essos sent to handle whatever happened on Earth today?"

Finn looks surprised at my question. "He told you that?" He spins me away and then pulls me back to him. "More or less. A god who will be at the Calling Ball was acting out of turn. I'm not the right person to keep him in check, but because Essos is preoc-cupied here, I was sent to deal with it."

"What did that entail?" I hope I'm able to keep with this line of questioning, since Finn is being vague. Maybe he'll let some information leak, although, if I've read him right, I doubt he will.

"In this case, it meant going to bars and getting hammered. Essos is usually more diplomatic, but I do what I can. I'm not allowed to bring the heat; only Essos is. Instead, I get to booze up the troublemaker and remind him that he can't throw temper tantrums in the form of ending mortal lives." Around the room, Essos chats politely with a few girls before moving to the dance floor with Madison. Finn catches me watching and shakes his head.

"So, he's a tough leader?" I counter.

"He's hardly a fire and brimstone guy, despite his job title, but he has done a pretty good job of keeping people in line for the last few millennia."

I catch sight of Zara stepping outside alone, and I let go of Finn abruptly and excuse myself to follow her. He looks surprised but lets me go.

When I reach her, Zara is breathing in the cool night air.

I grab her arm and spin her around to face me. "So, what, Tiffany tells you my idea, and you decide to market it as your own?" I ask.

I'm not sure where she came from, but Cat is suddenly at my side, followed by Finn. Zara feigns shock and stands up a little taller so she can tower over me. It makes me want to kick her in the shins. Zara might be taller, but I'm scrappier. While I had mostly good foster homes growing up, I was smaller than a lot of kids, which meant having to fight for everything I got before I was adopted.

She tosses her long dark hair over a smooth bare shoulder. "I made my own suggestion, based on a conversation Tiffany and I had, based on a conversation that you two had. I'm hardly responsible if you take every last minute to come down to dinner looking mediocre at best."

I step toward her, but Finn and Cat each grab one of my arms.

Finn moves swiftly so he is directly in front of me. "If you hit her, you will get tossed out and you will never get to prove me wrong about getting better at dancing. She is so beyond not worth it." Finn says it lightly, but there's an undertone of seriousness in his voice.

Over his shoulder, Zara looks smug. My face burns, and I want to hit her all over again, but I loosen up. Cat and Finn both let go of me but look ready to jump back in.

I'm turning to walk back inside when I catch sight of a bed of flowers that just moments earlier had been in full bloom and are now wilting. "You are so poisonous, Zara, that these flowers—" I gesture at them "—are literally dying in your presence." I push my way back inside, thankful that no one else seems to have paid any attention to us.

As I pass Tiffany, she grabs my arm, her eyes full of regret. "I am so sorry. Never in a million years did I think she would do something like that."

I soften at her words and take her hands in mine. "Am I furious? Absolutely, but not at you. That was a dirty, underhanded way to win brownie points. But I hope it was as cathartic as we hoped it would be."

Essos appears at Tiffany's elbow and gives me a cordial nod. Tiffany looks like she wants to say something more but leaves with him instead.

Finn offers me his hand, and we step onto the dance floor again. I try to relax as we move into our usual box step.

"Can I ask what that was about?" he presses, trying to get me to look into his beautiful dark eyes.

"Why, so you can pretend like you don't know?" I snap. I'm

taking out my frustration on the wrong people, and I know it. Releasing a shaky, calming breath, I explain the conversation I had with Tiffany earlier in the day, already tired of rehashing it.

"Essos is an excellent judge of character. He knows when someone is genuine and not. I have to imagine that he saw through Zara's bullshit when she told him about it," Finn tries to reassure me.

"I'll have to take your word for it," I reply glumly, this time accidentally stepping on Finn's foot. It hurts me almost as much as it hurts him. My shoes grind against my toes, and I wonder why the heels aren't imbued with magic to avoid blisters. I decide that when I do get a chance to talk to Essos or Sybil, the shoe complaint is going to the top of my list.

"You have to give Essos a chance. He sees more than you know."

I think about how his gaze has a way of piercing me, making me feel like he's looking into my very essence. "I can trust you, right? We've got some sort of escort-client confidentiality?"

"That's what I tell all my Johns, or in your case, Janes."

I stick my tongue out at him, wondering if I should let myself retreat and burrow back into my shell. No, I can't do that. If I really want this, if I want to become a queen, I can't hide when I'm scared of what the answer might be.

"Who is Dion?" Finn is the one who stumbles this time, stepping on my foot. "Ow."

"Sorry, I'm sorry. You shouldn't know that name yet. He's... he's my, uh, wow, okay."

"He's your what?"

Finn stops dancing abruptly and looks at me. "How did you hear his name? Tell me the truth. I can tell when you lie."

There is something in the way that Finn is looking at me that makes me want to lie to him, but I'm not willing to risk finding out how he knows when I lie and what will happen if I do. "I had a dream." That won't satisfy him, but I try anyway.

Finn startles me by grabbing my wrist and hauling me off the dance floor and back outside so we're alone. He's not rough, but he's never handled me like this before. "Do go on, Daphne. I'm not a dentist. don't make this like pulling teeth."

"If you weren't so cagey, maybe I would be more forthcoming."

Finn doesn't seem amused by me. "Please," he deadpans.

"I had a dream, and in it, I was on a beach, talking with someone, Essos I think, and the name Dion was mentioned. It felt real —it felt like I was going to find sand in my bed when I woke up. Essos confirmed that Dion was a real person—well, god."

"Have you had other dreams?"

"Yes," I admit.

Finn cups my face, slouching so he's eye level with me. "Understand what I'm about to say to you. Stop poking around for answers. You'll get them when you get them, but right now, this will lead to nowhere good."

"What does that even *mean*?"

"It means a good queen knows she needs patience above all."

He doesn't give me a chance to respond, just skulks off before leaving altogether.

I stare after him, trying not to scream. A waiter comes by with champagne, but I wave him off, remembering how sloppy I got the night before.

I never get a chance to dance with Essos, because my feet are bleeding and blistered, and I call it an early night.

When I get to my room, Dave is sitting outside. I hold up my shoes, and he looks at me, head tilted.

"You were wrong about the footwear. This is the last time I take fashion advice from a dog." I open my door, and he bounds in and onto the bed, ready for a night of snuggling.

Asking questions of Finn only made me more confused. It leaves me wondering what that dream was...and how I knew a god's name.

II

We fall into an easy pattern wherein every day, we listen to Sybil impart myriad facts and figures about the world of Solarem, and each evening we don our finest gowns to dance and party. Each night, Finn accuses me of murdering his feet, and each night, Essos accuses him of being a drama queen. Every night, I watch girls try to get closer to Essos, but he seems aloof toward almost everyone. Zara is the only one brazen enough to kiss him goodnight.

Essos has become a recurring presence in my dreams, which feel more and more like memories. One night, I dream about him outside.

Essos floats lazily in the tide pool his brother-in-law has kindly created for us. The water is calm, and the full moon and stars are my only light as I walk down the beach toward him. The moonlight glistens off his honed muscles, and a fire lights inside me. His erection stands tall and inviting and I actually lick my lips at the sight of him.

"My love, why are you out of bed?" he asks as I close the distance.

His tone is nearly chastising. He's not wrong to scold me; I've been rest-
less at night, unable to sleep when he doesn't come to bed. I'm wearing
a silk robe, and only the robe, as I dip my toes in the water. It's the
middle of the night, and I know his work makes him keep odd hours,
but this is a bit much.

"Why don't you come back to bed?" I plead as I untie the robe and
slide it off my shoulders. He swims to the lip of the pool with a wolfish
smile on his face.

"On a beautiful night like tonight?" He watches me closely, and I
drop the robe to the ground and slip into the water beside him. His eyes
never leave mine.

"I suppose it would be a waste with this beautiful sky above us." I
swim away from Essos, and he follows me, as if attached by an invisible
tether. The air is warm, and the water is cool on my skin, even though I
feel like I'm on fire around him. He swims close and is finally able to
grab my hand and pull my naked body against his. He doesn't say
anything as one arm snakes around my waist and the other slips up my
back and into my hair. Being with Essos never gets tiring; hundreds of
years together, and every time he touches me my blood sings for him.
We behave like two teenagers driven by hormones; it's why I've needed
to take an office separate from his. We would get nothing done other-
wise. I lean my head back, dipping my hair in the saltwater as he
presses a kiss to my collarbone. With every kiss, Essos awakens a desper-
ation deep inside me, a need to have him and only him in my arms, in
my heart, in my bed.

"You undo me," he says with a laugh. "I am King of the Under-
world, and the sight of you drives me to my knees."

I smile, loving the power I have over him. "My naked body has that
effect on men," I tease, not that there is any truth to the statement. The
only man to see what's hiding under my clothes is the man currently
worshiping me, and it's going to stay that way.

"I'd better be the only man who has the privilege of this vision," he
huffs, pressing my back to the hard-packed sand on the side of the pool.

It grates against my skin, at odds with the pleasure coiling in my belly. He grabs my wrists then slides his fingers between mine before covering my mouth with his. At first, the kiss is demanding, but then it gentles, and he nibbles on my lower lip. He's teasing me, and I love him for it as he releases one of my hands so he's free to explore other parts of my body. He lets his fingers dance along my skin under the water before resting that hand on my hip.

"I will gladly exalt you for the rest of our long lives." He kisses my lips once more before swimming away. "That is the glory of being gods, is it not? Having forever with the one we love, knowing that we will have a thousand more nights just like this."

I WAKE feeling weighed down with a stone. Each of these dreams fills me with the deepest sense of a love that goes beyond carnal pleasure, but waking and feeling its loss makes it a struggle to get out of bed every time. On numerous occasions, I've swept into breakfast late, the last one to arrive, having to scarf down whatever food is piled on my plate before going to lessons.

I've wondered what these dreams could mean. It feels like it's me in them, like it's my skin lighting up with every touch, but how is that possible?

I assume that no one else is having similar dreams, because Cat confirmed that she's not. I'm not close enough to anyone else to ask if they're having sex dreams about Essos, but I suspect if others were, they'd be talking about it. At the very least, Zara would make it well known that she's had dreams about knowing Essos carnally.

Just the thought makes me dig my nails into my palms.

I grimace. Calling them sex dreams is a disservice to the emotion in them—they're about so much more than sex and touching; they're showing the partnership between Essos and this woman. Who in my dreams is me.

AT SOME POINT during the first two weeks, Dave started sleeping outside my door. Eventually, I started waiting for him before going to bed, at which point he began climbing onto the bed while I finished my nighttime routine. Now, once I settle in, he cuddles with me like the big baby he is.

Essos questions us about it one morning.

"Has Dave been staying with any of you?" he asks, flipping a page in front of him, then glancing at us. I'm seated next to him today and catch sight of the top of the page, which says *Emerald Production.*

"He's been sleeping in my bed," I admit, and take a sip of coffee.

Essos looks pleased and nods. "That's because he knows he's not allowed to sleep in mine," he says with a chuckle. He reaches out and gently touches the back of my hand. "If it bothers you then I won't allow it." It's not a question or a command, but an offer.

"If it bothered me, I would have said something," I point out.

Essos buries his grin, accepting this before slipping some bacon to the dogs.

Once all 15 of us are in the room, he stands. "Ladies, today we will have a group date."

There is some interest at this announcement, and some groans. Over the past two weeks, Essos has gone on a handful of solo dates, but this is the first time there'll be a group of us. Partnership was apparently something that Essos could not see with Penny, the sophomore with red hair, who was his latest dismissal. Essos never reveals why someone is leaving, though if she wants to fill in the blanks, she can. Even Essos was tight-lipped about her dismissal, though they both agreed it was for the best.

"Ordinarily, it would be a small number of you, but in the interest of being more equitable with my time, today we will all be together. I fear I've been neglecting you." His eyes do a sweep of the room. "This isn't on your schedules. I've cleared my calendar to accommodate our time together, so please put on some comfortable athletic wear and meet me outside on the beach in two hours." Essos sketches a bow. "I will see you ladies then."

He steps out of the room, bribing the dogs with bacon to follow him, and we erupt in excited chatter. Zara was delighted when she received the first solo date with him a few days after the gallery tour, so she feels confident about this group date. After our altercation on the deck, we've been steering clear of one another as best we can. She seemed elated after finding out that I was one of the few who did not have a one-on-one date with him. It feels like at every opportunity she's loudly gossiping about her time with Essos with a smug glance in my direction.

It takes a lot to remind myself that tripping her would be unqueenly, but fuck, it would make me feel better.

We all do as we're told, and I am the first to meet Essos on the beach. I'm surprised when I see yoga mats for each of us lined up and Essos chatting with a woman I haven't met before. She's short with dark hair and skin and full lips, and she's wearing a crop top that says *Namaste in bed* and high-waisted shorts. Essos is dressed the most casually I've ever seen him, and more shocking is that he's not in head-to-toe black. He's dressed in a dark blue tight-fitting T-shirt that shows every muscle I imagined was there and sweatpants that hang dangerously low on his hips. I am thrilled to get to admire this all on my own.

The woman spots me first, and Essos turns. "Daphne!" he says with surprise, walking toward me. I love the sound of my name when he says it.

"Yoga?" I ask, gesturing at the mats. I'm rewarded with a smile for my observation.

"A bit unconventional, but I've noticed things are tense. I want to give you all a chance to unwind. But yoga comes later. Are you adjusting well?" he asks, studying my face closely. His hands are clasped behind his back like he's trying not to reach out and touch me, but I wish he would. Rather than leaving it up to him, I reach forward and pluck some imaginary lint off the collar of his shirt, letting my fingers brush his skin. He tenses and wets his lips as he watches me. It's like Victorian times, where just the brush of a hand could soak panties.

"As well as can be expected. Sybil is jamming more information into the two hours they have us each day than I learned in my three and a half years of college. Who is this?" I ask, gesturing to the woman.

She steps back and away from us, finding something about the mats to fuss with.

"Luminara—she is—"

"Unimportant. Carry on with your conversation. Ignore me!" She gives me a secretive smile before striding away from us.

Essos blushes and shakes his head with a laugh, and I want to lean into the sound. We may not have had any intentional one-on-one time like he's had with some of the others, but each night, he finds me across the room, each night, his fingers are light on my skin, and each night, I relax into dancing, letting him lead. Sometimes he remembers himself and excuses himself to dance with another, but I've noticed, more often than not, we have to be interrupted by someone else seeking his time.

"It is a lot, I know, but some of the gods are rather particular about their roles and their histories. I imagine it's similar to the quarterback in high school, forever regretting that he peaked early, forever chasing that high."

I smile ruefully. "I know the type. I even dated one or two." I shake my head, and I notice Essos go perfectly still, watching me.

"I don't think I ever considered..." He trails off and clears his throat. "I mean, you didn't mention a boyfriend at the memorial dinner. I didn't think..." Now he's visibly unnerved. I wonder if he's uneasy about dating women with boyfriends, but I consider Tiffany and Madison, who both had boyfriends and are both still here. I reach out to touch his arm, unsure if it's okay but doing it anyway. This touch is meant to convey so much more than an "accidental" brush of fingers earlier.

"I mean, I dated a guy named Chad in my meteorology class, but never seriously. I always felt a little too lost in my own life to find someone really worth my time." It's not a lie. I would get as far as a handful of dates before realizing the person wasn't right. I wasn't expecting the Mia Thermopolis "foot pop" or anything, but I was hoping for a spark that was never there.

Essos looks like he could fall over with relief.

"Good! I mean, not *good*, but I'm glad you didn't leave someone behind. I know Tiffany has been struggling with losing Steve." Essos reaches out to touch my arm, but other girls start to arrive, and his fingers barely graze me before he turns his attention to them. The look on his face makes me feel like my disappointment over their arrival is mutual.

Zara runs to him and leaps into his arms, wrapping her legs around his waist. I am grateful when her long black hair acts as a curtain and blocks my view of what I can only assume is her kissing him. My relief is short-lived when she pulls back and shifts her hair over her other shoulder before kissing him again. I could swear I caught her glancing at me before doing it to make sure I saw.

Cat walks over and hip checks me before following my line of sight. She immediately steps between us, breaking the spell.

"Look at you down here all early and shit," she teases me as she tightens her high ponytail.

I look at her and frown. "I'm not always late."

Cat's eyebrows shoot into her hairline.

"Literally every meal and every class, even when we were alive," Zara says, having managed to disentangle herself from Essos. I swallow the urge to trip her. She knows this about me only because of Cat's constant teasing about having to run on Daphne time.

"Ladies, thank you all for joining me today for this group date," Essos begins. "You can see there will be some yoga later, but first we will do stress relief in the form of flag football. I understand that your sorority participated in something called Greek Week, where you would compete with other fraternities and sororities. Today is about blowing off some steam, and then yes, there will be yoga to help you relax afterward."

"What about flag football makes a queen?" Cat murmurs to me. I know she's not quiet enough, based on the look Essos gives us, but it's one of mirth and not admonishment.

"How to lose with grace?"

"How to make an enemy a friend?"

"How to play dirty but look fair?"

"How to shut up?" Zara hisses at us, leaving us to dissolve into giggles. With each little task Sybil has given us, each crumb of knowledge, we've tried to understand how it matters. Like when we learned about the introduction of sliced bread. Cat and I continue to ask questions about Solarem and the gods that we're going to have to interact with, but we're told only that we'll learn in due time.

There are general murmurs of excitement at his announcement, and Sybil provides a list to Essos, which he reads off.

"We have two team captains. Catalina is going to lead one team and Daphne the other. I have your teams here." Essos reads off the list, while I motion to Cat that I'm watching her and she crosses her arms, sticking her tongue out at me. I'm not paying attention to the names until he mentions Zara will be on my team. Zara looks like she tasted something sour, but quickly covers it up. Cat looks understandably concerned. I would be more concerned if Zara was on Cat's team—at least she has to have my back.

I don't expect Essos to know what's going on, but I'm positive that Sybil sees all. When I glance at where they're watching from the deck, they meet my eye with a mischievous glint. Sybil knew exactly what they were doing when the teams were created.

After reading the names, Essos says he will be a wild card, flipping between the two teams.

The first round is fun. Cat is the first to run off with the ball, and she heads toward our end zone. There isn't supposed to be any touching, but I playfully tackle her anyway, and she laughs. Madison, who is on my team, grabs the ball and runs in the wrong direction, reducing Cat and me to tears of laughter. We manage to stand only to collapse in another fit as she celebrates her non-touchdown.

"Two points for Cat's team." Essos declares with a laugh after Madison jumps in his arms.

"Wait, what?" Madison asks, confused and disappointed. Essos explains the rule as we all reset, and Madison pouts and apologizes. I laugh it off, knowing this is all in good fun, but Zara looks furious.

We continue playing, earning points back and forth, and Cat's team has the lead when the ball slips out of her hands. I watch the fumble and dive for it at the same time Zara does, and I wind up with a mouthful of sand and an elbow in my face. I barely have time to react before Zara takes off with the ball and scores a touchdown.

I lay there for a moment, more stunned than injured, before spitting out the sand. I feel a gentle hand on my back.

"Are you all right? It looked like you hit the ground hard," Essos says.

I look up at him, wiping my mouth. He offers me his hand, and I take it gladly, watching the muscles in his arms tense as he hoists me to my feet.

"I'm fine," I say, absently touching what I'm sure is going to be another bruise on my cheekbone.

Essos gently grasps my chin with his thumb and index finger, tilting my face to the side to get a better look. "I'm not sure; you may need to lose the whole face," he teases.

"You mean, I could get that nose job I've always wanted?" I ask, feigning excitement.

He surprises us both when he taps my nose. "I would have to object. I like your nose." I smile at his compliment as he drags the backs of his fingers along my jawline before cupping my face. I think for a moment that he's going to kiss me. The entire world feels distant as I search his eyes for any clue that I'm right. I get lost thinking about how it's felt to kiss him in my dreams, and how I wonder if that's what kissing him would feel like in real life. His gaze dips to my lips, and I know I must be right. The lean has started, like it's finally going to happen.

I've lost track of the events around us until Zara leaps onto Essos's back, celebrating her touchdown. Essos almost crashes into me, but he manages to catch himself, never breaking eye contact. We finally look away from one another and get back to the game, the chance of the kiss lost to time.

The elbow to the eye is not the last time that Zara and I collide. More than once, as we run side by side, I wind up on the ground as she feigns innocence over having lost her footing in the sand. I could have forgiven it the first few times, but after one more incident of her "accidentally" shoulder-checking me, I get in her face.

"We're on the same team," I say through gritted teeth. Zara plays innocent with a dramatic *oops*.

Cat steps between us, draping her arms over our shoulders. "Isn't this fun, ladies?" she says cheerfully. My eyes roll so far into the back of my head, I worry they might get stuck there. To appease Cat, I shake it off and keep going.

While we're resetting, Essos switches to my team and stands next to me in a defensive position. "You all right? New legs today?"

I flash him a fake smile. "All good over here." I adopt the same perky tone Zara has been using all day.

The next time Zara and I are on a collision course, she drops to the ground, grabbing her leg and feigning injury better than a professional soccer player. I pull back from her so fast, I almost fall over, but instead, I collide with Essos's chest. His hands grab my shoulders, steadying me, and then he kneels beside Zara. She has managed to twist her ankle in her rush to both get in front of me and away from me and is bawling, holding her foot.

I want to scowl, but I think she might genuinely be in pain, even if it is self-inflicted. Cat jogs over to see what happened. I cross my arms as Cat leans on my shoulder, peering over me. I don't want to crowd Zara, because Tiffany is now by her side and so is Essos.

"Oh no, please don't touch it," she whimpers as Essos reaches out to test her ankle. She actually swings away from his hand. I can hear him quietly trying to reassure her as he again reaches out to take her ankle. I can't bear to watch and am thankful for the distraction of Sybil sprinting down the stairs to Essos's side. I assume that it's to render aid, but the panic on their face makes me second guess that.

"My lord, you have a meeting that you must attend immediately," Sybil relays.

Essos looks up at them, Zara's ankle cradled in his hands. "Can't it wait?" he asks, clearly annoyed.

"I'm sorry, but this is in regard to the incident the other day. He's here to discuss it." Sybil's voice is grave, and Essos nearly drops Zara's foot but seems to catch himself. He gently places it on the ground.

"I'm sorry, Zara. Sybil will have to attend you—this is an urgent matter that I absolutely have to address." He stands, looking frazzled. I reach out to touch his arm, and he nearly jumps out of his skin when I do so. His eyes meet mine, and this seems to relax him for only a moment. He searches my face, and I see the concern deepen.

"Ladies, please enjoy some yoga and a relaxing day. I'm sorry that I won't be able to spend the rest of it with you," Essos says before jogging away and taking the deck stairs two at a time.

I feel uneasy, as if I've eaten something rotten. As Sybil heals Zara, I take a staggering step back, gasping as a sharp pain lances through my stomach and side. Cat is quick to put a supportive arm around my back, and I cry out as the pain intensifies. My vision narrows until all I see is white and gold, the world overtaken by the sting and burn of a repeated stabbing sensation in my chest. My heart is pounding so loudly, the rush of my pulse becomes the only thing I can hear, until it feels like my heart will burst, and not in an *I'm-so-full-of-love-for-you* way. There's a constant ringing in my ears, and hollow laughter that sounds far away.

Cat eases me down to the sand as the ringing gets louder and louder. Then, just as quickly as it all started, it stops. I take gasping breaths and clutch my chest. No more pain, no more ringing, nothing. Cat's eyes are as big as saucers, nearly bugging out of her face as she sits next to me, her hand on my back. She rubs gentle circles, searching my body for some sort of indication as to what that was.

Sybil is towering over me, shaking their head. I notice now that Zara is standing beside them, arms crossed, and I am decidedly not a fan of everyone standing over me. I scramble to my feet and dust off the sand. Cat remains on the ground, brow furrowed. The mental calculations she runs in her head as she solves a problem are playing out on her face. Her brow twitches periodically until Zara distracts her.

"What was that, drama queen?" Zara asks, looking at me like I've grown another head.

"I'm sorry. I have no idea," I say, averting my gaze from everyone. I wrap my arms around my middle and hug myself, uncomfortable with the scrutiny. That chill from the first day settles into my bones.

Sybil watches me closely, no expression on their face. "Do you feel up to yoga, or do you want to go inside and lie down?" they ask kindly.

I shake my head, not wanting special treatment. It doesn't help that Zara is shooting daggers at me through her eyes. There will be days as a queen where I may not feel up to doing what I have to, and I want to keep going now. Even though Essos isn't here to witness it, Sybil is.

"I'll stay with everyone else," I say weakly.

Cat rises and dusts the sand off her legs. "This has actually been a lot of excitement for me, so, I think I *will* go inside." She shrugs, watching me. "Why don't you keep me company, Daph?" she pleads.

I see right through what she's doing, and I love her for it. Sybil gives a small nod of approval to Cat. She holds my elbow as we make our way up to my room, where I collapse on the bed.

I curl up, and Cat sits behind me and pulls off my shoes. "Are you okay?" Her voice is soft. My insides are shaking as I look at her. I can barely shake my head, unable to find the words to convey how I feel. "Can I get you anything?" she prods.

I manage to squeak out, "Water," and she gets up in search of it. When she opens the door, I'm not surprised to see Dave on the other side. He bounds up and settles himself in the crook of my knees, with his head resting on my hip.

"Dave will take care of me while you're out."

Her eyes look uncertain, so I wave her on. I take comfort in having Dave by my side while Cat is gone. What happened was terrifying, and I have no reasonable explanation for it, which makes it all the more scary.

I close my eyes, and when I open them, Cat is returning with a tray in her hands. Not only does it have water, but a grilled cheese sandwich as well. She sets the tray on my nightstand and hops onto the bed beside me. I sit up, much to Dave's chagrin, forcing him to resettle.

"How do you feel?" she asks, studying my face.

I take a small sip of water. "A little better. Mostly just confused. How long were you gone?"

"About 45 minutes." She holds out a triangle of grilled cheese to me. I take it and nibble at the long corner to appease her. "I was talking with Sybil, and they insisted that I bring you some food."

I am grateful to both of them. "Did I miss much?" I say, and take a bigger bite.

"No. Everyone was ass up in downward dog when I went downstairs. I did overhear Essos shouting." She takes a bite of the other sandwich.

"Are you going to make me beg?" I glance at Dave, who is literally begging for food, before looking back at her.

"Not in your current state, but otherwise, maybe. I'm not sure what was happening, but he was yelling at someone named Galen about coming here and acting out of turn. Whoever this Galen is yelled back about Essos not following procedure. No clue what they were really going on about, but it sounded heated."

"This is probably about what happened last week. There was

some sort of event in the mortal world—Finn mentioned that he was sent to handle it because Essos was busy with us." I wonder who Galen is.

A shiver runs down my spine.

"Well, whatever it was about, clearly Essos is not having it. Do you think this weird phantom pain has anything to do with those dreams you keep having?"

"Why would you think that?"

Cat pushes her half of the grilled cheese into my mouth. I chew noisily at her to show that I'm eating, and she sticks out her tongue in retaliation. Dave is still begging, even as the last of the food disappears.

"Because you didn't see yourself. Your body was thrashing like you were actively being stabbed."

"It felt like I was being stabbed."

"Maybe your consciousness isn't compatible with being in Solarem or the Underworld or whatever. Maybe you're having memories of another soul, and your mind is just filling in Essos. You said that in one dream you were wearing Elizabethan clothes, and another time, you were in a slinky ball gown or, you know, naked. Maybe you're prone to sympathetic vibrations. I don't know, but you know who you can ask?"

I don't get a chance to answer. There's a gentle knock on the door, and I call out for whoever it is to come in.

Sybil enters. "Are you feeling all right?" they ask, and I am so tired of people asking me that. Gingerly, they sit on the edge of my bed, giving Dave a scolding look. I swear the dog looks away from them and pretends he doesn't notice that they saw him on the bed.

"Fine. I'm not sure what happened. I'm feeling much better now that I have some food in me." I gesture toward the empty plate and water glasses. Sybil reaches out, and the water glasses refill instantly. They hand me one, pushing me to keep drinking.

"Good. I'm glad to hear it. I was hoping you could describe what you experienced outside. I was helping Zara, so I missed most of it. I just heard you cry out. Did something happen?" Sybil's voice is gentle, and their dark brown eyes are imploring my honesty. I wonder if they're a walking-talking truth serum.

"I don't really know how to describe it. At first, I felt physically sick, like I was going to throw up, and then, it was like I was being stabbed—it took the wind right out of me." I think about the sharp pains and rub a spot just below my collarbone.

"Has anything like this happened before?" Sybil presses.

I drink more water and shake my head. "Never. It did remind me of finding out we had drowned, but I can promise, I've never been stabbed before," I assure them, still rubbing the same spot.

Cat reaches out and takes my hand. Sybil stands, bringing a hand to their mouth and chewing on their thumbnail. They look stressed, and tendrils of hair have come loose from their usually meticulous braid.

"Ask them," Cat presses.

For a second, I'm confused, but then I realize she's talking about the dreams.

"Ask me what?"

"Well..." I think about Finn's words, about needing to be patient and how I should stop poking for answers. "Hypothetically, if someone were having dreams about Essos, what could that mean?"

Sybil goes preternaturally still. It's easy to forget they're not like us. "Hypothetically..." Their eyes flash to Cat. "Hypothetically, it could get them dismissed for having an unfair advantage. And if someone else were found to have concealed this knowledge, that could also be grounds for dismissal. I suggest that, since this *is* a purely hypothetical situation, there is no reason to put anyone at risk or risk their friends being removed. If you value your place here, *hypothetically*, say nothing."

I lie there, stunned.

Fortunately, Cat isn't.

"How can a *dream* be an unfair advantage?" Cat demands.

Sybil doesn't seem to have an answer for this. "I suggest you both leave it alone. I can promise you won't like the consequences of not complying." They brighten suddenly, giving us a serene smile, as if they didn't just threaten us. "Please let me know if something like this sudden painful sensation happens again. I'll be sure to let Essos know. He may decide to cancel the dancing tonight in favor of you and Zara getting your rest."

As much as I want to push Sybil about the dreams, I'm not interested in getting both Cat and me kicked out. I shake my head emphatically. "Please don't let him know about today. It was nothing, really. And please don't cancel tonight—I promise I'm feeling up to it."

Sybil sighs, as if they already knew this was going to be my answer. "I will not tell Essos if you promise to tell me if you feel this kind of pain again."

Not likely, after their reaction to the dreams. "Done. Just please, *please* don't tell Essos. I don't want him to worry. He seems like a worrier, and I have to guess that he's preoccupied with whatever or whoever drew him away today."

Sybil's eyes narrow at my mention of the mystery guest. "No, we wouldn't want that." With a heavy sigh, they give in. "Fine, but you should start getting ready now if you want to even pretend you're going to be on time." They take their leave of us.

Cat looks at me and takes a breath, and I hold up a hand, stopping her. "It's not that late. We should get ready—I know I need a shower after rolling around in the sand."

Cat bows dramatically to me, worry still radiating off her. "As you wish."

As she goes to leave, I get up and throw my arms around her. I pull her close in a hug, surprised that my strength is back. "I'm sorry if I didn't say it before, but thank you for everything today. It's days like these that I don't deserve you as my friend."

Cat hugs me back tighter. "I hate when you say shit like that. I love you. I'm worried about you. That was scary earlier—I didn't know what was happening, and honestly, things have been weird since we got here. You keep having those dreams, and I don't want to crowd you with my concern. I know that you're not big on that, but I *am* worried."

"Crowd me whenever. Your burdens are mine, no matter how small you think they are. I want to share them with you—that's what best friends are for, right? Never feel like you need to tiptoe around shit with me. You're my ride or die."

"You fight, I fight," she says back. "Go shower—you smell. Hell, I smell!"

I listen to her advice and take a long shower, catching sight of a few bruises and scrapes on my knees from when I hit the ground earlier. The bruise on my face isn't as bad as I thought it was going to be.

I listen to Dave again, picking a blue gown with metallic gold and silver threads through the bodice. He insists on heels, but I choose a different pair that is a little lower and hopefully more stable. I make my way downstairs, not wanting to admit that I'm still a little shaky. I'm surprised to find no one except Essos waiting at the foot of the stairs. There are fresh worry lines creased between his brows, and I want to smooth them out with my thumb. I give him my brightest smile, and he responds in kind.

"Were you borrowing against how early you were this morning?" he asks, holding his arm out to me.

I slide mine through his, letting him lead me. "I'm not that late," I protest.

"Everyone is already in the dining room. I heard there was some sort of incident—I wanted to check on you."

I scowl, making a note that Sybil can't be trusted. "I'm fine. I think all the activity just got to me." While not an explicit lie, it's enough of one to make me feel guilty.

"I'm glad. Zara made it sound like you collapsed in protest of me giving her attention and then rudely running off."

I mentally apologize to Sybil for so quickly assuming that it was them. We pause before entering the dining room.

"I waited for you because I want you to sit next to me. I feel as though I've been neglecting you, and I don't want *you* to feel that way." Essos reaches forward and brushes a tendril of hair out of my face, tucking it behind my ear. His fingertips linger a moment longer than necessary, grazing my neck the way mine did his this morning. He's not as neglectful as he claims, though today is the only day that I've been early enough to snag a seat next to him at breakfast. This will be the first time I sit beside him at dinner.

I smile. "Hardly. I stumbled backward, and Cat caught me and helped me sit. I think the constant all-night parties got to me. College didn't prepare me for having to dance all night and entertain people. Now, pong on the other hand—college prepared me well for that, and binge drinking, of course."

He laughs, and I could live the rest of my life hearing only that sound. "Pong?"

"Seriously? You're an immortal and don't know what pong is? Like beer pong?" At his raised brows, I continue, "Okay, tonight after the dance, me, you, Finn, and Cat—is that okay? Can we do that?" I'm hopeful. I think about how much fun it would be, especially with the people I am closest with.

"I'll see what I can do. Shall we?" He gestures to the dining room, and we stroll in side by side.

Sitting next to him at dinner and being on the other end of the eye daggers people are hurling my way is a different experience. Essos is magnetic, and everyone has their attention turned toward him, but I'm the one he's focused on. With each laugh and smile, I find myself leaning closer and closer to him like I'm a budding flower and he's the sun I need to bring me to life. When he's done eating, he slips his hand under the table and rests it on my knee, his thumb stroking my thigh.

"Will you show me the gardens?" I ask him abruptly. I don't know what it is about him that has me wanting to lay myself bare to him. I want to tell him about the foster mother who demanded that my Mother's Day gift from school be for her and when it wasn't, she destroyed it. I want to tell him about how nervous I was to believe I was actually being adopted, and how I cried into Waffles's fur the first night we got him and he actually stayed in my bed. I want to tell him how ticklish my sides are, and that I have stubby toenails on my baby toes.

Essos squeezes my knee gently. "I'll have Sybil make time for it," he promises.

He summons Sybil and whispers in their ear. I catch them glancing at me, one delicate eyebrow raised. I smile at Cat, who gives me a broad grin, but I can see apprehension in the wrinkle of her brow. Sybil's words to us earlier have certainly made Cat more wary of Essos's assistant.

The meal seems to fly by, and when we move on to the dancing portion of the evening, Finn gives me a pout when he doesn't get the first dance. I feel like I'm floating in Essos's arms as I let him lead me around the floor. I don't fight it the way I do with Finn, and I can see how much better it is. My hand is loose on the back of his neck, my head bowed close to him as we move as one. I take a deep breath, knowing that the song is almost over. He smells of sandalwood and cinnamon, a hint of vanilla intermingling. More than ever, the smell of him is so familiar, and it feels safe and like home.

The song ends, and we stand there for a moment, his breath tickling the hairs on my temple. Essos seems to have to remind himself that it's not just us. I feel bereft when he steps away from me with a deep bow.

"Thank you for the dance," he says, his gaze staying on me before he forces himself to turn away. Finn is right behind me, ready to sweep me off my feet, and I let him lead me away. Finn and I are quiet for our first dance, my focus on not stepping on his toes.

"You seem to be improving," Finn teases. I look up at him, my concentration broken. I step on his foot, and he doesn't hide the wince. "Well, you were."

"Maybe if you would quit gabbing and let me focus on what I'm doing, you wouldn't be suffering," I snap.

Finn laughs at me. "And here I thought you would be 'miss cool and collected' after getting such special treatment."

My eyes narrow as I glare at him. "Rough day," I grumble before explaining to Finn how we had flag football and I took an elbow to the face. When I get to the part about almost passing out, I hesitate to tell him. I'm not sure why I don't, but this moment doesn't feel right for it.

"I can imagine that being unpleasant." He lets me off the hook and leads me from the dance floor to a bench. "Sounds like you could use a break."

We sit in silence, watching the girls and their escorts move gracefully around the floor. Essos is dancing with Tiffany, their movements perfunctory. Whereas most of the other girls have continued to grow closer to Essos, Tiffany still has him at arm's length. He's tried night after night to break through to her, but I haven't seen him make any progress. This furthers my belief that she's here only to support Zara and play along with the game.

As the night winds down, I snag Cat and tell her about the game of pong we're going to play with Essos. She's excited about the prospect, and we slip away to set up, with Sybil's help.

Sybil manages to magic up a table that fits the size regulations. Cups are set in their spots, empty of liquid courage. We keep getting distracted, watching the end of the glittering night inside. Finn steps out, holding bottles of champagne with a grin.

"Did someone say drinking games?" he asks, placing a bottle on one side and walking over to Cat on the other to help her set up. He wraps an arm around her shoulders and pulls her close, kissing the top of her head. "We need to wreck them. Do you have that in you?"

Cat affirms with a nod.

Essos emerges with Sybil behind him. Right away, Sybil sits in a chair against the house and crosses their legs, ready to watch. Time moves in slow motion as Essos takes off his jacket and tosses it onto the railing. His hands deftly roll up his sleeves, exposing his muscular arms, and my breath catches. If I wasn't already hot for this man, this would have made me want to jump him. When he gets on his knees before me, I go totally still, unsure what he's planning. I can't stop thinking about having his face between my thighs, and more. I want his featherlight touch to skate up my legs the way they did in my dream. My heart can't take much more of this teasing relationship between us. The fact that he's getting bolder in how he touches me makes my soul trill in delight with each graze. He's careful, slipping off my heels and tossing them to the side.

"If we're going to win, I want you on steady feet. So, tell me more about this...pong," Essos says, shaking me out of the waking wet dream I'm having.

"Get ready to be schooled, old man," Finn says, pouring champagne into the red cups. Sybil magics up our other needs, including a ball and paddles, as instructed by Cat. Finn casts aside his jacket and rolls his shoulders, ready to go. Briefly, we explain the rules to our partners, showing them how to volley. I appreciate that Finn chose Cat as his partner, giving me a chance to partner with Essos.

"So, you're going to want to sink this ball into one of those cups. If you do, the other team has to drink the whole cup. If we hit a cup, they have to drink half of it. When we serve, the ball has to bounce on our side and then their side. During a volley, it should only bounce on their side, or ideally, we sink it. We need to keep the ball shoulder height or higher."

Essos nods, confirming his understanding. "And the paddles?" he asks, holding up his paddle, which is missing the handle. I palm my own paddle with my fingertips, gripping the edges.

Cat and I volley a few times, demonstrating how to play. Finn has one arm crossed over his chest while his other hand is lifted to his mouth as he studies our movements. I glance up and catch Essos watching me, and my cheeks flush.

Cat is wearing a strapless navy blue dress that flares at the knees. I suspect both of us are going to struggle in these gowns, which will level the playing field. When Cat realizes that I'm barefoot, she kicks off her own heels and asks the boys if they're ready to play.

We fall into an easy cadence, Essos and I easily playing off each other. He moves out of my way as if knowing when I'm coming, and I do the same, almost predicting his movements before he makes them. Finn and Cat, on the other hand, keep colliding and laughing as they alternate trading drinks. They celebrate by hip-checking each other every time they make a sink or a hit.

"You know, I know that you were lying earlier. That's okay—you don't have to tell me if you don't want to, but I am here for you."

I'm holding a cup after Finn sank it, not looking at Essos when he says the words. I look up, and that cagey feeling I had when I first got here is gone. I want to open up to him, tell him what's been going on.

I'm silent, contemplating.

"You're a worrier." I drain my cup and stack it neatly with our other empties.

"You're right. I am." He reaches out to take the ball from my hand. One small brush of his fingers against my palm, and I'm practically panting. Is this what it was like to be courted without modern dating and sexting? "I appreciate you trying to protect me, but I need to protect you. Things may not be what they seem." When he says that, I think of the dreams I've been having and how Essos is now at the center of them. I wonder if the dreams are not quite what they seem, either. Sybil's reaction earlier today warned me off mentioning them for sure. Was Cat onto something, and they're actually the memories of another soul? I'm dying to ask, but the threat of repercussions falling on Cat means I can't.

"I just got overwhelmed, probably tired from being early the one time. I don't think there's anything to worry about."

From across the table, Finn gives me an odd look, and I wonder if he can hear us. Essos serves, letting me put the conversation to rest. The first game finishes, and to be fair to Cat, we switch partners. I team up with Finn, and the results are spectacularly bad. Essos and Cat are not as in sync as Essos and I were, but Finn is all over the place, making throw saves in an attempt to try to keep the game going.

"What lie did you just tell?" Finn asks when we're teamed up.

"What?"

"I told you, I can smell the lie you told Essos. It was tart."

"He asked me about today." Without prompting, Finn sets his paddle on top of the cups, effectively pausing the game.

"What about today?"

I glance at Cat and Essos, who start chatting. I think Cat's giving him pointers on serving. Still, I lower my voice, not wanting him to overhear. The urge to confide in Finn is strong, and while earlier didn't feel right to tell him, now I feel like there isn't a choice. "I don't know—something weird happened. I felt like I was dying, and then it was over as quickly as it began. Cat has a theory that I'm not compatible with Solarem and the Underworld, or maybe I'm too compatible and I'm feeling something from a soul."

Finn drums his fingers against his lips. "And when Essos asked what happened, you told him it was nothing?"

"I did."

"It's probably nothing, but you're right not to tell Essos. He's a worrier."

"Right? That's what I said."

Finn lifts his paddle and calls, "Are you ready for us to whoop your asses?"

After another game ends, we switch partners again, girls against boys this time, and it is a decisive victory for Cat and me. Sybil is still sitting in the same chair, looking amused as we win without them sinking a single cup.

"I think that's the night, boys." I laugh, watching Essos knock back the last cup I sank. The adrenaline is starting to wear off, exhaustion settling in my limbs. I doubt I would be able to hit the ball at all if I played another match. With the games played over such a long span of time, what we did have to drink hasn't really affected Cat and me. For the most part, the boys were the ones knocking the drinks back in a show of chivalry.

"I want a rematch!" Finn protests.

Essos places the cup on the table before waving it all away. "Perhaps another night, but for now, I do have a full day of work tomorrow and likely another meeting to attend." He walks over and gives Cat a hug as Finn high-fives me.

"Killjoy," Finn accuses, before giving Cat a hug as well. He squeezes her arms, lifting her off the ground and spinning her. "Ah, good game all around. Let me walk you in." Finn offers Cat his arm, and she takes it, giving me a wink and walking off with him.

Essos grins at me, brushing the hair from my face. "I truly needed this. I can't remember the last time I had so much fun."

For a moment, I think he might kiss me, and my eyes flick to his lips, prompting me to wet mine. He lets out what sounds like a disappointed breath before pressing his lips to my forehead, and I share in that disappointment. Although...if he's so disappointed, I don't get why he won't just kiss me. He hasn't kissed anyone but Zara, as far as I know, and the times I have caught them, she's been the one who instigated it. I have the urge to get on my toes to kiss him myself, and the brave part of me that told him I wanted him to bite pushes me forward a step.

Essos takes a step too, closing the distance so we're chest to chest. The thin tulle of my dress grates against my skin, and I can feel my nipples harden in anticipation. I tell those hussies to relax, because if he's not even going to kiss me, then they're definitely not seeing any action from his mouth tonight.

"I'm glad. You work hard—you need to do something to relieve some of that stress." I keep the disappointment from my voice.

"I didn't used to be like this. Once, my life was very different. I'm hoping that I can find that again, somewhere in this group. I think I will. God, I want so badly to kiss you." It sounds torn from him. Essos reaches for me, pulling me against him by the waist, anchoring me to him. I didn't think we could get closer, and yet here we are, in a tight lovers' embrace. I'm sure he can feel my heart beating wildly against my ribs, eager to break free and crash with his. I reach up and press my hand over his heart, and I can feel the same frenzied beating. His admission comes with something rare—a blush spreading over his cheeks. But just as quickly as he pulled me to him, he releases me, staying close.

"Why don't you? I know you've kissed Zara."

"Because this is not the perfect moment, both of us half-drunk on champagne. You deserve better, and the best things are worth waiting for. I would wait a thousand lifetimes for you."

I swoon at his words, the corners of my mouth pulling up into a smile. He does lean down and brush the corner of my mouth, missing my lips.

"Let me walk you to your room." He offers me his arm again, and I notice Sybil is trying to look very interested in the notebook in front of them. The way they're staring at it, I would bet money that it's a blank page.

"You can always join me in my room," I say, then immediately blush, and he laughs.

"Always so bold." Essos's voice is husky, like he wants to take me up on the offer but thinks better of it. We walk to my room in silence, my thoughts repeating the same thing—*I can't believe I just said that to him.* When we reach my door, he gives me another deep bow. "Thank you again for an amazing night."

He doesn't give me a chance to respond, but the gleam in his blue eyes lights up something in my chest before he leaves. I go inside and lean against the closed door in a full swoon, knowing that he's walked away with a piece of my heart.

12

Our new normal involves breakfast with Essos before his workday and before our classes. Information is being shoved down our throats with each passing day, and it's hard to keep up with the who's who. Luminara, who was meant to be the yoga instructor after flag football, is the Goddess of Harmony. When talking about her, Sybil seemed quiet and almost moony. Then there's Dion, and talking about the God of Wine made my stomach turn. While other girls were joking about how much fun he must be, I was left wondering why I mentioned him in my dream and why no one could tell me the godsdamned truth. We've talked about everyone below the royal family, but Essos's siblings are still a giant question mark.

Every evening, we attend dinner with him, followed by a dance. I never thought I would tire of pretty dresses, but having to be "on" every night is exhausting. Slowly, our numbers dwindle. It's always quiet; the girls say their goodbyes one night and are gone the following day. One month into the process, we have only twelve girls left.

We are at breakfast one morning, a little hungover and too

tired to do anything but quietly enjoy our meals, when the sound of the front door banging open startles us all.

Essos stands quickly. "Stay here," he orders, but before he can take two steps toward the door, a man enters the room. The hairs on my arms rise.

If Essos is the night sky, all dark colors and hidden beauty, then this man is the sun personified. He's a touch shorter than Essos but seems take up more space. His hair is a golden blond, his eyes hidden behind a pair of aviators, as if he's too bright even for himself. He takes them off once he's in the room, facing away from Essos, and I glimpse light brown eyes flecked with gold. He flashes us all a grin with brilliantly white perfect teeth. He's casual to Essos's formal, a T-shirt and cargo shorts not the only thing setting them apart.

"Big brother. You've been keeping secrets!" He gives Essos a tight hug as he says this. Essos frowns, reluctantly returning the hug. I swear I can see him seething, but he tries to cover up his anger and frustration by straightening his suit. The room warms by several degrees and I'm not the only one who notices. The stranger raises one pale eyebrow.

"Baby brother. How good of you to come by. I'm afraid your visit is inconvenient. If you could check with Sybil for my availability, perhaps we can arrange a visit at another time."

His brother doesn't seem to care what Essos is saying. He walks right past him and into the room with us.

"Hello, ladies." He whistles before turning back to Essos. "What a fine group you have this time; much better than the nuns in 1706. How many did you start with—and you're down to what, 12 now? You are fast, big brother. If it were me who had the Calling, I would take my sweet, sweet time with them." He winks at a few of the girls. He stops at Madison and wraps one of her curls around his finger.

"Everyone, this is my brother, Galen," Esosso says. "Galen, these are the participants of the Calling.

He walks around the room, looking at each of us in our pajamas, not yet ready for the day. When he reaches me, he stops, a big shit-eating grin on his face. Essos doesn't move, I don't think he even breathes the entire time Galen is looking at me.

He turns to Essos again. "Secrets, secrets brother. You're supposed to be playing by the rules."

"Galen, might we have a word in the hall?" Essos's voice is hard, only getting more rigid by the time he reaches the end of his sentence. He's giving the impression of some internal tether ready to snap.

Sybil walks into the room and stops short at the sight of Galen. They try to catch Essos's eye, but he doesn't look away from his younger brother.

Essos doesn't give Galen a chance to respond; instead, he drags his brother from the room by his arm, Sybil following closely behind. His grip on Galen's arm looks bruising, but Galen only chuckles in response.

Although we all strain to hear what's happening, none of us can make out what they're saying. The only thing I hear is Essos warning Galen not to interfere. Galen's laughter at this gives the impression that he will not heed this warning. Galen says something low that I miss, followed by pure silence.

A moment later, the three of them return. Essos looks pale, a grim set to his mouth as he watches his younger brother. When Galen settles in the empty seat beside Zara, there is a slight easing of tension in Essos's shoulders.

"Please, explain to me, big brother, why you literally get your pick of the ladies, and I have to fight like a dog to get one to look at me." He flashes his dazzling smile again.

"Maybe because you fail to leave anything to the imagination," I say, buttering my toast, not sparing him a glance. Cat giggles, hiding behind her mug.

"Well, maybe this time around, my big brother will learn to share," Galen says, and I look up just as he grabs a slice of bacon off his brother's plate.

Essos sits back down, and I think I see actual steam coming out of his ears. "Not likely," he mutters and returns to the paperwork before him. Whatever happened in the hallway has Essos much more subdued toward his brother.

Ever the diplomat, Cat tries to diffuse the situation. "So, you're Essos's baby brother? Will you be staying here long?"

"No," Essos replies as Galen offers his own answer.

"Till the ball." Essos looks up sharply as Galen continues. "I think today, we play hooky from the classes that I know Sybil is putting you through and just hang out by the pool and beach. Big brother clearly has so much work to do that he can't even enjoy a nice breakfast with you all, so I figure I will entertain you."

Essos looks at Sybil. Before either of them can say anything, some of the other girls start pleading for a beach day.

"I suppose all work and no play makes me a dull boy," Essos says begrudgingly, scooping up his papers. I can tell it physically pains him to put his work aside. "Fine, just for today, I think we all can take a beach day. Sybil, will you please arrange meals, et cetera? Ladies, please go ready yourselves. We will go down to the beach in an hour. I have to catch up with my brother first."

It's a race up the stairs as everyone chatters about getting out of the house. While we haven't been under house arrest, it feels like we have, with the mountains of memorization Sybil has had us doing. As discussed, when we first started our classes, they haven't offered any information about Essos's family—just that Essos has brothers and sisters—and now here we are, faced with one of them.

I pop into Cat's room first to look over her bathing suit options.

"Well, this is certainly a change of pace," Cat calls from the closet as she changes, excitement raising the pitch of her voice. My shadow, Dave, sits at my feet, tickling my toes as he licks them. "Still, I think we could use some livening up. I'm enjoying the balls and dancing, but I think this will get Essos to open up more to us. Is it just me, or is he shut tight as a clam?" She steps out in a fire-engine-red suit. I whistle at her, and Dave perks his head up, before lowering it, realizing nothing is going to happen. I scratch behind his ears, giving Cat a chance to finish putting herself together.

"I think Essos has been through this before, and it's made him cautious about getting attached. I can hardly fault him for playing things close to the chest. Tiffany was telling me that Anna told Madison, who told Tiffany, that Essos was the one who dismissed Anna, saying they weren't a good fit."

When we go back to my room, Dave follows us, eager to play his part in picking my bathing suit.

I pull out a few options and ultimately don a yellow string bikini with polka dots, the only one that caught Dave's attention. Cat is amused that I let Dave pick my outfits, but he's never wrong.

"I've got to admit, the dog has good taste," Cat says as I pull on a pair of shorts and some wedges. Dave licks her hand in agreement, and I grab a white sun hat from my closet. At times it feels like the closet is sentient, knowing my needs before I do. The only exception was the blue dress Sybil found for me. I could explore the idea more, that maybe the closet is tied to Sybil's or Essos's magic, since they know what we'll need on any given day. I could see Essos being uncertain that I would give him my trust in such a display. It makes me want to protect his little cinnamon bun heart.

As we walk down the stairs, Cat stops and grabs my arm. "Do you think they miss me?"

For a moment, I'm confused, but then I realize she must mean her family. After the first week, we never really talked about our families again. No matter how often I left the option open to Cat, she never seized it, quick to change the subject instead. Pushing her wouldn't have done either of us any good, so I did my best to follow her lead.

"Of course, they do. They love you so much." I take her hand and give it a squeeze. The time I spent with her family is among my happiest memories, including mornings when her mom would trick her brothers with blueberry pancakes, telling them she made chocolate chip. She was always ready with a smile or platitude to make a day brighter. Her dad was often busy with work, but breakfast and dinner with the family were sacred, and he always made me feel like part of his brood.

"It just feels wrong, living this life, as if I should be sadder that they're gone." Cat's voice dips low.

I start walking with her again, leading her down the stairs. "I think that they probably feel the same way, like they shouldn't go on either, but that's why you have to—you wouldn't want their lives to stop because you're gone. You have this second chance, and I don't think you should feel bad about it." I hope my words are reassuring to her.

"I don't mean to interrupt, but I agree," Tiffany says, coming down the stairs behind us. "When I think about Steve, I know I want him to move on and keep living his life, even though I wanted it to be with me. I know it's best for him to move forward. Even if a small part of me wants him to mourn me forever."

"I'm sure in his own way, he will." I take her hand in my other, and the three of us walk outside. In the time it took us to get ready, Sybil had a cabana set up by the water, complete with drinks and snacks and towels. Knowing that sand and shoes are a terrible idea, I kick off my wedges and feel the sand between my toes. This moment, with the wind blowing my hair, the smell of the saltwater, and the sand beneath my feet, feels like the most real experience I've had in a month.

Galen looks up at us and smiles. "Glad to see that you aren't covering up your itsy bitsy yellow polka dot bikini. That would be a crying shame indeed."

I grab a towel from the cabana before stepping back into the sun, refusing to acknowledge him. I hold the towel against my body, feeling a chill deep in my bones. These moments of chilliness have been plaguing me since I died, and I have yet to figure out if there's a trigger, but right now, in the sun under Galen's gaze, I feel cold to my very core.

I set my towel on a lounge chair and rub my arms until warmth spreads through my insides to my limbs. I look up from the coast toward the cabana and see Essos, still in his business suit, chatting with Zara. He might be talking to her, but his eyes are on me. There's a storm brewing within him, visible in the stony set of his mouth. I give him a smile and a nod, which he returns before focusing on Zara.

As Cat and Tiffany stake out chairs, I opt to head for the water. I'm still not the most comfortable with it. I shower more quickly than ever before, and the idea of a bath isn't even in the hemisphere of thought. As I stand there, I rationalize that, now that I am dead, the water can't hurt me. I miss that feeling of weightlessness that comes with drifting in an open body of water, slowly rocked by the waves. I want to capture that feeling again.

I hoped for solitude in confronting this newfound fear, but the footsteps behind me send that hope far away.

"Hey!" Galen calls, as I dip my toes in the ocean for the first time. "It's Daphne, right?"

I turn toward him, crossing my arms. "That's my name." I turn back toward the water. I'm hoping he gets the hint. He comes closer and grabs my arm, and a jolt of static electricity buzzes through me.

In my mind I see a flash of Galen's face, hovering over mine, flushed red as he says my name, his golden curls matted to his forehead as sweat drips off his face. I feel so many things at once —the way the bedding I'm lying on chafes my back, and the sheets fisted in my hands. I feel the pounding of my heart and a moan scratching against my throat. The brief flash makes my heart race.

"Daphne, are you okay?" Galen's voice pulls me back to the present.

I swallow, my mouth suddenly dry. "Yeah, but I'm not big on people touching me without my permission." The feeling of ice in my veins battles with my red-hot skin. I might not have gotten a complete memory from the flash, and there was no emotion behind it, but I have an idea as to what was happening. I've never had sex with Essos in my dreams, but there's something more intimate about how we kiss and our bodies press together. I can't imagine any reality in which I would do that with his brother, of all people.

"Sorry, I just...I was hoping to talk to you. I want to get to know all the girls who could someday become my sister-in-law." Galen has a strange expression, as if he's trying to memorize my face.

I wonder if he saw the same thing I did.

"Sure," I agree, not willing to fight him over something as trivial as getting to know me. My brain is too busy trying to figure out what it means that I had that vision of Galen, who certainly seemed to be saying my name with passion. I feel my cheeks burn at the thought of how his hair was askew, how his body was definitely moving above me.

"How have you been enjoying living in the lap of luxury? I hear Essos has pulled out all the stops for your group. All-night dance parties, champagne flowing. What escort did you get stuck with?" He fires off questions faster than I can answer them.

"I'm with Finn. He's been great." Galen wades deeper into the water so it's up to his knees. While shorter than his brother, he still has an easy height advantage over me. I go past him a bit farther until I'm up to my hips, secretly relieved that I have someone there if I freak out. Reminding myself that I'm still on the sand bar, I focus on taking calming breaths in through my nose and out through my mouth. I thought I wanted to face this alone, but I don't. Galen might not be the person I want by my side, but he'll do. The person I do want is still at the beach dressed in a suit, something I may never understand.

"Ah, he's okay. I'm looking forward to seeing you in a gown tonight. I'm sure it's a spectacular sight."

I glance at him over my shoulder and find that he looks genuine. I smile, loosening up to his charm. "I always am," I tease. Once the words are out of my mouth, I regret them and want to claw them back. It's the kind of flirty comment I would have thrown out with friends, but even if my feelings toward Essos are complicated, I shouldn't have said that to Galen. He grins at me broadly, and it makes me feel *wrong*.

"You're a bit cheeky, aren't you?" Galen glances at the shore, where the next closest people are walking toward the water, far enough away that I can't make out their words over the crash of waves around us. "Look, we're far away from prying ears now. I want to let you know that you can always come to me if something seems off here. Please, know that I'll make sure you're protected."

A flurry of thoughts crosses my mind as we come off the sand bar, and suddenly I'm treading water. Without the comfort of the sand directly under my foot, I feel sick, my stomach dropping. It's too much to deal with at once, the overwhelming fear of drowning again, and Galen's insinuation that I'm in danger.

Sybil's threat about the dreams resurfaces, and I suppress a shudder. I know that we aren't being told everything; Finn has even counseled me to be patient, but I want answers, and I'm wondering if, since Galen isn't directly involved with the Calling, he's able to give me some.

"I'm sorry, but I don't understand what you mean. What would I need to be protected from?" I paddle my way back to the sand bar, thankful to find my footing. I need to be on two feet for this conversation.

"I love Essos—he's my brother—but he's used to running his realm alone. It's been him and Sybil for so long. I'm not sure they'll look kindly on some woman invading their turf."

I think about how close Sybil always is to Essos, their ability to anticipate his needs on an almost psychic level. I attributed that to how long they've worked together, but maybe it's something else. I think of the disdain they occasionally have for some of the girls, and how they always touch Essos when coming to deliver a message for him.

"I don't expect you to trust me. You've only just met me, and I know trust is something to be earned. But Daphne, I am trusting you with this, because I see the way he's looking at you, and I've seen what Sybil is capable of when Essos is leaning toward someone they can't control. If the way you've spoken to me is any indication, you're strong-willed. I would hate to see something happen to you. I'm just sorry it took me so long to get here."

It's like he's reading my soul when he says that he under-stands trust is something to be earned. Essos told me right away to trust him while giving me a superficial trust—there would be no consequences if I told someone that he liked to wear blue. It would be a breach of that trust, and was likely a test, but all the same. It's validating to have someone agree that trust is not something easily given.

I study Galen's face, trying to see if I can get a good read on him. His brow is furrowed in concern, presumably for my well-being, but I just don't know. There are too many questions running through my mind to focus on the signals he's sending with his body language.

"What do you mean, took you so long? What is Sybil capable of?" I ask, deciding to tread water again. From the shore, I hear laughter; a few other girls have started wading in the water but aren't coming as far out as we are.

"The Calling is an old tradition, one that Essos has been participating in with displeasure for a long time. There are rules, just like the ones that you ladies have, that he is also supposed to be following. I'm sure Sybil has started to educate you about the sycophants that surround our family, correct?" Galen is watching me closely. He glances over his shoulder before continuing.

"Once the Calling began, Essos was supposed to notify the citizens of Solarem by inviting us to the ball. He was explicitly told this by the head of the Council, but he still hasn't sent out the invitations. You see, the last few Callings ended before the girls could get to the ball, so certain people want to ensure that this Calling doesn't fail. I only found out about it because I was here a few weeks ago on business and happened to catch sight of some of you. I came here today to confirm my suspicions. When I confronted him about why rule-abiding Essos hasn't invited everyone yet, he explained that he doesn't want to waste everyone's time preparing for a ball in case it doesn't happen. I have so much more I want to say, but I know you need time to feel me out for yourself." He glances at the shore again. "I should head back before he gets suspicious of us talking, but think about what I said. Please." The tone of his voice is imploring, as if there is so much more he wants to say but can't. He wets his lips and glances at mine before turning away from me.

I watch him wade back. He ignored my question about Sybil, and the whole conversation left me more confused than ever.

With Essos, I've gone one step forward, then two steps back in a dance of balance that can never be kept. Every time we talk, I try to open up a little more, but with him, it's like peeling an onion—beneath every layer is more onion, which leads to frustration and tears. I haven't cried over him, but I could. Galen seems completely open with me, and willing to answer my questions, at least at a later time.

I consider heading back to shore but instead embrace the solitude. I'm not bold enough yet to submerge myself, but as the waves gently rock my body, I let myself float, thinking of the dream where I approached Essos in the water in a silk robe. I think about how my dreams have added to my confusion about Essos, how there is a familiarity there, but I don't know where it comes from.

Something wraps around my ankle and drags me under.

I have no time to get air in my lungs before I am submerged. I don't even have time to scream before whatever grabbed me has pulled me farther away from the surface. Seeing as I have no interest in drowning again, I bend over and reach for my ankle. The skin of the creature is velvety and smooth, like a dolphin or other aquatic animal. It must be a tentacle of some kind holding tight to me. I dig my feeble nails into the tender skin as hard as I can, angry that they're too short to do much damage. The thing's skin is too slimy. The pressure on my chest already hurts, and I want to pull in a breath, but I can't. I promise myself that, if I survive this, I'm going to stop biting my nails. I try to slide my fingers between the tentacle and my leg, and I make some headway. Thankfully, the creature loosens its grip enough for me to kick for the surface.

With my head barely over water, I try to force out a scream, but my lungs are fighting to do two things at once. I inhale deeply but, instead of screaming, I'm pulled under again. This time, I at least have more air in my lungs. I try to kick with my left foot, but a second tentacle wraps around my free leg, giving the creature a better grip to drag me down. The farther it pulls me, the more intense the pressure I feel in my lungs.

I open my eyes and stare at the surface, watching it get farther and farther away. Surprise at how deep we're going is suffocated by the fear that no one saw me get dragged under. I glance down into the abyss and see nothing below me, not even the creature. The memory of what it was like to be on that bus with no hope of escape crushes my chest worse than the pressure of descending. Doubt creeps in. Maybe this is the way it's supposed to be— maybe I'm supposed to surrender to the depths of the ocean.

There is a flash behind my eyelids—

—I'm no longer in the ocean but kneeling in a field, the air around me crisp like a too-cool morning in spring. No one can tell me my worth, not the God of Luck with his sideways glances nor the Goddess of Rain and her ability to draw a cloud at will. I will decide my worth and what I can do.

The dead grass that surrounds me is still, despite the cool breeze that tickles the hairs on the nape of my neck. Digging deep, I find the magic at the core of my being before I plunge my hands into the soil and release what I know I have. Around me, life blooms.

My eyes open, stinging in the salt water. I will not give up this fight. Whatever that was, I try to dig deep to find a kernel of that belief in myself again. I close my eyes and focus on my fight.

Suddenly, there's a mouth on mine, and air is forced into my lungs. I get another flash, then, of Galen tucking a flower behind my ear, telling me that I will be safe with him forever and that no harm will ever come to me. I open my eyes to see Galen holding my face.

When he sees my eyes open, relief flashes in his own. He swims down to the beast and grabs the tentacles around my ankles. I don't see what he does, because my eyes start to burn, but the creature suddenly releases me.

Galen wraps an arm around my waist, and we both kick furiously upward. Once we break the surface, I start to cough, trying to get the water out of my lungs. I fight to take several deep breaths, tears springing to my eyes, and whether I'm crying or they're just trying to cleanse the salt water, I'm not sure. Galen is holding me around the waist and dragging me toward the shore. When we reach the sand bar, he stands and lifts me into his arms. I am grateful that I am wet so my tears are disguised, and the coughing covers the sobs that wrack my body. I am so grateful and happy that I get to see another day.

"That's right, take a deep breath, keep breathing, my flower, keep breathing. It won't do to have you die on me now. I've just found you again. Rest now, I've got you." I don't know what he means, but I let my body go limp now that I'm not fighting for my life. I hear the sounds of splashing and more people rushing into the water, and then I'm scooped into someone else's arms. It's uncomfortable for a moment, but then the warmth of the body and the familiar scent of sandalwood and cinnamon settle me. I let my body fully relax, with no fight left in me, and I pass out.

13

When my eyes flutter open, all I see is blinding white, and I think that maybe I did die. Waves crash in the distance, and I realize that I'm not dead, I just almost wish I was. I take a few seconds to re-acclimate myself. I'm still on the beach, now under the cabana. Essos is in a chair next to me, watching me. He brushes a strand of hair out of my eyes, letting out an audible sigh of relief.

"I really wish you would stop trying to drown on me," he says, trying to keep it light, but his voice breaks. I cough before responding.

"It's a character flaw, what can I say?" I croak, my throat raw. It hurts, and despite having inhaled more water than I want, I'm eager for water to soothe my throat. I struggle to sit up, tired of feeling helpless. Essos reaches behind me to readjust the lounge chair so it's upright. It's helpful, but I feel like an invalid.

"Other than your bravado still being intact, are you all right?"

I'm sure he knows the answer just by looking at me. I mentally take stock of myself, stopping when I come to my ankles. I sit up a little more and see that not only are they bruising, but they're also red and blistered. Looking at them makes me wince.

"You know, I missed having bruises. I figured I'd get some more." I smile at him sheepishly.

"Your wit knows no bounds. Even after facing certain death a second time, you can't stop making jokes." Essos speaks wryly, but there are creases on his forehead, and he looks haggard.

"It's called comic relief; otherwise life would be too sad. Where is everyone?" I ask, looking around. The beach is deserted, as if everyone just vanished, the lounge chairs and towels left behind along with the food. I wonder how long I was out.

"I sent everyone to the pool. The rules say we're not to be alone behind closed doors, but I see no doors here. I figured I would keep an eye on you myself. You scared the life out of me, you know. Seriously, what happened? One minute you were talking to Galen, the next Tiffany was screaming bloody murder."

I take a deep breath in, savoring the feel of air in my lungs. "I don't know. Galen and I were talking, and he decided to head in. I was floating in the water, and something grabbed my ankle and pulled me under. I thought I was a goner—it had both my ankles. Galen came out of nowhere, gave me air, and made it let go." Essos listens intently, frowning. I omit what we were talking about and what Galen said to me while pulling me to shore. He unloaded more meaningful information in that one interaction than I've received the whole time I've been here.

Essos looks as though the weight of the universe is bearing down on him in that moment. "Would you like to go in and rest? I can cancel the rest of the evening, the dance and everything. Whatever you need. Just tell me." He takes my hand in his, and his thumb gently grazes my skin as he rubs my hand like a worry stone.

"What I want is to know why you're wearing a suit at the beach. Are you so pasty under there that we'd all be blinded?" I say, trying to break the buildup of emotion between the two of us. He lets out a big laugh, even if it is somewhat forced. I scared him today.

"I'm a formal person. I was raised in the lap of luxury but with responsibilities. Responsibilities Galen didn't have, lucky for him. So, I'm known as the one with a stick up my ass, because I would rather keep my heart close to my chest and not wear it on my sleeve the way he does. I suppose I can try to be a little less formal going forward." He discards his jacket and unbuttons his collar. Even this little bit of skin sets my heart racing, and I wish he'd keep unbuttoning his shirt. Then his pants. I want to feel the thick length of him pressing against me and see if it's anything like it is in my dreams. I want to know if he feels the same pull toward me, and if he lights up like the New Year's ball at Times Square when I touch him. When he comes, is he loud? Is he a generous lover, or does he take what he wants and leave his partner desperate for more? Somehow, I doubt the latter is true; he strikes me as the type of man to give himself entirely to his partner. I want to give myself entirely to him.

When Essos meets my eye, I think maybe he can read every filthy thought in my mind, because his eyes burn into mine with a need that has the heat of desire coiling low in my belly.

He unbuttons another button before swallowing hard and leaning back.

I realize there's a line of dried salt water on his pants and jacket. That he ran into the water to meet me doesn't escape my notice. He still holds my hand, not letting go, as if he needs the reassurance that I'm still here.

"You do realize that this is the most I've learned about you since this all started."

"I'm not sure I believe that," he says, as if shocked by this. It would be more shocking to find out that Essos doesn't have every single conversation he's ever had meticulously cataloged away somewhere.

"Well, you should believe me. If I told a lie, my nose would grow." I turn my head as if to showcase that my nose has not in fact grown since we started talking.

Essos reaches out with his free hand and taps the tip of my nose. "We wouldn't want that, now would we? I like to think of myself as an open book."

I laugh, loud and bawdy. "On what planet are you an open book? You have more secrets than the Kremlin."

Essos feigns offense. "I resent that statement wholeheartedly. What do you want to know about me?" He opens his free hand, still holding mine with his other. The question is more, what don't I want to know about him? There is so much to him that I don't even know what I don't know, but I get the feeling that Galen would happily fill in the missing spaces. This whole situation feels like I'm applying for a job, getting the dressed-up version of Essos and this life. No one will tell you the pitfalls of a new gig right off the bat.

"Okay, for starters, how many Callings have you had, and why weren't they successful?" I sit up fully, swinging my legs over the side of the chair so I can face him instead of lying down. He leans back in his chair, finally letting go of me. Despite my current misgivings, I'm sad that I made him do that.

"Wow, straight for the jugular. All right then. I've had 12, and for the record, if we're going to play this game, it's going to be tit for tat. You hold just as many secrets."

"You still haven't answered the second half of my question. It was one question with two parts."

"Are you sure you didn't want to become a journalist? You may have missed your own calling."

"Hard to be a journalist when you're dead. Nice deflection. Answer."

He looks away from me, his face falling as he stares at the horizon, no doubt thinking back on his previous Callings. "They all failed for one reason or another. What I think you all fail to realize—and this is not just true of you and your friends, but of all the women in the previous Callings—is that you're facing down the rest of forever. It will take a unique person to spend eternity by my side. For starters, I snore, and whoever it comes down to needs to be able to put up with that. My turn. What happened to your birth parents?"

"Wait, I'm sorry, you snore? You did say that at any point, we can opt out, right?"

For a moment he looks stunned, as though I've hit him. Once he realizes I'm joking, he laughs. "Now you are deflecting. Answer."

I frown at my own words being used against me, and then sigh, considering how best to answer him. "My parents died when I was a baby, after deciding to take their first solo trip since I was born. There was a mudslide that buried their resort." I pause, reaching out to take his hand for my own comfort. I can never stand to look at people's faces when I tell them; they're always horrified by it. I hate the pity that comes with people realizing I never knew my parents. They think that I'm inherently damaged because of it. But I can't miss what I didn't have.

Essos, as if sensing that I have more to say, waits patiently. Maybe Finn was right, and patience is a sign of a good ruler.

"I was a late-in-life baby, so my grandparents were already older. Only one set was still alive when I was born. They never got over losing their daughter. My grandfather died shortly after my mom, and my grandmother passed when I was five. My adoptive parents did a great job of making sure I didn't forget any of them."

"They sound wonderful."

Essos gingerly reaches over, and the soft pad of his thumb wipes away a tear that I didn't realize had escaped. Usually, I'm more in check with my emotions and can handle conversations like this without a breakdown. Twenty years steeled my emotions about it.

"I'm sorry, I don't know why I'm crying." Another tear slips free, and he brushes that one away too.

Essos lets go of my hand and cups my face, using his thumb to catch each stray tear as it slips from my eyes. I pride myself on not being a crier and, in this moment, I'm angry with myself for these tears.

"It's because you died last month and almost died again today. I would say that's enough to knock anyone off-kilter. There's nothing wrong with it—grief is a normal emotion. I've never understood why people fight it. You're allowed to rail against the injustices of the universe. I think I should cancel tonight—you'll hardly be in dancing shape. Let me do this for you. Take a break."

"Now you're just challenging me," I say and push out a laugh that sounds as fake as it is. I lean away from him, wiping the tears from my cheeks. "I'm positive—please don't cancel tonight on my account. Your brother is here, anyway. Don't you want to show off how marvelous we all are?"

A dark look crosses his face. "How about I have the chef make your favorite tonight? Whatever it is, that's the menu."

"You ask as if you don't already know my favorite foods. Don't you have a dossier on each of us? You seem to know everything about us, including our measurements."

His gaze slides over my body at the mention of my measurements. For the second time today, I'm feeling self-conscious that I'm wearing a bikini.

"Knowing something and being trusted enough to have someone share it with you is entirely different."

Yep, there's no doubt in my mind that he was just undressing me with his eyes. A blush spreads over my body as I think about how badly I want him to undress me with more than his eyes. The trust issue aside, I wouldn't mind letting Essos take me out for a ride.

"Macaroni and cheese, with dinosaur-shaped chicken nuggets."

He laughs, leaning back and crossing an ankle over his knee. "I'm sorry, are you twenty-one or five?"

"You judge, but there's nothing wrong with those two things except when they're apart." I don't say that these are the foods my grandmother used to make me.

"Nothing wrong when you're five."

I stand up then, crossing my arms, and he shoots out of his chair, so close to me. "Another mark on your permanent record," I say, trying to fight back the pinch of pain in my ankles now that they're bearing my full weight.

He tilts his head at me. "I'm sorry, permanent record?"

"Yes. You admitted that you snore, and now you've told me my favorite meal is for children. Before I know it, you're going to tell me that you don't pull string cheese—you just bite it, like a heathen. No, I don't think I can see anything more between us." I shake my head, shrugging my shoulders and holding up my hands dramatically.

"I think I deserve another shot to show you that it could work." He leans his head down and presses his forehead against mine, then closes his eyes. I think this might be the moment, that he might kiss me. "Please, please be more careful with your life. I couldn't bear it if something bad happened to you."

I lean away from him, a burning question on my mind, the potential kiss forgotten. "What would have happened?" I ask, considering the worst. The look on his face is grim, his mouth set in a hard line, and I know that I'm right.

He seems to contemplate how to answer me, but he paces away before coming back. "I don't know," he nearly snaps, frustration seeping into his voice. "It's not like this has ever happened to me before. Your soul could have been lost forever," he whispers, as if not wanting to say it too loud.

I snort, the only reaction I can bear to have. "Well, that would have sucked."

"Indeed. And I do think you should go upstairs and rest. You were out for almost two hours, and I think you need the rest badly. Especially if you want to be a hero for tonight. Dave will go with you." At the sound of his name, Dave perks up from under the lounge chair where I was sitting. Essos signals to someone, and I'm not surprised when Sybil appears by his side. He relays to them what we just discussed, and that I'm permitted to miss the rest of the activities.

Before walking away, I turn to Essos. "I'm a little tired of being ordered around. I'm not this frail damsel who is going to fall to pieces. If I need rest, I'll rest. But stop assuming it. I'm stronger than you think." I pause. "That being said, I'm going to go rest."

A ghost of a smile crosses his face. "Understood," he confirms with a bow, and Sybil leads me away. Their arm wraps around my waist, holding me up. I'm putting more weight on them than I would care to admit, so I'm grateful to have them by my side. We take the stairs slowly, one at a time.

Once we're inside, away from everyone else, they finally speak up. "You gave us quite a fright." We arrive at my bedroom door, and they pause, taking both of my hands in theirs. "Why don't I have the cook send you up some lunch, and you can relax up here? Doesn't that sound nice?" Their tone is a little patronizing, but I let it go, since I made such a spectacle of myself earlier. I nod and open the door to let Dave in. Sybil watches as he jumps up on the bed, and they give a half smile. "You spoil him so." With a final look, Sybil leaves.

"Thank you, Sybil," I call as they walk down the hall. I go into my room and lean against the door, looking at Dave. My emotions feel like they're all over the place. My bravado can only get me so far and, now that I'm mostly alone, I start to shake, thinking about how close I came to actually dying.

"Oh, Dave." His ears perk up at his name. "What am I going to do?"

14

I'm dreaming in black and white. This time, I'm wearing a heavily-beaded black dress with a risqué hemline ending mid-thigh, and my hair is cropped short with finger waves. Galen looks suave in a black suit and matching fedora. We're dancing before a live band, our faces close, but never touching. My body and his move so clearly in sync. My feet and lower legs are moving in ways that I never thought I could with a level of coordination I never knew I had. As the song ends, he takes my hand in his, pulling me insistently away from the dance floor. He looks both ways down the hall before pulling me into an empty coat closet. His mouth is on mine in a flash, kissing me hard, as if time is running out. I respond in kind, pressing against him as if he is the air I need to breathe. He lifts me onto the counter, kissing down my neck and breasts. I lean back, a small moan escaping my mouth, but he pulls me closer, putting his hand over my mouth.

"Shhh, my love, we can't get caught."

But I don't care. I fumble with his belt, undoing it, so I can thrust my hand into his pants. I grab hold of the length of him, and he groans, thrusting into my hand. I bite my lip and gently drag my nails over him, watching his reaction. Galen groans back between clenched teeth *and thrusts again. I'm admiring the responses I elicit, my thumb rubbing over the head of his cock, a bead of liquid there.*

I press my mouth to his ear. "Shh, my love, we can't get caught."

I nip at his lobe. He pushes my skirt up to my hips, ripping a seam on the side. One hand finds the slick wetness between my legs while his other hand finishes undressing. He fumbles, righting himself before thrusting inside me. I cry out, causing him to clamp his hand over my mouth again. With each thrust, our care of the outside world hearing us slips away. All that exists is our bodies, fusing together as one. My fingers run through his silky blond strands, causing some to slip into his eyes. I press my forehead against his, riding the rising wave inside me, as we both climb toward climax—

I WAKE with a start to find Cat sitting on the foot of my bed, petting Dave. My breathing is labored as I sit up to look around.

On my nightstand is a bowl of soup that looks long-since cooled, along with a small vase and single blue cornflower. I can feel the thump of my heart as it beats hard, trying to break out of my chest, and the warmth of pleasure between my legs. As the dream fades, the desire I felt slips away as well. It's like that flash I had earlier by the water, and this new vision confirms that what I thought was sex with Galen must have been. My stomach heaves, and I go utterly still to try and control the urge to throw up. The desire to close my eyes and push the images away is strong, but I can't. I tell myself that it was just a dream, but it felt so real.

I can't open my mouth, so I focus on breathing in and out through my nose.

"Please don't scare me like that again," Cat says. When our gazes meet, I see that her eyes are puffy from crying. I open my arms, and she crawls across the bed and hugs me. "This wouldn't be worth it if you weren't here."

I smile at her. "Same, sister, same." I look at the clock and see that we have only one hour to get ready. Thankfully, I showered before climbing into bed and passing out, but I'm not sure Cat has. I turn to the closet and see a dress bag hanging from the door with a note. I give Cat a questioning look before walking over to it. I read the note aloud.

"'As a thank you for saving your life, please wear this dress. – Galen' Well that's a tad presumptuous," I say, tossing the card aside. Cat nods in agreement, but once I open the bag, I gasp at the beauty of the dress. It has a tight bodice and a loose skirt with a slit all the way up the thigh to the hip. And it is *red*—not "I'm trying to show off" scarlet but a deep crimson. I marvel at it and see that Galen also provided gems to go with the dress, including a statement diamond necklace that has three large stones connected by smaller ones, as if three suns were connecting.

"Super presumptuous." Cat agrees, eyes wide.

I stare at the dress, and my throat feels like it's closing. As gorgeous as the garment is, I'm not sure I should wear it. The whole point of the Calling is to try to win Essos's heart, and accepting this gift from his brother feels like a test. Is that it? Am I meant to prove that I can look past biases and adversity and still work with someone?

Slowly, I change into it to see how it fits and, of course, it slides on like it was made for me, like everything else in my closet. There's a box under where the dress was hanging, and I open it to find another note and red satin slippers.

I flash the note at Cat and read this one to her as well. "'I figured your ankles needed to rest too. Dance on, princess.'"

Dave is watching me get dressed and keeps letting out huffs of disappointment. I go over and scratch behind his ears to reassure him he's still my number one consultant.

"That settles it for me. Forget the guys, let's have you and me run this bitch," Cat teases.

I laugh and follow her across the hall so she can get ready

while I fill her in on what happened to me. Thinking of Sybil's warning, I leave out my visions of Galen as well as his warning about Essos.

"You and Essos looked like you might have kissed," she muses, putting on her makeup. She's watching my reaction in her vanity mirror.

I look at myself, wondering how finger waves would look with my hair length and dress. "That would be a hard no. I thought we might, and then nothing. He's concerned over my wellbeing, and I keep giving him good reasons to be. But it's not like he's kissed anyone else, so maybe he's not really allowed to?"

"Except for Zara," she points out.

"Except for Zara," I confirm with a scowl.

I consider how to approach Galen tonight to get more information from him away from the prying ears of others. At the very least, there doesn't seem to be an excess of love between the brothers, and I want to know more about that. The thought of all this back-channeling exhausts me. I consider not going, but it might be my only shot to get information from him.

Realizing I forgot the necklace, I pop back into my room. When I open the door, I find a bouquet of closed flowers on my nightstand in place of the cold soup. I walk over and pick up the card leaning against it.

I never thought you were frail.
—E

I hold the card to my nose, and it smells like Essos, vanilla and cinnamon and sandalwood. The scent soothes my nerves, helping the pent-up stress from the day seep away. Essos's comment earlier about my bravado wasn't off base. Eventually, I'll have to process how very close—again—I came to death. Dying once was enough.

174

I set the card carefully on my nightstand and gently touch the bouquet. The flowers might be dahlias from their shape, and I'm sad to have to wait a few days to see for sure.

Cat's waiting for me in the hall, her mouth pinched from holding back what I assume are all her comments about how early we're going to be. Since I'm in flats, I sweep down the stairs ahead of her, laughing back at her as my dress billows behind me, making me feel as if I'm flying. I'm not paying attention, because I collide with a solid force at the foot of the stairs. I hear Cat's heels stop short.

Essos is holding me, steadying us both as Cat presses her hands against my shoulders to stop herself. A smile brightens his face as he looks at me.

"I'm glad to see you've made a full recovery. You look beautiful, as always. Your dress is stunning. Did you get some rest?"

I blush, remembering my dream about his brother. My dreams of Essos are never so erotic, always ending before the real action.

"Yes!" I squeak, stepping away from him to give him more space.

He holds out his arm to me. "Marvelous. Shall I escort you ladies in, then?" He looks at Cat as well.

Cat steps forward and takes his other arm. "We would be delighted."

Because our numbers have whittled down, the escorts are now invited to dine with us each night. Tonight, it's Cat's turn to sit beside Essos, and I try not to be jealous about it, but that ugly green bitch rears her head, saying he should be doting on me. My stomach is turning so fiercely, I might be sick.

Finn is standing behind my seat, waiting for me. His eyebrow twitches when he sees me, and he gives a soft, dignified whistle as he pulls out my chair. "I heard you had an exciting day." He takes his seat beside me.

Before I can fill him in, a hand slaps on his shoulder. "She's lucky I was there," Galen gloats before taking the seat on my other side. "That dress is very becoming on you." He winks. Finn looks just as happy to see Galen as Essos was, and I wonder if this feud runs deeper than just brotherly rivalry.

"Incredibly lucky, otherwise some monster would have carried me away, and I would have drowned a second time. I wouldn't have recommended it the first time." I am shockingly uncomfortable, sitting between the two men. Finn has never given me the impression of an alpha male, but since he saw Galen, his chest has puffed out, and he's sitting a bit taller.

"We wouldn't want that," Galen says, his gaze running the length of me. Goosebumps break out along my arms, prompting Finn to reach out and rub my back. Essos catches the movement, and I feel the warmth from his power spread out along my body. He must have assumed I was cold. It tracks, but how can I correct him from across the room that I'm not cold, it's from a prickle of awareness?

Galen turns to Essos. "Brother, what are we feasting on tonight? I've been craving that pork belly your cook makes."

Essos looks at Galen and smiles. The smiles I've seen from Essos usually make his eyes brighten and his whole face soften, but now he looks plastic and perfunctory.

"It's a surprise I'm sure everyone will enjoy," he says, and turns his attention back to Cat. Still, I catch a small tick in his jaw, as if he's clenching his teeth.

Galen calls out to Essos again. "Brother! Doesn't Daphne look smashing in the dress I chose for her tonight?"

Every muscle in Essos's face tenses, causing my stomach to clench uncomfortably. I put that look on his face by wearing this dress. He reaches out and touches Cat's arm apologetically before turning to his brother. "She does. You missed your calling as a stylist to the stars. Daphne, will you do me the honor of the first dance?" Essos says easily.

I expect Cat to look hurt, but instead, she smirks, watching Galen.

Galen looks like he's about to blow up but then seems to remember that he's playing chess and needs to be cooler than that. It dawns on me that I'm a pawn in this game between brothers.

My eyes narrow. "I would love to, so long as *Finn* isn't too hurt by it." Finn waves his hand and I grab it, willing him telepathically to say no to giving up the first dance with me. I've come to take solace in my moments with him. Telling him about my day helps me relax.

"Not a problem at all. I would love to catch up with Galen, anyway. It's been too long, *pal*," Finn says.

I stomp on his foot in retaliation for being unable to read my mind. The tension between the three males is so thick I'm surprised I don't see sparks flying. I consider locking them in a room so they can get it out of their systems.

"I think that sounds *swell*, Phineas," Galen replies.

Things calm down as we wait for dinner to be served. Usually, the servers work their way around the table, but this time, they all take their places behind us, plates with covers in hand. In one synchronized motion, they place the plates in front of us and remove the covers all at once, revealing mac and cheese and dinosaur-shaped chicken nuggets, to my endless amusement.

Everyone else seems confused. After all the fine dining we've had, from stuffed Chilean sea bass to prime rib and artisanal salads, this is such a departure that even Galen is at a loss for words.

Essos stands then, opening his arms to us all. "Bon appétit!"

Once the words are spoken, I shove a forkful of mac and cheese into my mouth in possibly the most undignified way I can. The mac and cheese is elevated and most definitely not from a box with powdered mix. The thick cheese and pasta goodness takes me back to my childhood, and I almost want to cry from the thought of my grandmother and all that I missed out on. Instead, I catch Essos's eye and mouth my gratitude across the table.

Once dinner is cleared, Essos approaches me and guides me out of the dining room, as he should have done for Cat. I shoot her an apologetic look as we pass, and she gives me a little head shake, motioning me forward. I take Essos's hand, and we move into the ballroom, where the string quartet is already playing. I could pretend that getting used to this is impossible, but then I would be a liar, and my nose would grow.

Once Essos and I reach the center of the dance floor, we begin to sway. My dancing has improved over the past month, even if Finn remarks that now he's icing his feet for only 30 minutes afterward instead of the hour he needed when we first became partners.

I look at Essos. His face is tense. I lean closer to him. "Please relax. You're going to step on my toes, and I think my feet have had enough at this point." Essos glances down at me, and the tension drains from his posture. I feel him relax into my arms, and I smile.

"I'm sorry about this dance—about making you a pawn in this stupid game with my brother. You deserve better. I shouldn't have done it. He gets under my skin like no one else." His hand slides down to the small of my back, our box step unparalleled in its smoothness.

"To be fair, he made me the pawn first. What happened between you two?" I ask, hoping to get some answers from Essos for once.

"That doesn't mean that I should stoop to his level. What happened is what always happens—we're brothers who were raised differently. He was the golden child who could have anything he wanted, until I got something he couldn't have. Our parents were overindulgent, so it caused a rift." I snicker at this as he spins me, the folds of my dress billowing, before he pulls me tight against him once more. Our noses touch, gently. Once I would have expected him to kiss me then, but I've learned that I'm going to be waiting forever to feel his lips on mine. He pulls away, looking as if he's shaking cobwebs from his mind.

"It's hard to imagine the King of the Underworld fighting with his brother and being put in time out."

He smiles at me. "I wish it were more like that, but it is literally centuries of fighting. It's like all those old wars that go on for so long, no one even remembers why they're fighting anymore." The look on his face tells me he knows exactly why he and Galen are fighting. For once, I decide not to press him as the song comes to an end. "If you'll excuse me, I owe Catalina an apology and a dance." With a bow, he sweeps off to find my best friend.

Behind me, someone clears their throat. When I turn around, I'm not surprised to find Galen standing with his hand outstretched.

"You asked me not to touch you without your permission. May I please have this dance?" he asks, with the look of a hopeful puppy. My annoyance is forgotten at his pleading look. I have mercy on him, sliding my hand into his—

—*the sky above me is clear enough that I can make out various constellations above me, but I'm hardly able to focus on the bright lights through the haze of lust. Galen is kissing down my body before he plants his face between my legs, his tongue stroking my* —

—I'm shaking my head, breaking the moment.

Galen has his arms around me and is whispering my name. This time, I don't play coy.

"What was *that?*" I ask firmly, flushed and frustrated by the sensations coursing through me. It's a confusing narrative, like waves crashing against an aging shoreline, eroding the cliff. These visions I keep having of Galen are wearing away at the fragile foundation I've started to build with Essos. Sybil warned me that mentioning dreams of Essos could lead to me getting dismissed, but seeing Galen isn't the same as seeing Essos. I don't see how the consequences could be the same, since there is no advantage to seeing Galen.

"You saw something," he states, his tone neutral. He never stops dancing; instead, he holds eye contact. My steps become jumbled, confused, and I step on him more than once, but you wouldn't know it by the way he pushes forward.

"Yes. Now explain it. You clearly know what's going on."

Galen looks frustrated but pulls me closer to his body. My dream of him comes back to me, causing my breathing to become quick and shallow. I'm going to start hyperventilating if I don't focus. I look down at my feet, trying to stay on the beat. *One, two, three, one, two, three.*

"I *can't*," he says.

"Can't, or won't?" I challenge, trying to slow our movements to force him to talk.

"Can't. Essos and Sybil surely explained that there are rules, yes? One of those rules prohibits me from telling you anything independently. If you come to certain conclusions on your own, I can verify and provide embellishing details. I can't initiate. Otherwise, the Calling will be canceled, and I'll be back to square one."

I pick up my pace to match his tempo, trying to split my focus between the steps and his words. "But if I ask you questions, you can answer?" He nods, and I take this as a sign I should continue. "Was it a memory?" He nods, his gaze casting around the room, and my breath stops for a moment. "Was it *my* memory?" He nods again. "What about my dreams, are they memories?"

He looks at me suddenly. "Dreams? More than one? I stopped in your room earlier, and you seemed to be sleeping so peacefully. You actually sighed in your sleep when I brushed a hair from your face. Were you having dreams about me before I arrived?" He stares at me, his gaze fierce.

I stumble another step, surprised that not only was he in my space while I was asleep, but he was close enough to actually touch me. "Stopped in?"

"Yes. I caught one of the maids bringing the food up and offered to take it in myself. I had the idea to gift you a dress while I was there, so I conjured it for you. Essos wouldn't let me get within a foot of you after *I* dragged you out of the ocean." Galen looks into my eyes. "Tell me more. Have I appeared in any other dreams?"

I clear my throat and look away from him. "Not all of them. In this one, you and I were dancing, and it looked like the 1920s." I avoid mentioning the hot sex in the coat closet.

He grins, clearly remembering. The look he gives me makes me blush deeper. "Real, very real."

I watch his face as he looks me up and down like a wolf eyeing a sheep that has strayed too far from her pack. "Why were you able to warn me about Sybil but not tell me about this?" I ask, thinking back to our conversation in the water.

"Because Sybil isn't a strict party to the Calling. I wouldn't be surprised to find out that what grabbed you today was their doing," he hisses. His hand clenches mine, hard.

I frown, remembering Sybil's concern when they walked me to my room, and how they've been nothing but kind. The memory of Sybil's implied threat about the dreams rises to the forefront of my mind in support of Galen's theory. It's hard to not have doubts when they flat out threatened Cat and me. Even thinking of that conversation drives me to suppress a shudder.

I choose to play dumb with Galen to see if he has any other insight. He doesn't need to know that I already tipped my hand to Sybil. "Do Sybil and Essos know that I have memories that are, I don't know, locked away or whatever?"

He sighs deeply at my question. "I have my suspicions—that's why I came as soon as I heard that Essos had a new group of girls.

Just as badly as Sybil doesn't want to share Essos, he doesn't want to share his power. It's all he has going for him. He'll play along, and in the end, dump all the girls. Keeping you away from me again."

The song comes to an end, but my questions have not. "*Again?* What does that mean, keeping me away from you?"

He shakes his head.

If these are memories...have I lived a life before this that I can't remember? The vision from when I was under the water rises to my mind unbidden.

Do I have powers?

I want to keep pressing him, but he steps away from me. "I've said too much." He strides off, and before I can follow him, I feel a hand on my wrist.

Ripping my hand out of the grip, I turn to find that it's Finn. "Let him have his diva moment. It makes him feel cooler if he gets to storm off into the night for dramatic effect." Finn holds his arm out to me.

"I don't find it entertaining." We walk off the dance floor in the opposite direction of Galen to where the drinks are. I grab two champagnes and hear Finn start to thank me, until he realizes that they're both for me as I knock them back.

"I need some fresh air," I say and walk away from him to the back porch, where I immediately regret my decision.

Essos is seated outside with Zara in his lap. She's got her mouth on his neck while his eyes are closed with one hand on the curve of her ass. He looks almost pained, and I wonder if it's from having to restrain himself from taking this further. They don't seem aware of my presence, so I stalk past them quickly.

My teeth clench so hard that my jaw aches. I try to scrub the image from my mind as I storm down to the beach. I reach the waterline, discard my shoes, and stand with my feet in the surf, not caring that I'm ruining the red dress.

Finn comes to stand beside me with his pant legs rolled up. "Not in the mood for dancing tonight?"

I shoot him a dirty look but stay where I am.

"Listen, you should know by now that you can talk to me about what's going on. I know that this process is stressful, but I am here for you. If you think the escorts' only purpose is to show you how to dance, you're wrong. I want to see you succeed, but I have to know what's going on in that brilliant mind of yours if I'm going to help. I want to think I've earned your trust. If you're upset about what was happening up there, it's probably not what it looked like. She's been throwing herself at him since you almost drowned again."

"Can gods die?" I ask abruptly. Like Sybil, Finn made it clear that I shouldn't poke at the bruise that is any dream that Essos might or might not be in. He's likely to shut down again if I mention that I've seen flashes when touching Galen.

Finn's nostrils flare, and he presses his mouth into a thin line as he regards me. "No, gods can't just die, Daphne. W— They're immortal."

"Immortal and invulnerable are not the same thing."

"You're right, but if I even—"

"Let me guess, you can't answer me because of rules, blah blah blah. I'm sick to death of your rules. You're, like, the opposite of helpful right now, holy shit," I say, giving him a light shove. He barely moves when I push him, and that irritates me more.

He laughs and grabs my arms. "Yes, I am, but you know what? I'm really fucking awesome too, and I promise you—I *promise* that all these non-answers I'm giving you will eventually make sense," Finn says, trying to soothe the wound he just caused.

I step farther down the beach, away from the house. "So, there is something to know? Am I supposed to wait for the ball?"

Finn looks excited by the idea. "That is *exactly* what you're supposed to do. Be a good little chicken like the rest of your friends and don't push the status quo. I can't—"

"I know, I know, you can't say anything. Are you, like, a doll with a pull string always repeating the same thing?"

"Something like that, but please, promise me you'll stop pushing. I know I've already asked you to, but these new questions make me wonder if you haven't been listening."

I look at his pleading face and reach up to ruffle his perfectly slicked-back hair. Finn freezes in shock at this offense.

"Fine, but I also want you to acknowledge that I don't have the full picture of what's going on here. There's a lot that I don't know. Would it help if I asked you a direct question?"

"No, not even then. Because I'm an escort and part of the Calling, I physically cannot answer certain things. Even this conversation is making my stomach roil, and the last thing I want to do is throw up all over this very sexy dress you've got on."

"Ew, you shouldn't find me sexy. I know I just met you, and this is crazy, but you're like my brother. Don't find me sexy." I singsong the words to the beat of a popular song. My confession in song seems to soften Finn a touch. There is a small lift to the corners of his mouth.

I want to make our conversation more serious, knowing that retaliation is close, but Finn scoops me up over his shoulder in a fireman's carry and calmly walks deeper into the ocean, with me kicking and screaming behind him, pounding on his back.

"Don't do it!" I shout, too late.

"You're right," he says as he hurls me into the water, not caring that he's also getting wet. There's a moment of panic as I remember the feel of the creature burning my ankles. The burns were healed when I woke up from my nap, something for which I assume I have Essos or Sybil to thank, but the bruises and the mental trauma are still there. I settle the pounding in my chest with a reminder that I am safe, I am okay, and I am in the shallows where the thing can't get me. Still, I splash Finn.

"You asshole, I almost drowned out here today." I kick the water at him, and a stricken look crosses his face.

"I am—"

I tackle him into the water. "An asshole. Accept your judgment." I laugh.

He hangs his head, his mess of blond hair no longer perfectly gelled back.

To say that we both look like drowned rats as we come back up the porch laughing would be an understatement. Finn is right —over the past month, we have grown close, and I do trust that he knows Essos better than anyone else.

Zara and Essos are still sitting there, their heads bent close in conversation as Finn and I walk back as if nothing happened.

"What in the world...?" Zara says, the first to see us.

I turn toward her, pushing a wet lock of hair out of my face.

"Oh, Zara, Essos, how nice to see you both enjoying the beautiful night air," Finn says, buttoning his sopping wet tux beside me. "I must recommend the water. It is lovely this time of night." He tries to hold back a laugh. I try to remain just as composed, but when Essos quirks his eyebrow at us, we both lose it, trying to lean on the other for support.

Essos looks at Zara. "What do you say, fancy a dip?"

At first, Zara looks appalled, but she quickly recovers. "Absolutely," she responds, climbing off him, and offering her hand. My laughter sobers as we watch them run toward the water. Before they reach the surf, Zara shimmies out of her silver dress, her long black hair cascading down her back as she gives Essos a coy smile before splashing into the ocean.

I can't see Essos's face, but I can his gaze running over her naked body as he takes in the full sight of her. I watch him kick off his shoes and cast off his jacket before I can't look any longer, and I walk back into the house with my head held high, dripping wet.

The sight of the two of us must be something else, because the cellist jerks her bow across two strings, resulting in a screeching noise and stopping the party. Everyone turns to see what caused this, and they catch sight of us. I pull back my shoulders and lift my chin, trying to force my 5'3" frame to appear taller, though I know it's no use.

"Finn bravely tried to help me slay the beast that almost drowned me today, to no success. If you will excuse me, I believe I need to change." The sound of my bare feet slapping the marble floor is the only thing that can be heard as I make my walk of shame toward my room. As I reach the stairs, I hear Cat clap and demand that the band begin again.

The wheels in my head turn over all the new information the last twelve hours have wrought. Finn is, unsurprisingly, unable to answer my questions. As much as I wish he could give me more, I'll have to get what I can from the only source able to give me the information I need.

Essos wants me to trust him, but he used me as a pawn in his game with his brother. This whole fiasco is wearing on me, especially knowing that he and Zara are out there right now, their bodies wrapped around each other.

If he's going to play games like this, I'm going to show him I'm not the type of woman to test.

15

I stand outside my door for a long moment, doubt already
creeping in. Maybe it should be less about the game and
more about putting all my cards on the table.

No. I'm a minnow swimming with sharks—I need to stick to
my guns.

With a deep breath, I turn the nob and step inside.

A figure looks up from the chair in the corner of the room, and
I stop short, a scream catching in my throat. I turn on the light.

"You can't be in here," I whisper to Galen, unsure what to do.
I'm surprised that Galen just comes and goes from my room. I'm
hardly prudish, but it doesn't seem right for him to have that
access. This is my space—my safe space. Sybil never explicitly
said no men in our rooms, but then again, we're all trying to earn
the affection of one man, so I think it should go without saying.

I look past him out the window and see Essos and Zara
splashing water at one another. Unable to bear another second of
it, I cross the room and snap the curtains closed before turning
back to Galen.

"You can't be in here," I repeat, as if he didn't hear me the first time.

He stands, towering over me. "I know, but you saw something earlier when I touched you, and I want to see if I can help you remember more. Since I can't explicitly tell you anything, maybe I can show you."

I look at him, weighing his words. Taking my time, I recross my room and close the door, slowly turning over options in my head. Do I trust Galen? I've only just met him, but if these visions are real memories, then I used to know him *quite* well. He's also been more open with me than anyone else.

What about the dreams I had of Essos? Were those memories as well? Was I stuck in some menage-a-trois between two brothers? There are lines you don't think you'll cross, and then there are *lines* you don't *cross*. I've made Essos work for my trust, but Galen seems to be offering me answers I've been unable to get—such as, maybe, an answer to why I'm having these dreams.

I need all the information that I can get, so I return to him. Reluctantly, I hold out my hands, permitting Galen to try. He slides his knuckles across my cheek before cupping my face instead, prompting flashes of images.

WE'RE LYING IN BED, *no sheet to be found, both on our sides, our bodies bare. Everything feels like it's been muted, the colors dull and lifeless.*

"Husband," I say haughtily.

He turns to me, a big smile on his face. "Yes, wife."

I slide closer to him. "If you don't perform your husbandly duties, I shall have no recourse but to divorce you and find a man who will ravish me hourly."

He rolls on top of me, propped up on his elbows, before kissing me fully on the lips. "You are an insatiable woman. It's only been 15 minutes." But 15 minutes has clearly been enough time, as I feel his cock harden against me. Galen uses his knee to push my legs apart before settling between them, but instead of immediately giving me what I want, he opts to tease me, kissing my neck and breasts, stopping to suck on my nipple. My back arches, and a sound I had no idea I could make escapes my throat. He nuzzles my neck, working his way down. Impatient, I roll over so that I'm on top of him and in control of what happens. I slide myself onto him inch by inch until he's seated inside me completely. A guttural moan slips from me as I move against him until we're both satisfied.

I OPEN my eyes and look at Galen in real time, pulling out of his reach. "What did you mean to show me?" I feel the flush on my skin, and I can see it on his too.

"I can't say it. You need to be specific about what you saw."

This game might be more frustrating than the one Essos is playing. I grind my teeth at this stupid rule but play along. "Our first night as husband and wife," I state. It's not a question.

He smiles. "Insatiable."

I take another step away from him. He looks confused, then hurt.

"I think you need to leave," I say firmly. I'm just as confused about this whole situation. Why would Essos want me to stay if he knew I was his brother's wife at some point? Or does Essos not know—is that why I'm not allowed to tell anyone about the dreams?

I huff. They're both using me in their game. I point at the door, not wanting to repeat myself.

He runs a hand through his hair and sulks toward the door. "You can't tell anyone about this, Daphne. If Essos or anyone else knows that I'm opening up your memories, they will shut down the Calling. They will take you from me again. I won't lose you to Essos again. When we were on the dance floor, you mentioned that you had a dream. Was it of Essos?" I don't answer him, so he plows on. "I think he's messing with your memories. If he's not fabricating them, then he might be modifying them somehow. To help souls with traumatic pasts, he's able to alter their memories so they can heal. Just be wary that he might be doing that do you."

A chill runs through me, and I fight my shudder. "Don't ambush me again," I say as he opens the door and walks out. After I hear his footsteps receding, I dare a peek out the window to see if Zara and Essos are still there.

They are.

She's in his arms, but it looks like she's got a blanket or towel or something wrapped around her, so he's not holding her naked body.

I wonder if these visions would be considered my own past. It feels wrong for Galen to trigger my memories—but can I even call them mine? They seemed that way at first, but now they feel as though they happened to a different person.

I decide not to return to the party; instead, I take off the ruined dress and throw it in a corner. My hair is still wet and smells like the sea, and I suddenly want to wash the memories of the day away. I go to take a second shower.

I turn the temperature all the way to hot until the flush on my skin is from the heat of the water and not the memory of Galen inside me. These memories, for lack of a better term, feel wrong, but maybe that's because I'm getting them before I'm supposed to. Finn all but admitted that something is going to happen at the ball—something besides Essos choosing his bride-to-be. I chew on my lip, trying to find a spark of emotion from these new memories the way my dreams of my mystery man—of Essos?— left me feeling so bereft. There's nothing but a sense of embarrassment over being so carnal with Galen. My current feelings are so twisted that even I'm having a hard time figuring out which emotions are real and which are reactions to the memories and dreams.

I scrub my body and look at my ankles, glad that they're only bruised and not blistered the way they were when I first woke up on the beach. As I change into my pajamas, I catch sight of the flowers on my nightstand. I expected them to take days to bloom, but they're all colorful and open now. I lean close to them, inhaling their floral scent, and gently stroke the bright pink petals. I wonder if Essos's magic extends to these, or if maybe it's my own power.

It seems too farfetched, too strange, to consider that I had abilities—or have abilities? I want to curl up and have someone explain what the hell is happening to me. Finn, Sybil and Essos seem unable to do so, but since Galen isn't as constrained by the rules of the Calling, maybe I should let him help me.

I go into Cat's room and wait for her, hoping to talk to her about what a walking train wreck of a person I have become.

While pondering this, I decide that I have to tell her about Galen. This is something that I can't keep to myself, and I know that her loyalty is to me and not Essos. She won't tell anyone and get us kicked out. I trust her with my life.

I fall asleep waiting for her, and somehow manage to not dream about Galen or Essos. Instead, the monster from the water continues to drag me down, down, down to the bottom of the ocean, where it meant only to have tea with me. The sea squid keeps offering me a choice of two teas. I can take my English Breakfast tea black, or I can have a lighter tea with milk, but every time I make a decision, I forget what it was.

I wake when Cat enters the room, laughing, and she stops short upon seeing me in her bed. Beyond her, I can see Tiffany continuing on to her own room.

"This bed was juuuusst right," I snark, as she launches herself at me.

"Goldilocks, get to your own bed," Cat grumbles into my neck.

I push her away from me, scoffing. "Hey now, if anyone is Goldilocks here, it's you, the one who keeps making herself at home in my bed." Cat rolls her eyes but climbs off and changes quickly into leggings and a T-shirt. "How was the rest of your night?"

She looks at me in her vanity mirror, where she's removing her makeup. I still. There is discomfort on her face, but I reason with myself that we're best friends and we should get whatever it is out in the open so it doesn't fester.

"Actually, I do have something to tell you." She sounds nervous, so I sit up, waiting for her to continue. I'm trying to keep my expression open and calm, but it occurs to me that she's about to tell me she's leaving, and if she doesn't hurry up and spit it out, I might throttle her. "Essos and I actually kissed tonight. It was really an accident," she rushes on. "He was leaning down to kiss me on the cheek, and I turned my head, and it was like barely even a kiss, but I wanted to tell you because I think the Calling means a lot more to you than it does to me."

My emotions are so all over the place that I need a second to process what she said. The fear of her leaving almost choked me; the news that she isn't is such a relief that I almost sag into her mattress. When it finally sinks in that she kissed Essos, I'm back on a dramatic upswing that now he's kissed Zara *and* Cat, accident or not. She doesn't sound excited about the kiss or even that it happened—could this mean that she's no longer proceeding? My hands twist in the comforter as the terror that this might mean she's leaving recaptures my focus.

"So, are you...?" I let the sentence trail off, not wanting to think about being left here with Zara and Tiffany. She turns to face me fully, her brush in her hand.

She points it threateningly at me. "Babe, you're my ride or die. It actually happened after we had a long talk, mostly just him checking in with me about the process. It sort of forced me to admit that I don't actually feel anything for him. Being queen would be cool, but I'm not as invested as some people I know. I was honest with him, and since he knows how close we are, he agreed to let me stay until you're through with this whole process. He explained that he has some latitude, including letting girls stay until they're ready to move on to their afterlife. As King of the Underworld, he should encourage them along. He's supposed to provide an update to whoever on the Council is overseeing the Calling, mostly to confirm he's following through with it for real. It's why he's been periodically dismissing girls, but somewhat irregularly."

I have noticed that. After one month we were down to twelve girls, and since then, only Becca chose to leave, after learning of her half-sister's death.

"I have grandparents I could go to, but that wouldn't be nearly as fun as staying here with you." I could cry at the thought of her staying, and I almost do. "But no one can know that's why I'm still here. It's not breaking a rule, per se, but the women remaining are supposed to be contenders. So, we have to play it cool, as if I'm still interested in him, even though Essos admitted that Tiffany has the same deal for Zara."

I climb off the bed and hug her tightly from behind. "You know your secrets are safe with me. I almost took them to the grave again today."

She whacks me hard with the flat side of her brush. I wince and rub the spot.

"Too fucking soon," she says, hitting me again on the same spot, guaranteeing it's going to bruise. "So, tell me about your night, and your second swim of the day."

I groan, falling back on the bed, staring up at her ceiling. "I learned something today, and it's really weird. I need to know that I can tell you and know that *you'll* take it to your grave. I mean, you remember what Sybil said, how certain information can get us kicked out?"

Cat nods, putting down her brush and giving me her full attention.

"So, when Galen touched me earlier today, I got a sort of memory flash. First, it was like, just us kissing, but then a few other times, we were more...intimate."

She raises her eyebrows. "Intimate, or like *intimate?*"

"I'm not sure of the difference in emphasis, but I'll go with *intimate.* He also told me that he can't tell me everything outright because of those stupid rules. He can only answer yes or no, so if I don't ask the right questions, I'm not going to find out anything more substantial. But he admitted we were married."

She gasps and clutches at her chest dramatically. I'm not sure if it's mocking. "That is so weird. Why would Galen let you stay in a contest to marry his brother—also, why would Essos let you stay if you were married to his brother? Also, *also,* why can't Galen tell you anything—that's, like, extenuating circumstances. And *finally*—you have like past lives? Were you mortal, or immortal like them? I am so confused."

I laugh, glad to hear all of my thoughts come from Cat, because if anyone will be able to help me figure it out, it's her. It's a relief knowing that these questions aren't as outrageous as I thought. "*And!* He also made it seem as though Sybil is not to be trusted. He insinuated that what happened today with the sea monster was Sybil's doing. Also, I...might have powers?"

The look Cat gives me could make a grown man weep. "You might have *magic* and you lead with boy troubles? What am I going to do with you?"

There's a whine at the door. I climb out of bed to let Dave in, and he wastes no time jumping onto the foot of the bed and snuggling in.

Cat takes in a deep breath and slowly releases it. "This is a lot of information to digest at four in the morning, and I, for one, need a lot more sleep if I'm going to puzzle out what the fuck is going on. It's making my brain hurt. Also, please don't have sex dreams in my bed, that's gross."

I stick my tongue out at her and roll onto my back. "It's not like I'm trying to have sex dreams. They just happen."

"I do think we should keep this between the two of us. It's not even should—I think we *need* to. I don't want to be here without you and, as great as Essos has been, there are still a lot of unknowns here. Sybil's threat to not to talk about the dreams makes me wary. They never said what sort of consequences we would face for not keeping them a secret, although *hypothetically,* they totally already know it's one of us having the dreams. But also, I don't trust Galen. I need to get a feel for him, other than douchey little brother. In summation, don't trust anyone."

I nod and then voice the last thing on my mind. "Essos and Zara seem to have really hit it off. They went skinny dipping tonight."

"Oh, who gives a shit."

"Me. *I* give a shit." I swing my arm in her general direction, but she catches it and turns on her side to face me.

"I know. All I'm saying is, if just touching Galen gives you sex dreams, I can't imagine what kissing Essos will do to you. You might explode."

The thought sends a huge grin to my face. I knew that talking to Cat would help give me the perspective I need on the matter. "What would I do without you?"

"Probably run away with Galen, now that all you can think about is his penis and the sex dreams he's giving you."

I hit her with a pillow. "I would be so lost and confused without you. Thank you for staying. I know that even if you do still want to be here, you're sacrificing seeing your grandparents."

"All in a day's work as your savior. Now, will you kindly shut up so I can sleep? I'm going to have bags the size of Alaska under my eyes if I stay up a wink longer."

Cat falls asleep almost immediately, and Dave is snoring at the foot of the bed, but I can't stop more thoughts from running through my mind.

All of her points were valid, but it gets lonely quick when there's no one else I can trust. I think about it and wonder what would happen if I were to kiss Galen. Having some sort of a past life would make sense, but if I was a god, can you really kill a god? And if I was married to Galen, why is Essos keeping me here? Galen made it sound like Essos knows exactly who I am and is keeping me here intentionally, but to what end?

Could I have been with both of them?

There are so many unknowns and no way to find answers unless I know the rules of the game, but the game keeps changing, and I don't know which rules to follow. Cat is right though—these are not thoughts and worries for the wee hours of the morning. Under the harsh light of day, maybe we can banish the shadows of lies.

16

Galen showed up two weeks ago, and we've found a new normal with him constantly lurking at breakfast and the balls. Each night he tries to charm everyone, and for the most part, people embrace his glowing energy. Zara, however, doesn't seem charmed by him and rebuffs him every time he asks her for a dance. Still, he tries to get to know all twelve girls who remain.

I both yearn for him to show me more memories and hate that I do—the magnitude of my craving to see more makes my skin crawl. There might be this whole side of me that I was unaware of. I wonder if I used to like the things I love now, like tequila and tacos. Do the gods have these things? I wonder if Galen is able to show me only memories of us, or if he could show me something else, like a memory of Finn. It's a reasonable leap that if I was involved with Galen, and Finn was Essos's best friend, then the two of us must have interacted with them both at some point. My dreams probably can't be guided, but maybe Galen can show me something specific.

It occurs to me that if Finn and Essos are close, then perhaps

Finn and I weren't so close in my past life. It's obvious from their interactions that Galen and Finn get along as well as drinking and driving. The trouble is that I can't ask without giving away the fact that Galen has started to help me remember. If anyone finds out, I don't doubt that this entire process will end. Did a past version of me already go through this?

Galen and Essos both asked for patience, for me to make it to the final ball, and I'm going to try my damnedest to do just that.

Today, Cat, Tiffany, Zara and I have a group date with Essos. He's leading us toward the garden when the sound of wheels draws our attention. Essos freezes for just a moment, and then the man runs in his three-piece suit toward the driveway.

"I'm guessing no one is supposed to be able to drive here?" Zara says with a shrug as we jog after him to see what the commotion is.

"No, they're not," Essos hisses, stopping at the lip of the drive-away between the gardens and a van speeding toward him. My heart lurches in my chest, and I consider that we might find out whether the God of the Dead can die. I don't want to know; I need more time with Essos, and I find myself stepping forward so I'm almost at his side.

The van comes to an abrupt stop just short of hitting him, the rear tires practically lifting off the ground from the force. A tall Asian man climbs out of the driver's side. Once I get a good look at him and his guitar, I realize who it is.

"Steve!" Tiffany cries and tries to run toward him, but Essos flings out his arm and catches her around the waist.

"You can't be here," Essos warns him. Steve tries to walk toward Tiffany, and Essos takes another step back, pulling her with him. "You need to explain yourself before there are any joyful reunions. How did you get here?" It is not a question, but a demand.

"I got a voicemail from Tiff, saying that she was in a better place but missed me." Essos looks livid, his ears turning red as Steve continues. "So, I drove to the spot where she died. For days and days, I drove there, right up to the edge of the cliff. I blocked traffic and had the cops called on me a few times as I parked there, just staring at the horizon line. Today as the sun started to set, I saw this weird light. The sky flashed, and I floored it and drove right at it, but my car didn't plunge off the side—there was a roadway. I thought I went blind, and the next thing I knew I was barreling down this road and almost hit you." Steve lets out a big breath. "You need to let me see her." Steve makes another desperate attempt to reach Tiffany. His hair is a mess, pointing in every direction, and he looks as if he hasn't slept in days or even weeks. I doubt he's showered either.

"You can see her from where you are. Everyone inside—now, please."

He hands off Tiffany to Zara, and as we start to walk away, Essos gestures to Steve, looking exasperated, and they bring up the rear. Zara is holding on tight to her friend without being told to do so. It's clear that Essos wants to keep her and Steve apart.

When we get inside, Galen looks smug as he leans against the doorway of the dining room, sipping his coffee. "Look at this little surprise. Someone is losing his touch."

Sybil emerges from the hallway and freezes as they catch sight of a mortal in the foyer.

"Brother, now is not the time," Essos says curtly. He is seething, his anger palpable. None of us have seen him like this, but I'm sure Sybil and Galen have. Essos strikes me as the type of man to keep his anger and rage carefully bottled away until the right—or wrong—moment undoes it. After existing for thousands of years, I'm sure he's unleashed it once or twice before.

Some of the remaining girls who were not on the group date wander in, looking curious.

"Daphne, Catalina and Zara, if you would please come along."

Essos might say the word *please* but his tone leaves no room for argument. For whatever reason, he wants us there, and I'm not going to argue. Maybe it will satisfy at least some of my aching curiosity.

Essos leads Tiffany and Steve down a different set of stairs, carefully keeping himself between them, and I wonder if the house is actually a labyrinth. I've never seen this staircase before, but as Essos approached it, the stairs appeared. How many other elements of his home are hidden away, only to be revealed when the time is fitting?

Only Cat, Zara and I are permitted to follow. I stick close to Cat, and a flicker of surprise hits me when Zara slides her hand into mine as we descend the stairs. They're long but wide, meaning we have space to walk three abreast. When Essos ushered Steve down the stairs with Tiffany hot on his heels, it was like she momentarily forgot Zara. We might not get along well, but if this were happening to Cat, I would be terrified. So, I grip Zara's hand tight, vowing to be her lifeline if she lets me.

We enter a room that we have not been in, but its purpose is obvious. *Room* is such a mundane word for the space around us. If I thought the ballroom above was opulent, then this is on a whole other level. It's not as bright as the upstairs rooms. The walls are a solid matte black, giving the illusion that the space is wide open while also giving the sense that the walls are closing in. It is an impressive and terrifying feat. I don't want to be in this space any longer than necessary. My steps stall as I look around, and Zara releases my hand to quickly catch up to Tiffany.

Opposite the entrance are two thrones, each equal in size, clearly intended for Essos and his queen. The walls seem to stretch up endlessly, making the room feel more like a cavern than an actual room, though I can just see a beautiful vaulted ceiling high above. Hanging from no discernable point are heavy metal chandeliers with candles that have black wax dripped down their sides. The room is larger than the ballroom.

This is what I would expect for the King of the Underworld.

I feel dizzy crossing the room, not because of the size, but because I have a disorienting sense of déjà vu. At some point, I must have been in this room. I grab Cat's arm to steady myself, unsure if I'll have a vision. But instead of a flash, I have this over-whelming sense of pressure. I squeeze her arm as the sensation continues to assault me and my emotions swing like a pendulum with no real direction. First, I'm burning red hot, wanting to tear the space around me down to the studs, but that's preferable to the sensation of my chest trying to cave in on my lungs, forcing tears to my eyes. With each emotion, I feel the urge to pull my hair out to make some sense of what is happening. Mostly, I want to flee the room to escape them.

While our presence is likely not necessary, all of us are eager to find out what will happen. I choose to focus on that emotion rather than my fight or flight instinct, which wants to send me far from here.

Essos takes his seat on his throne, sparing a glance at the empty seat beside him. The thrones are large and solid and seem to have grown out of the same obsidian slab as the floor. They look uncomfortable, but I notice that they have the same moon and flower symbol as Essos's necklace. It feels achingly familiar, but maybe that's because I've seen the symbol. I wonder if this is the room where Essos usually conducts his business.

Essos gestures for Cat, Tiffany, Zara and I to stand behind him, off to the side behind the empty throne. I'm not sure what urges me to do it, but as I pass him, I drop my hand onto his shoulder and give him a comforting squeeze. His fingertips brush the inside of my wrist just as I pull my hand away.

Galen and Sybil follow the congregation into the room as well and stand behind Steve. Dave, Shadow and Spot take their stance guarding the door. Essos levels them with a scolding look, and they tuck their tails between their legs, as if ashamed for letting a living human into the Underworld.

Before Essos can demand an answer as to how he managed this trip, Steve pulls his guitar around and starts to strum it. Essos leans on one armrest and rests his chin in his hand as he rubs his temple. I think his head might actually explode from stress.

Steve is a passable guitar player at best, and when he starts to sing, his vocals could use some work. But what he wrote is beautiful, and it transcends the wrong notes and offkey singing. He plays a song he wrote for Tiffany, about how he missed her and loves her with his whole heart and that he'll do anything he can to love her for eternity. He sings about her accepting his hand in marriage, and he ends the song there, getting down on one knee.

Tiffany is crying beside Essos, and she goes to run for Steve again. Essos has to physically restrain her. Zara and Cat step in, grabbing her to hold her back. Essos looks bewildered by all of this.

"What exactly are you asking?" Essos demands.

Steve rises and walks toward Essos. "I thought that was obvious. I want her to marry me."

Tiffany starts to struggle against Zara and Cat to get to him.

"I love you, baby!" Tiffany shouts, breaking free. Essos grabs her wrist, preventing her from going farther. She starts to yank away from Essos, trying to break his grasp, but he's a god, there isn't much she can do.

"ENOUGH," Essos booms, his gaze swinging from Tiffany to Steve and back again. "Yes, I understood that much. However, she is no longer part of the land of the living the way that you are. How do you plan to carry forward with this request?"

"I want you to give her back." Steve squares his shoulders and puffs out his chest. He looks like he's ready to fight Essos for Tiffany, as if a physical altercation will do the trick. His hands even tighten into fists and he raises them slightly so they're around his midsection. Steve looks like he doesn't want to fight, but rather to convey to Essos that, if it comes down to it, he'll let them fly. From the back of the room, all three dogs stand and growl, looking ready to jump in. Essos just seems exhausted and releases his grip on Tiffany so she can finally embrace Steve.

Essos steps back up on the dais and sits heavily on his throne. As Tiffany and Steve reunite, all eyes are on them, but I watch Essos. His thumb rubs the length of his lower lip then back again as he studies the young lovers.

"Very well. Under one condition." His voice is soft and quiet when he says this. Tiffany and Steve separate, shock making them still. Tiffany is the first to come to her senses, and she turns to face Essos, her eyes brimming with tears. He speaks directly to Steve. "You will leave, and she will follow you, but you cannot touch her or look upon her until you are back in the mortal world. If you do, I will reclaim her, and she will pass forward into her afterlife. There will be no second chance. I am understood?"

What is it about Tiffany and Steve that has the King of the Dead releasing one of his own back into the mortal realm? Is this king of darkness a romantic at heart? The task he lays at Steve's feet is not an easy one, considering that he has hardly taken his eyes off Tiffany the entire time. The man has found a way into the Underworld, but there could be talking animals around us, and he would still have eyes only for her.

Steve has to give Essos a level of trust that he will uphold his end of the bargain. I realize I have no doubt that, if Steve succeeds, Essos will follow through.

He is trustworthy. At least in this.

Steve looks elated, like he could jump through the sky right now. He actually fist pumps and jumps in the air, unable to take his eyes off Tiffany.

"Yes. perfectly. There is no limit to how far I would go for her. Can I hold her until we get to the driveway?" Steve questions.

"No, you may embrace only now. After that, you will have to trust that I am upholding my end of the bargain," Essos confirms.

Tiffany jumps into Steve's arms, and he holds her close, his nose in her hair. If they were any closer, they would become the same person.

I sense that Essos wants to be happy for them, but that Steve's ability to show up here is a much larger issue.

"This is awfully generous, brother. You're not up to any tricks, are you?" Galen asks.

Essos ignores him, gesturing to Sybil to take Steve and Galen out of the room.

Once they're gone, he leans forward in his seat and turns his attention to Tiffany. "You are under no obligation to go if you don't want to, but know that if you decide to go, you will not remember any of this, and neither will Steve. It will be as if you were not on the bus at all. So, I have to ask, is it your decision to leave?"

"Yes," Tiffany answers without hesitation.

He leans back in his chair and nods. "Then you shall follow him into the realm of the living. He will not be able to hear you or sense you—he will need to do this on trust alone. If he turns to look at you, then you will be sent to your afterlife." He pauses to let this sink in. Tiffany glances at Zara, who gives her a nod. Tiffany then looks at Essos and nods. "All right then, please be well, no matter where you wind up. You may take a moment to say your goodbyes." Essos stands and exits the room. My throat tightens, and I have to stop my feet from following him. I don't want him to leave; I want to slide my fingers between his and affirm that this was the right call.

What he has done today for Tiffany and Steve is no small thing. They are two lovers, separated by death, and he's allowed their reunion. There is probably more to why Steve was able to get here, but it speaks to his determination to not let something as silly as death keep him and Tiffany apart.

A surge of pride rushes through my chest for Essos and his kindness today. He could, and probably should, have said no, but he's doing the right thing for Tiffany and Steve, I'm sure of it.

Zara is the most emotional of us all. She and Tiffany hug, whispering in each other's ears, tears streaming down their faces. Zara pulls back and holds Tiffany's face, swiping at the tears, confirming that she will be fine without her. Zara means herself, but I think it goes both ways. Tiffany gives Cat and me long hugs too.

When we open the door to the throne room, Essos is just outside the door, waiting for us. It's been weeks since anyone has left, and seeing Tiffany prepare to go now brings into perspective how much closer we're getting to the end. Our numbers will only continue to decline.

We walk upstairs, Cat and I behind Tiffany and Zara, who are holding hands, neither seeming ready to say goodbye forever.

I think about how much I will hate it if that's ever me having to say goodbye to Cat.

When we reach the main level of the house, Essos looks to Tiffany again. "You're sure?"

"This is the most sure I've ever been in my entire life." She smiles at him through tears.

Outside in the driveway, standing in the bright sun, are Galen, Sybil, Steve and the rest of the girls. We wait as Tiffany says her cursory goodbyes to her sorority sisters.

With a wave of Essos's hand, the van disappears.

"You are not to look behind you, ever." Essos gives Steve this final warning, and Galen snorts. Steve nods and holds out his hand to Essos. Essos eyes the hand for a moment before giving it a firm shake. Steve begins walking up the driveway and away from the house.

Zara starts to cry again, and I reach out to hug her, letting her know that she has my support. We might have our differences, but no one should go through this alone.

Tiffany begins walking, not glancing back at us as she follows silently behind Steve to begin her second chance at life.

17

Zara is somber in Tiffany's absence, and Cat and I do what we can to help cheer her up. We chat with her as often as possible and include her whenever it's just the two of us. With our focus on Zara, I have no time for Galen and his antics. He's careful not to touch me without my permission. This doesn't mean I'm not still being harassed in my dreams, but they've been repeating, never showing more than what I saw before. The dreams are different now, showing Galen in what I assume was Essos's place.

Maybe it was never Essos in my dreams, but Galen.

Touching Galen must have triggered my dreams in a way touching Essos never did. It makes sense, if he was my husband, that I would get these memories from touching him. But if real memories didn't exist with Essos, what were those first dreams? A trick to lull me into trusting him? Or was my brain just trying to make sense of the memories, and Essos was the only man in sight?

I stare out the window, daydreaming, as the waves crash on the shore. Sybil is droning on about the creation of the known universe, and I try to listen, I really do. I lift my head and watch their lips move as they discuss the God and Goddess Supreme, and I feel furious with myself for being unable to absorb any of this. It's actually painful trying to get my mind to still, and I wonder if maybe these memories or dreams might be messing with my head.

"Daphne, really," Sybil scolds when I look away from them again. I'm chagrined that they called me out, and I try again to focus on them and the chalkboard behind them.

"Right, Seth and Octavia, otherwise known as Essos and Galen's parents, created the universe in the big bang."

"That must have been one big bang," Cat mutters under her breath.

Sybil scowls. "Yes. I was about to describe the different levels of the Afterlife—you know, the realm you're trying to convince Essos to let you rule with him?"

"Right, the Afterlife, the Garden of Evil, and the Deep. Got it." I click my pen and scribble it down.

"What?" Cat says, leaning toward me. "How did you know that?"

My brow wrinkles as I look at her. "What do you mean? It's right..." I gesture at the board that Sybil has just tapped, making the words appear.

"Looks like someone has been poking about the library," Sybil says, giving me a convenient explanation. Only it's not true. I haven't been to the library. Maybe I overheard Essos, because the explanation would be otherwise too strange.

"Yes...?" I say uncertainly. Zara glares at me over her shoulder, but I have no idea what I've done to her this time.

"What about reincarnation?" Cat asks.

"Mortal souls do not reincarnate, but you're getting ahead of yourselves. Most souls end up in the Afterlife. Those who have committed a middle-tier crime, such as theft or not signaling when making a turn, wind up in the Garden of Evil. Souls that have committed truly heinous crimes—murder, acts against children, rape, and worse—all wind up in the Deep, named such because it is akin to being locked in a box and dropped into the bottom of the sea, forever conscious, drowning over and over again, left to go insane. The consort came up with that punishment. Those of you who make it far enough in the Calling will receive a tour of the Afterlife and the Garden of Evil just before the ball."

All the information about the layers of the Afterlife eddies out of my brain, but Cat is quicker to the punch. "Consort? Who is that, and why is this the first we're hearing of them?"

Sybil opens their mouth, only no sound comes out. Looking unnerved, they press their lips together before trying again. With a shaking hand, they write on the board behind them with a marker, *CAN'T*.

"Can't, or won't?" Zara demands.

A soul-splitting glare is the only response that Zara gets. When it becomes clear that Sybil physically cannot go on, we're all dismissed.

BY THE HALFWAY POINT, only ten of us remain in this twisted competition. During breakfast, Essos stands at the head of the table, waiting for everyone to take their places. Once we're seated, he begins.

"We are down to ten. The remainder of you are unlikely to leave unless you ask to be excused, so please settle in, knowing that. The arrival of my brother has prompted me to send invitations to the ball, and it is unlikely that he will be the only person interested in these happenings.

"You will now be placed into two groups. Tomorrow, I have proceedings that I need to oversee, first in the morning, and again at night. One group will join me during each set of proceedings to get a better idea of what it is that I do and what will be asked of you.

"On a final note, please ignore my brother and any attempts he may make to influence the outcome of the Calling. He isn't supposed to be here, and he knows it. Please don't encourage him by feeding the caged animal."

Galen snaps his teeth at his brother, a broad grin on his face.

"If he's not supposed to be here, then why is he?" Zara questions.

"He's not supposed to stay, but he's allowed. Technically, any god or goddess is allowed to drop in and see how the Calling is going and meet the participants. Fortunately, most prefer not to trifle with the King of the Underworld." It's the first time he's used his title as sort of a threat. My curiosity is piqued, and I wonder what he's truly like as a ruler.

"Big brother, you make me out to be some Big Bad, but I'm just here to make sure that all the rules are followed." Galen tosses a grape into his mouth, eyeing Essos. I'm going to have to get Galen alone at some point to tell me about the cause of their rift. That might be the key to learning more about the memories he's shown me.

"You know you have no actual requirement to do so. Sybil is here to ensure that the rules are followed and that the Calling proceeds correctly. Be grateful that I allow you to stay at all." Essos turns to us. "The rest of the day you have to yourselves. I know that Sybil has been stuffing information into your heads as if there is no end to it, so take some time to digest what they have taught you." Essos gives a little bow before walking out, not staying for breakfast this time.

Galen tries to catch my eye, but I won't look at him.

With the time that Essos has gifted us, I grab my copy of *The Iliad* to read, as Sybil asked us all to do a week ago for no reason other than it is one of Essos's favorites. I thought that one perk of dying would be no more homework, but here I am, with a difficult reading assignment.

In an effort to steer away from people, I head to the vast library that Sybil mentioned in passing during a tour of the house. It's located on the ground floor of the wing that has our bedrooms, and I'm convinced it's in some sort of pocket dimension like the Sistine Chapel. It's my first time exploring the space, and I'm instantly mad at myself for waiting so long. The library is a wide-open room with two stories of books shelved on its walls, each spine glittering, waiting to be opened and read. At the far end of the room, I see a maid on a ladder, dusting shelves.

I slowly walk through the room, happy to find myself alone with my thoughts. I decide this is to be my hideout, somewhere I can get lost in myself without any pressure from Galen to remember who I was or to be the person that Essos wants in a wife.

I take my time walking around, running my fingers over the spines of the books until I come to a small collection of thick short books with their spines cracked. I pull one out and laugh out loud at the cover. Glancing up, I make sure I haven't disturbed the maid, who doesn't seem to notice or care.

On the cover of the book is a woman in a billowing petal pink dress. Her back is pressed against a hulking tan man who is naturally shirtless. He's gripping her upper arms, their mouths about to meet in what is sure to be a passionate kiss. On the other side of the woman is a man on his knees before her, holding her hand tightly in a nearly crushing grip with a crown askew on his head.

The title of the book is written in a pretty script, *The Princess and Her Guard*. Succinct and to the point, but something about it nags at me. I flip through it, the pages opening to a well-worn crease in the book. My eyes widen at the vivid description of Lorelei getting her face fucked, and I can't help the bolt of desire that pulses through me. Gods, they're just like us. Face flushed, I slide the book back onto the shelf, full of a renewed curiosity about the citizens of Solarem.

There is a nook by the window overlooking the gardens calling my name. It's been weeks since I asked Essos to show me the gardens himself, and it keeps getting put off for one reason or another. When I asked Sybil if I could go by myself, they told me no. I settle into my seat, curling into a ball with my book in my hands. One glance out the window at the various flowers and walkways, and I consider relocating outside, but decide that the spot I'm in now is too perfect. I let myself get absorbed by *The Iliad* even when I'm tempted to go back to that well-worn romance.

I'm not sure how long I've been there when I'm startled by someone plopping into the seat across from me.

"You missed lunch, so I came looking for you."

I close my book and look around for something to tell me the time, but I already know there isn't a clock. Galen leans toward me, resting his elbows on his knees.

"I got so wrapped up in reading that I lost track of time." I rub my eyes, trying to re-adjust to the contrast of the bright day and the soft light of the indoor library. My vision is fuzzy from being focused on the page for so long.

"A maid said she saw you, so no one was too worried that a sea monster had carried you off. Glad someone tended to you." With a wink, he gestures at a plate next to me with a half-eaten sandwich and a mug of what I assume to be hot chocolate, from the whipped cream remnants on the brim. I don't even remember this food showing up, just that my stomach grumbled, and there it was.

"Well, thanks for this," I say, grabbing the sandwich and taking another bite.

He nods, then just stares at me.

"You know that's both rude and distracting, staring. I'm not loving this whole watching-me-eat thing."

He flashes a full toothy smile. "Would you believe me if I said I'm watching because I missed you?"

I consider his words, keeping my face blank. "Why don't you and Essos get along?"

Galen stares at me, his golden eyes flickering then going dark. I can see him contemplating how to proceed. His face, which is usually bright and open, shutters, turning off all emotion. "Why do most men fight? It was over a girl."

I sit up, unfurling from my seat to stretch an ache from my legs. I must have been curled up for hours, judging by the way my knees creak. I try not to show my interest in this subject, but I'm dying for him to continue. Maybe *dying* is the wrong choice of words—I'm *eager* for him to continue.

"Can you tell me about the girl?" The room is dead silent as I wait for his response.

He shifts, looking uncomfortable, almost sad. He glances toward where the maid was earlier, but we're alone.

"I fell in love with a girl. She was smart and funny and witty. Given how unusual my family is, I kept her from them, holding on to my own little spark of heaven for myself." He gives a half laugh, looking away from me to the garden.

I follow his gaze and see Essos with Zara, his hands folded behind his back as they walk. So much for this being our time alone to commit important details to memory.

"I fell in love, and my big brother decided that he was in love with her too, and so he pursued her. He could have and was with

213

anyone who caught his eye, but he wanted her." Galen rubs his mouth, standing then and pacing to the window to watch his brother. "He was relentless, and it was like every time she said no, it made him want her more. Even after we were married, he didn't stop, until he took her from me the only way he could." He pauses, getting choked up. "He took her soul."

My heart twists when I hear the pain in his voice. I try to remember falling in love with him, to remember the life we once had, but all I can access are the memories he's gifted me. He doesn't have to do this, clue me in to what my past self experienced, but he is. I walk to him and tentatively touch his shoulder. It takes a moment before I get flashes, not of one memory, but many—kisses that seem to span a thousand years, embraces, and joyful laughs. I see intimate moments where our love seems to pulse through the room. With each glimpse of that life, I have the impression of having a partner by my side, though I don't see his face clearly. The loss of a love so profound has to be heartbreaking, and it makes tears prick my eyes for what Galen must have gone through.

When the flashes end, I hug him tight. I expect the feel of his arms around me to be familiar, but it's not. Maybe these memories can only go so far—I'm no longer that woman, after all. I let go and step back from him. I want to know the *how* of all this, but he already seems distraught.

"Why can you tell me now, but you couldn't before?"

He smiles ruefully. "The wording of your questions matters."

I nod, contemplating what to ask next. "Has Essos kept us apart?"

He grins broadly. "That's my girl." He cups my face and rubs his thumb over my cheek. "Yes. As King of the Underworld, he held your soul until he wanted to release it. I don't know why he decided to release it now, but he did. Maybe he was hoping I wouldn't see when it happened. He almost succeeded." He presses his forehead to mine. "But I came here, and I felt you, and I knew that you were waiting for me to get you. Nothing can keep me from you—not time, and not my brother."

I think he's going to kiss me, and he almost does. His nose nudges my face, and I can feel his hot breath on my mouth. I part my lips, tilting my head up to him, but he steps away from me before it goes any further. My knees nearly buckle under me in relief. I have too many unknowns to kiss him right now, chief among them, what would happen to the Calling if I did. What would happen to Cat? As badly as I want answers, I'm not willing to risk my best friend.

"I don't know what game he's playing by having you in the Calling, but we can't let him win. I promised you I would protect you, and I will. You just need to make it to the ball."

"What's so special about the Calling Ball?" I ask, hugging myself. I'm glad I brought a sweater with me, because I'm chilled to my core. Finn has also told me to wait until the ball for answers.

"That's when he'll choose his new queen, but she has to accept in front of all of us. It's a long night, but I promise, if you make it til then, we will be home free."

I sit back down, shaking my head. "I'm sorry, this is just a lot of information, and I just don't—" Words fail me.

"I know that you need space to figure this out on your own, and I know that you need to find your own way to trust me, but I'm not going anywhere without you. I will be here every day, every step of the way. I hope you can find a way to trust that and the feelings in your memories."

The sound of a door closing pulls our attention away.

"Let me give you one parting memory," he whispers, and I nod.

Galen closes the gap between us, his hands cradling my head

and his forehead touching mine, the memory seeming to flow right from him into me.

I'm on my knees with my fingers digging into the soil when I hear footsteps behind me. For now, the space looks barren, but after some tending, I know that these gardens are going to flourish. It isn't necessary, but I want to grow these the old-fashioned way, with my own blood, sweat and tears infused in these flowers. Everything around me looks dirty, and not just because I'm in a garden; it feels like I'm looking through a dirty lens.

There is something therapeutic about being able to watch something grow.

"Do you have something you want to say to me?" I call out, not looking at my husband as he approaches.

"Dare I ask what I did this time?"

"It's very simple—just put the toilet lid down when you're done. We had the marvel of indoor plumbing well before the mortals. Put it to good use."

Getting to my feet, I finally look at him, dressed in a beige three-piece suit. His hands are shoved deep in his pockets.

"I'll try to remember."

"This is a new look," I say running my hands along his chest, feeling his finely honed muscles. This hardly counts as a fight, but maybe we can still have makeup sex.

Galen seems to read my mind, because he's not gentle as he tears my dress away.

"Do you know what a distraction you are? All day, my only thought was when I could get myself between your legs and feel you come around my cock."

My cheeks warm as my breathing gets deeper. He is not a dirty talker; this is different, and I love it. He kisses me deeply, one hand cupping my ass and pulling me as close to him as I can get without him being inside me.

"Then why are you still dressed?" I ask with a giggle as I pull out of the kiss.

"Propriety, my love. There could be eyes everywhere." He holds me to him as the bottom drops out of the world and we're transported to the bedroom in our apartment. Galen is naked this time as he presses me down onto the bed, positioning himself between my legs.

"Was my garden not good enough?" I ask him slyly.

"When it is as lush and full as you, it will be. I will make love to you on a bed of the softest petals you have, but no, I am not interested in cutting your back open on the rocks you're still clearing from the dirt. Now hush so I can make love to my wife properly."

It's the last warning he gives before he pushes inside me to fulfill his promise.

GALEN STEPS AWAY FROM ME, his fingers slowly threading out of my hair, before he turns and leaves me there with this memory.

I need to make it to the end somehow, and hopefully find clarity in that time.

18

When I get back to my room, there's a note taped to my door. I glance up and down the hall, as if the person who put it there might still be lingering. I open the note and read it.

Meet me in the gardens at 4 PM. Wear your finest.
– E

I check the time and see that it's already 3:50. I have no time to digest Galen's side of the story before meeting Essos.

I think about what he means by "wear your finest" and dig through my closet for a gown. I opt for a gauzy blush-colored one and style my hair into a quick fishtail braid. Since my ankles are still bruised and sore, I choose a pair of ballet flats. It's 3:59, and regardless of whether or not I feel ready, I can't keep Essos waiting. I do enough of that already.

I run down the stairs, glad to not be in heels, and head to the gardens. I slow my pace so I'm not out of breath, even though it does make me a little late. When I get to the entrance to the hedge maze, Essos is waiting with his back to me, fiddling with his cuff-links. I approach him and tap his shoulder, causing him to spin to face me. The smile on his face makes my heart stop, and I fight to remember what Galen said Essos has done. I cannot match what Galen has told me about Essos with what I have learned about him myself.

"Fashionably late, as ever," he remarks, offering me his arm.

I thread my arm through his with a smile. "Sorry about that. I was reading in the library and didn't see your note until I got back ten minutes ago."

"Not at all. You're worth the wait every time."

Giddiness spurs my steps along faster than I expect. Essos keeps pace, his eyes bright with amusement. Pleasure ricochets between us. Essos seems delighted by my excitement, and I find that with each smile or half smirk, I want to make him do it again. I'm sillier than normal, spinning, letting my dress catch around my legs. When I stumble once, Essos is right there, keeping me upright, his blue eyes intense as he looks at me. His chest is flush against mine, and the urge, the *need* to kiss him drives me to my toes, but I don't take it further. I could, if I wanted to do what Zara has done and take the initiative, take what I want, but I think there's a reason Essos has been so reserved.

"I take care of this space myself," Essos tells me as I step away from him, breaking the moment.

"Why's that?"

"It's a special place to me. I'm honestly glad that our joint tour was canceled. I was dreading it all morning. Perhaps that's why I was so generous with Steve. He saved me from disappointing you all when I changed my mind. I'll admit to telling Sybil to bar access to the space as well. I wanted to show you around myself."

"And yet you took Zara here earlier, and now me?" There is an edge to my voice when I say Zara's name that causes Essos to still before he drags his gaze to meet mine.

"No, Zara and I took the long way around the garden. I was showing her the vineyard on the grounds. She was interested in the wine we've been having at dinner."

I suck my lower lip into my mouth and fight the urge to step toward him. If what Galen said about Essos is true, he holds too many secrets for me to fall into a possible trap so easily.

"Oh." It's so soft, I'm not sure I would have heard it if I didn't know I said the words.

Essos doesn't call out my jealousy, he just holds his hand out to me, beckoning me to follow his lead.

Each type of flower he shows me seems to open up to me as if I were the sun, and I wonder if that is more of Essos's magic. I remember how the dahlias in the bouquet he brought me opened early.

"Is this you?" I ask, leaning in to inhale the scent of a plumeria.

"Is what me?"

"How they all seem to be blooming as we pass—is that your magic?"

He seems at a loss for words, his mouth opening and closing before he answers. "Yes and no. It is the magic of my realm that allows flowers with different needs to bloom, but I think—" He shakes his head stopping himself.

"What?" I ask, smirking.

He shakes his head again, laughing. "It's going to sound like a line, and you're worth so much more than a jumble of cliches."

I fist my hands in my dress out of his sight. Nothing about how I'm feeling is normal. I shouldn't want to have Essos woo me with pretty words in this garden while his brother is telling me that we were once married.

To diffuse the tension and the obvious want I think I'm reading on Essos's face, I drift toward some stargazer lilies that match my dress and inhale deeply. That *is* what I'm reading, I think—the tense set of his shoulders and how he has to keep his hands clasped behind his back to stop himself from reaching for me.

Or am I seeing what I want to see—a man besotted with a woman he can't or shouldn't want? My heart gallops over the implications that I want to see love in his eyes when he looks at me, but I can't think about that, not now, not on the heels of Galen's information, not when Essos is standing before me looking at me like I hold the sun and moon in my hands.

Essos picks a red lily and threads it into my braid. His hands are gentle, the stem seamlessly winding into my hair.

"They're my favorite." I gently reach back to touch the flower in my hair, gazing at him. "But then, you already knew that." I smile before turning back and picking a matching flower, then tucking it into the breast pocket of his jacket.

"I told you, I want to learn it all firsthand."

I'm still trying to perfect the flower in his pocket when his hand covers mine, pressing it against his heart. I can feel the rapid thumping through his three-piece suit. It's ridiculous how much I love that he wears them.

Something about suits nags at my mind, but I can't put my finger on it.

"This isn't even the surprise," Essos says.

I look up at him and try to imagine this man as the monster Galen portrays him. Essos hasn't been nearly as forthcoming as Galen has been, so I try to keep these budding emotions in check. But damn it, Essos makes it so hard. Galen's revelations may have come too late, as I know I've started to feel something for the man in front of me.

"There's a surprise?" I ask.

He slides his fingers between mine, as if it's something we've done a thousand times, and graces me with a smile. He leads me farther into the hedges, and in the distance I hear the static rush of the waves crashing. We come to what I think is a dead end, and Essos instructs me to close my eyes. I hear him step behind me and feel his hands cover my eyes as he slowly walks me around a corner before stopping again. When he removes his hands, I open my eyes to find two midnight-black horses standing there, tied to a bar.

I spin around and look at him. "You expect me to ride? In *this*?" I gesture at my dress.

Essos at least has the decency to look abashed as he walks over and pets the closest horse on the nose. "Yes, well, I might have been too intentionally misleading with my clothing instructions. I can change your attire, if you want. You don't have to ride if you don't want to, but I imagine you'll like it."

I take a step back as the other horse noses toward me, sniffing at my hands. "How about not." For now, this dress will be my protection against riding. I don't mention to him that I have never even seen a horse in person, let alone been this close to one. They are so much larger than expected, and they have powerful bodies. This feels like a terrible way to tempt fate after being pulled into the depths nearly to my death and having drowned once before. I would hate for the third time to stick.

He drops his hand from the horse, studying me. "I thought you were braver than that." He watches me closely.

I'm not sure what gave him that impression, but I'm happy to correct it. I refuse to tear my gaze away from the horse, which, upon realizing I have no treats, turns toward Essos and nuzzles him to see if he has something in his pocket.

"I will not be baited into this, Essos," I hiss.

Clearly, he does have something in his pocket, because the horse tries to gnaw on it.

Gently, he pushes the horse away and walks to me. He touches my shoulders before sliding his hands down to mine. He holds them a moment, ducking his head and forcing me to look at him.

"If you really don't want to, you don't have to, but I'm asking you to give Abbott and Costello a chance. Just five minutes, and if you're not comfortable, then we leave."

My eyebrows shoot up. "Seriously, with the names? Are you a comedian too?" I focus on that instead of the fear coursing through my veins. Essos won't let me get trampled to death if he really is hell-bent on one-upping his brother. I don't think Essos would let me get trampled either way, really. I let out a shaky breath, and peer around him at the horses. "Fine," I relent.

Essos is gentle in introducing me to each horse, starting off slow, petting them before feeding them some treats. While we stand there, he tells me the story of how he came to own them—a gift from his brother-in-law—and how they got their names. Finn named them, a joke that Essos didn't understand at first but now does.

Abbott nuzzles my hand for another sugar cube, and Essos produces one from his pocket for her.

After a half hour of me getting to know the horses, Essos grabs a brush and shows me how to use it. I eventually start to relax, and Essos seems to catch this change in my demeanor.

"Do you want to try riding? We'll start slow. I promise, you can trust me and these horses."

I look into his eyes and want so badly to trust him. I don't think I've ever wanted anything more. My heart is shouting at me to trust him, but at the same time, my brain is reminding me what Galen has said and shown me, and I'm not sure I'll be able to get past that. But Essos hasn't tried to harm me in any way since I've come here, and my gut is chiming in to trust him as well.

I place my hand in his, taking the leap. "Show me the way."

Essos leads the horse to a step-up block and helps me get situated on Abbott. I refused his offer to change—if I'm not long for the Calling, this might be my only chance to ride in a dress, because I am certainly never getting on a horse again.

Essos adjusts my feet in the stirrups and shows me how to keep my heels down. He takes the reins and leads us around the paddock so I can get used to being on Abbott while he's on the ground, ready to jump in at any moment. He gives me pointers on how to move with the horse, how to control her using my legs and the reins, how to stop and how to nudge her forward and ask her to trot. At first, I bounce around like a sack of potatoes, but Essos tells me to lean back and let my hips sway with Abbott's movements, and soon I'm feeling less like a disaster. Once I'm comfortable guiding Abbott at the walk, Essos climbs onto Costello. He leads us to the beach, his hands still holding my reins.

"Let me guess—horse riding was never at the top of your must-do lists?" he asks. His attention never leaves me as I navigate this new experience. The horses are walking slowly, never too fast for me, though any sudden movement from Abbott causes me to tense.

"What gave me away?" I ask, glancing at him. I can't bear to take in the sights right now, my gaze moving quickly from Essos back to the beast below me.

"How at ease you are with them."

I consider the ridiculousness of this moment, and I laugh. Who would have thought in a million years that I would be riding a horse on the beach in a ballgown? That's a perfume commercial, not my life.

"Is there anything you always wished you had done while still alive?"

I snort, readjusting myself on Abbott while I ponder his question.

When I move, I accidentally give her a kick in the side, and she takes off at a gallop. Everything that Essos told me about how to stop the horse goes out of my mind. I am straight-backed for only a moment, my hair coming loose from my braid as the wind whips my face, burning my eyes. Abbott, it would appear, was not happy with the slow walk and is welcoming the opportunity to show me what she's made of.

I lean down close to her neck and try to grab the reins, which were ripped out of Essos's hands. They flap uselessly in front of her, and I pray she doesn't step through them and flip tail over head. I think I'm supposed to lean my weight back and keep a steady hold of her mount or something to slow her down, but the idea of moving that much doesn't seem wise, so I close my eyes, grasp tight to her mane, and try to keep my tears in check. I know that animals respond to emotions, but I can't get rid of the heart-racing panic as I pray that she doesn't throw me off. I saw *Gone with the Wind*; I know what happens when you get thrown off your horse.

As we fly down the beach and I fail to fall to my death, something loosens inside me. My fear begins to mingle with excitement at the speed and the power of Abbott's body between my legs. A frisson of exhilaration has my hair standing on end, and I want to lean back and relish the feel of the wind blowing through my hair. Maybe when I'm a more experienced rider, I'll toss my head and laugh as the wind rips through my tresses, but not today and not now. I risk a quick glance over my shoulder and see that Essos and Costello are bounding toward us at a decent speed to catch up. Abbott surges forward, interpreting Costello's chase as a challenge.

I feel Essos grab my wrist before he catches the reins as they flap upward by Abbott's mouth. He tugs back on them and says, "Whoa." Thankfully, Abbott responds to the command, slowing to a stop. Shaking, I sit up, my hair wild and windblown with more out of my braid than in it. The flower is long gone.

Essos looks at me, concerned, studying my face. His brows rise when I grin at him.

"That. Was. Exhilarating!" I say between deep breaths. Essos laughs, his head tipping back, like this is the only way the full sound can escape him. My belly flips. There is a slight tremor in his hand as he takes mine and gives it a gentle squeeze. The reassurance in it might be more for him than for me.

"So, you haven't sworn off horses?" he asks.

I smile at him, petting Abbott with my free hand. "Not at all." I pause, considering my next words carefully. "I like the sound of your laugh—you should laugh more often."

I swear that he blushes at my comment, though he looks away as if trying to hide it. When he looks at me again, his brow creases, a fresh look of concern on his face.

"Daphne, are you all right?" I don't understand why he's asking, until my head starts to ache like a vise has settled around it, squeezing and squeezing. I'm surprised to feel something wet on my top lip, because it's not raining, and I'm not crying. I reach up to touch it and pull my hand away only to find it red with blood. My heart starts to beat an erratic tempo, and I don't think it's because of what just happened or my proximity to Essos.

I try to meet Essos's eyes, confused as to what's happening. I don't want to open my mouth, afraid that my voice will waver. Cold suffuses my limbs, and the only thought pounding in my mind is that this is how it felt when I was drowning. There was that momentary awareness, then cold before everything was different.

"Ess—" I start, but never finish. His hands grab my waist as my vision slowly tunnels to black.

19

I'm on a boat, my body swaying with the water below me. I've got on a tea-length navy dress and oversized sunglasses. I'm lying back, watching Essos. He's wearing a polo, and his biceps bulge with each stroke of the oars as he watches me intently. My lips pull into a smile, enjoying how serene the King of the Underworld looks bathed in light. I'm just as calm as I look at him, but his face blurs, and instead of Essos, I'm sitting with Galen. My sense of serenity is gone, and now I'm confused and alarmed, as if a glitch in the Matrix keeps changing their faces.

MY EYES OPEN, and I find I'm sitting up and swaying, gently propped against something firm.

"Look who has decided to join the world of the living," Essos quips, sounding amused by his own joke, and I realize he's holding me on Costello's back. I rub my head and touch my nose, finding the crust of dried blood there.

"How long was I out?" My voice sounds groggy.

"About 10 minutes. You got a nosebleed and passed out. Your

heart..." Essos pauses, and I think I hear him swallow. "I was able to heal you." I turn slightly in the saddle, accidentally grinding against him as I try to look at him. I see blood on the flower I put in his pocket, and I'm suddenly thankful he's wearing black. As badly as I want him to finish his sentence, I can't hear him say it.

"Stop the horse," I say firmly, and without question, he does. I go to climb off, and he steadies me before jumping off first and helping me down.

"Why does this keep happening?" I ask, my voice shaking. "I demand a real answer, not the 'Ring Around the Rosie' bullshit you keep giving me. I *deserve* an answer. It felt like I was dying."

"I don't know." He shoves his hands in his suit pockets. I pace in front of him, unsatisfied with the answer. When I meet his eyes, I see regret, and that makes me angrier. I shove him hard.

"I *said* I want an answer," I shout in his face.

He whips his hands out of his pockets to catch his balance. "*I* said, I don't know!" He runs one hand through his hair, leaving his dark locks unkempt. He continues shouting. "Don't you understand how frustrating that is for me? This is my domain— I'm supposed to have all the answers, and I just don't."

"Don't you know how frustrating this is for *me*? I keep almost dying!" I don't want to keep shouting, but I do. I have no one else to take out my frustration on, just him.

He walks past me to grab the reins of the horses and starts walking them toward the house and away from me. "I have Sybil making inquiries. If you could be so kind as to not almost get yourself killed for one godsdamned day, I would greatly appreciate it."

I have to run to catch up to him. "Hey, you don't get to walk away from me. You hold all the cards in this game, and I don't even know what game we're playing!"

"Then for the love of the gods, will you just play along like everyone else?"

I kick sand at him, but the wind just blows it back at me, leaving me sputtering. "You'd like that, wouldn't you? Me playing doll, like Zara. That way you can bend me and dress me any way you want."

I see the moment I go too far and he shuts down.

"I'm not going to be baited, Daphne. It's not happening."

Like I know the sky is blue, I know that if I push him a little harder, I can bait him into a reaction. I can bait him into shredding his cool veneer before he—I kill the thought.

Why do I think I know this man that well?

I lift my skirts to kick more sand at him but get woozy in the wind. My body feels effervescent, and I grab my head, starting to fall backwards. Essos is there in a flash to catch me before gently settling me on the beach. Our combined weight throws him off balance, his butt crashing into the sand, but he doesn't let me feel the jarring impact. He holds me practically in his lap and places a hand on my forehead, as if seeing if I have a fever.

"We can't even have a proper argument without you nearly passing out," he grumbles.

"Stop that. Don't touch me; I'm mad at you." My protest is as halfhearted as my attempt to push his hand away.

He silences me with a dirty look before he closes his eyes in concentration. My head feels lighter somehow, like the vise released my brain and the blood flow has returned to normal instead of gushing out my nose. I don't even consider what a tragedy my dress has become.

"I've done what I can for your head. You're not bleeding internally, but there's a deeper issue I can't fix because I can't find the source."

I pull my knees up to my chest and rest my chin on them. "You're infuriating," I mutter. "But thank you." I'm genuinely thankful for him helping heal me at every turn.

I can see he's just as frustrated as I am. I play with the hem of my dress, looking away from him, the fight draining out of me.

"And so are you. You're making keeping you alive a full-time job, and I already have one of those." He shifts, removing his coat and undoing the top button of his shirt. This is the most casual I have seen him since embarking on this journey.

"We get to see what that's like tomorrow, right?" I'm eager to move the subject away from my nosebleeds and near-death brushes. He's so close to me, the scent of him nearly overpowering now that my brain is able to focus on something other than maybe dying.

"You run hot and cold all the time, don't you?" He laughs. "Yes, that's the idea. For the most part, what I do runs itself with very little interference, but sometimes there are special cases that require my attention. Tomorrow, I happen to have two of those cases. It can be...disheartening at times. I'm looking forward to a time when I can share the burden again."

"Again? Sybil doesn't help?" I ask.

"Of course, they're immensely helpful, but there are certain things I can't share with them. They can help with the day-to-day, but there are elements of my work that having a partner with whom to share the emotional burden would make a huge difference."

I feel as though I'm finally getting somewhere with him. "Did you have a partner before? Your consort?"

His face shutters. "It's complicated. *Consort* is a clever word. I heard Sybil let it slip, and it got your very important lesson about the Afterlife cut short." He uses a seashell to dig a hole in the sand. Just like that, I get sent to jail, do not pass Go, do not collect two hundred dollars. I'm back to square one and have very little to show for it. I stand up.

"It's always complicated, Essos. I don't get you. Galen has been an open book to me, at least as far as your stupid rules allow, but you're always sealed tight like an oyster. You want me to trust you, but you're making it so difficult to give that trust."

Essos pauses, clearly choosing his words carefully. "Galen is held to a different standard than I am. As a result, he is able to be more free with his words and actions. As the main participant of the Calling, I *cannot* tell you more. I know you've been asking questions of Finn, and I haven't interfered because I didn't think I had to. Stop poking at it, Daphne. Stop trying to rip open the scab to see if it still bleeds. There *will* be answers when the time comes." Essos grinds his teeth, locking eyes with me. "Is Galen interfering in some way I should be aware of?"

I think of the memories that Galen has given me so far. If I want to learn more about myself, I need to keep him in the house. If Essos knew Galen was doing that, what would stop him from sending Galen away, or worse, canceling this Calling because I've been influenced? I try to think of some kernel of knowledge that I can use against Essos in this moment that won't stop things dead in their tracks.

"No, he's just been more free with information about you as a person and your history as the King of the Underworld. What is he the god of, anyway?"

I can see by his expression that Essos doesn't believe me. I see in his eyes that he knows his brother is up to something. Does he need proof to do something about it?

"He is the God of War and Suffering," he says, sounding disappointed, like he already knew the answer to the question he was asking but wanted me to confirm it. "We were close once but had a falling out quite some time ago. He's never recovered from the slight, and things only deteriorated from there. He's the reason I was called away abruptly. He started a skirmish that could have turned into a war, and since it resulted in mortal deaths, I had to step in. The King of the Gods was otherwise occupied. Galen acts out like that frequently."

"You make him sound like a petulant child."

"That's because he is one. He doesn't like being the baby of the family and will use any excuse to act out. It's no wonder that people treat him like that." Essos scoops up a handful of sand and lets the grains slide through his fingers, not looking at me. "I know it makes me sound like a bitter child, but after thousands of years being faced with his behavior, I'm...what do you mortals say now? Over it. Just...trust his actions over his words. Galen is always better at showing people who he really is underneath it all."

I hold his gaze. I can picture Essos as a small child, pouting over the attention given his baby brother, and I feel uncertain again of who to trust.

"If you want me along for the ride, I need to know what I'm doing."

He squints against the sun. If I suggested it, I wonder if Essos would just sit and play in the sand with me, casting aside his kingly demeanor. But I've already pushed him too far in the other direction.

"Fine." He shakes his head and stands up, then dusts off his hands on his pants and offers me one.

I think about the past few days, and I reach out and take it.

The world spins around me for what feels like an eternity. I wonder if maybe I have permanent brain damage, or if I got up too fast. When Essos drops my hand, I open my eyes. It takes a second for them to adjust. Gone is the sunbathed beach with its cool ocean breeze. Instead, we're standing in a dark cavern with moist, stale air. I see nothing identifiable, just a long hallway extending before us.

"Where are we?" I ask, knowing that the answer is obvious. Essos is busy grooming himself—dusting the sand off his suit, running a hand through his hair to slick it back. He refastens the top button of his shirt and closes his jacket. He misses a few stray hairs, and I instinctively reach out to brush them into place. He stills as I do it, and I imagine him grabbing my hand and kissing the inside of my wrist, as if this is a dance we've done before. I want him to do it, want to feel the press of his mouth against my skin, even if it's not my lips.

"We're in my realm. The Underworld. This is where the queen will spend her time by my side. No better place than among the worms. Ashes to ashes and all that." His tone is different as he says it, flat. This is another face of his, trying to fill the role everyone expects of him. It almost sounds like the opposite of a sales pitch, like he's trying to talk me out of proceeding, which only makes him more perplexing.

He starts walking, his back ramrod straight as he ventures forward. The side chamber he leads me into looks like the DMV—long, slow lines and unhappy people. There is no end in sight for the line in either direction.

"Consider this your sneak peek of tomorrow, except, because I don't want to send you all away screaming, I keep the demonstration tomorrow more civilized and in another location, not underground," he murmurs to me.

"Why show me then?" I ask.

He looks down at me, his ice-blue eyes softening for a second before he hardens himself. He needs to be a different version of himself to do this job. I wonder which is closer to the real Essos—this man without an ounce of pity in his voice, or the man who played with sand just minutes before.

"Because you're relentless, and I know that you won't be satisfied without the whole truth. Daphne, I can't show you everything, but believe that I am pushing the limits of what I am absolutely allowed."

I trail behind him as we walk past the endless lines of people, most of them looking bored, some crying. "But you're not giving me the whole truth—just a convenient part of it."

We stop in front of another door.

"That's because I can't tell you everything you want to know without ending the entire process, and then this will be all for nothing. Is that what you want? I can promise you that it's not what I want. My hands are tied by other people. I'm not my brother—I cannot flaunt rules for my own gain." He is frustrated with me; I can feel it. But if he thinks I'm just going to be some pretty accessory that won't ask questions, he's barking up the wrong tree. "Do you have any other questions before this gets started?"

A flush of embarrassment crawls up my neck. "How is this not breaking any rules now that we're alone together? What are all these people waiting for?"

"Sybil is able to keep an eye on what is happening at all times. They know when I have pre-scheduled time with someone and are able to watch, so we are never technically alone. We never have been, but I ask them to keep their distance."

He blows out a long breath before giving me as detailed an explanation as he can.

"At the end of the line is the Register, which contains the name of every person and what type of afterlife they are going to have. There is so much death in the mortal world, and this space acts as a holding place before people pass on. Forget what you've been taught in religion classes about gods and St. Peter and the Pearly Gates—this is the reality. I'll do a better job of going over the details tomorrow, if you'll have the patience. Then it will make more sense."

"Don't ask me for questions and then get pissy when I ask," I snap.

Essos stifles a smirk.

He turns to the door and straightens to his full height again, his posture having relaxed as we talked. His face changes; gone is the beaming smile and deep concern from earlier. In its place are a frown and indifferent eyes. He seems practiced in this transformation. Thousands of years of doing this have to wear on a person's soul; I can't imagine the mask he needs to don here.

Before pushing both doors open, he glances down at what I'm wearing and waves his hand, turning the bloodstained, blush-colored tulle to black. I feel my hair twist back and away from my face into what I think is a tight bun, but I don't dare check. I stick close to his heels as we walk down the center of what looks like a courtroom, only the viewing gallery is endlessly filled with people.

He walks into the judge's box and conjures a chair behind him for me. He gives no instructions, but I know to sit and be silent all the same. I perch on the edge of my seat, my shoulders pulled back, sticking out my chin a little, trying to adopt the same unbothered look as Essos. His gaze lingers on me for too long, and his mask cracks a little. Essos's nostrils flare as the muscle in his jaw ticks. His hands are clenched so tightly I'm afraid his knuckles might break the skin. Then he releases the tension, seeming to remember where he is and why we're here.

From out of nowhere, a man appears in front of him and calls the already silent room to order. This man looks at his clipboard and calls out a name, prompting someone to stand and walk forward. Essos looks at the papers in front of him.

"James Blane?" Essos asks. "Are you aware of the charges against you?" The man is slouched with bad posture. He has shaggy, greasy hair hanging in his eyes, and it sways when he shakes his head to Essos's question. Essos looks down at the paper, then back at the man.

"You ran and operated an online celebrity website on which you ridiculed people for no other reason than their social status. Is this correct?" The man nods. "Is it also correct that you paid special attention to Bonnie DeVille, a 17-year-old starlet, shaming her for everything from her looks to her singing ability to her family?"

The man senses where this is going and swallows hard, his Adam's apple bobbing as he nods his head. The man is looking everywhere but directly at Essos. His gaze snags on me, and I feel his stare as he takes in my exposed neck down to my chest and gown.

Essos catches his leering stare. "*Look at me,*" he orders coldly, the lethal tone leaving nothing to be misinterpreted. Essos doesn't need a show of force, like slamming down his fist or shouting—the power is in his words. The man's gaze immediately shifts to the space directly in front of Essos. "Is it also true that when she made a personal plea to get you to stop, you told her—and I quote—'I'll do it only if you suck my big fat cock?'"

The man now has beads of sweat rolling down his face under Essos's glare as he waits for an answer. James Blane attempts to shake his head, but nods instead.

"And did she?" Essos's voice is dangerously low, an edge to it that I haven't heard before. The man nods his head, lowering his eyes. I bet if he was capable of collapsing in on himself, he would.

"So, to summarize," Essos says loudly, "you bullied a 17-year-old girl into giving you a blow job that you then bragged about all across the internet, and when people demanded proof, you provided it in the form of video evidence. Correct?"

My skin crawls, thinking about this happening, that men like this still breathe air, although in this case, he doesn't anymore.

"Did Bonnie kill herself after you shared this?"

The man drops to his knees, nodding his head.

"Why should you be permitted to go to a better afterlife?"

The man starts crying, blubbering, not making any sense. Essos lets him whimper and cry until he holds up a hand, silencing the man. "I demand an answer. Why should you be allowed to have a peaceful afterlife after the pain you have wrought? You knew that this young woman had depression—you wrote about her being medicated for it. You knew the ugly things people said in response to what you wrote." Essos waits for him to respond.

"Sir, because, sir, one mistake doesn't make a person, sir."

Essos appears to consider it for a moment but no longer. "Not sufficient. Denied." He waves his hand, and the man disappears.

Essos does a few more of these, including war criminals and negligent parents, making a different decision each time. He is efficient at his job, asking only a few questions before making his declaration. After he's had enough, he holds my hand and leads me out of the room, then takes me home.

20

We're back at the beach in an instant, only it's dark now. I walk forward and sit in the surf, letting the water lap around me, not caring that I'm damaging another dress. Essos sits beside me, getting wet as well. He has the common sense to kick off his shoes first.

"That wasn't easy," I say, looking at him.

He takes a deep breath, nodding. All of the terrible things that he had to read and say felt like they chipped away at my soul. My heart is heavy, and I feel my shoulders have turned in on themselves. The weight of what I witnessed bears down on me, the words and the actions of those people, while not my own...having to hear them made me feel dirty inside.

"And that is why I need someone to take on this task with me. I've done it on my own for a long time. I need someone to share this with. What you didn't see was how I prepare for every case that needs to be heard. I spend hours pouring over a dossier of their lives, knowing when they stole a candy bar from a store or a handful of rocks. I learn what they fear, what drives them. All these reports are compiled by the worker bees that actually keep the realm running. I'm not so arrogant as to think that I'm what keeps the wheels turning. I offer a very competitive healthcare benefits package to all who work for me." He sounds tired. Tired of this burden that he has to carry alone.

"What about Sybil? Wait, you have other employees?" I ask. I wonder if they want this role at all. But knowing what they do, I have to doubt Galen now. Taking this on requires a special kind of person, and I'm not sure it's something that even I want.

"Of course, I do. Like any other business, the Underworld requires accountants and assistants and managers. Roles like this are filled with lesser gods, nymphs, dryads and other creatures. I can't get into details yet, but Sybil is just the tip of the iceberg. A very important iceberg. Sybil is tremendously helpful, but like I said, it's not the same. They can't adjudicate with me or know how it feels to send people to a terrible afterlife. Sure, Sybil can handle the paperwork, but when it comes to handling the souls, that burden rests on the king and queen." He stares at the horizon. "I have to carry this with me, knowing that some of these cases are not cut-and-dried. Knowing that there are people suffering for my judgment. I've been making these decisions for a long time, but when I had someone to share that with, it meant that I wasn't alone in how I hurt for these people and those impacted by their choices."

I take his hand in mine, sliding my fingers between his. I don't miss that he had someone once whom he shared the burden with, and I wonder who she was and why she is no longer in the picture. I don't press him on it, knowing he can't give an answer. Instead, I'm grateful for the glimpse he has given me. "Thank you for sharing that with me."

Essos looks like he has so much more to say but won't...or can't. I want him to be able to open up, to let me in. I'm not sure I'll ever be able to fully trust him while he keeps this wall between us. Even if it's not a wall of his own making, it is a wall that prevents me from really reaching him.

But now, seeing what his job entails, seeing him in action, I do understand him a little better. Why he needs someone in his life, why it has taken him so many tries to find the right person. Is that why he so doggedly pursued his brother's wife? Because he felt that I—or rather, she—was the only person who could help him handle all of this? Is that why whenever anyone asks if there was someone before, the answer is always, *It's complicated*?

"I've kept you out much later than I should have. You must be hungry." We stand and step away from the water, both of us wet from sitting in the surf. I'm about to say as much when Essos waves a hand, drying our clothes.

"Neat trick."

"It comes in handy."

We head back inside and find everyone in the ballroom, mingling. It's clear that we missed dinner and the ball is well underway. Zara tries to hide her jealousy behind a smile as she crosses the room to us. Not caring that I'm right there, she gets on her toes and kisses Essos on the lips. He's stock-still a moment before his hands gently hold her away from him as he pulls back. Essos slides his hand into mine, making it clear to Zara that now is still my time. He makes excuses and apologies to everyone else about needing to get food. He doesn't let go of my hand as he leads me toward the dining room.

Cat and Finn are chatting with champagne glasses in their hands. They look smug as we walk past them. I watch as they clink glasses, not taking their eyes off us, their conversation continuing without missing a beat. They're cute standing side by side, and I wonder if, since Cat is allowed to stay without actually dating Essos... If she can... Maybe she can start fishing in this wider, very good-looking pond.

I catch Galen's eye as I pass. His head dips toward me, his

golden eyes catching my hand in Essos's. I could swear his eyes flash red. A fleeting thought enters my mind about what must be going through Galen's head. I decide that I don't really give a shit. He has far more information than I do about what's going on, so if I have to keep some secrets too, I will.

We wind our way into the kitchen, where a stout redheaded woman is commanding a roomful of people as they run around making food. One of the younger servants comes to a dead stop and drops a platter.

"Well, now you've gone and done it! Dropped the canape! What am I supposed to feed these people now? Do you know how much Finn puts away alone?! Get this cleaned up. What will the king say when he sees this!"

"I imagine he will say 'sorry,'" Essos responds, fighting a smile.

The cook looks up at him. She turns a furious shade of red to match her hair. "Now you've *really* done it!" she says. "Embarrassed me before the king! What have you got to say for yourself?"

The boy is frozen in his spot. I assume that he doesn't interact with Essos on a daily basis.

I pick up the food and place it on the tray, which gets her started all over again. I hope that I'm not making things worse for him.

"Please, Estelle, it's okay. I startled him. It was my fault." Essos gets on his knees beside me to help clean up. Essos helping out finally spurs the young man to action, and he grabs a napkin to wipe the floor and cover the soiled food. We finish clearing the mess, and the cook looks as though she might drop dead on the spot.

"Daphne and I were hungry, and we hoped that might be something that you could help us out with."

Estelle claps her hands, turning away from us and barking orders as she goes.

Another young man leads us to a table in the corner. Eager to impress the boss, he sets out a tablecloth as well as candlesticks, then adds plates and silverware. I bite down on my lips to bury a smile over how everyone is tripping over themselves for Essos.

"I keep waiting for a fat Italian man to start playing the accordion behind us," I tease as we settle in.

"Shall I use my nose to pass the meatball to you?"

My retort about him promising to kiss me as we share spaghetti dies on my lips. If Galen touching me can show our love affair, what would kissing Essos show me?

Would I see his plans to steal me away from Galen? Is that why he won't do it?

Essos drags me back to the present by trailing a finger over the back of my hand. "How's your head?" He's watching me closely.

I wonder if he can read minds, but I dismiss the thought. If he could read minds, then he would already know what Galen has shown me.

"Much better, but I feel like the headache is still lurking."

"Please tell me if you get any more nosebleeds or headaches. I want to make sure we monitor that in case it has anything to do with whatever attacked you a few weeks ago."

I lean away from him, astonished. "That feels like a lifetime ago." I can't see how my current health issues would have anything to do with the sea monster. If I were a betting woman, I would say they're due to the memories Galen has shown me.

"My brother tends to have that effect when he's around." Essos takes a sip of wine and chuckles.

"It's nice to know that even the King of the Underworld has some sibling rivalry. If you don't get along, why is he still here?" I can't help but hope he answers this question of mine. Hedging my bets, I push further. "What can you tell me about your other siblings?"

Estelle has two chicken pot pies delivered to us in record time.

242

The smell of the chicken prompts my stomach to give an undignified growl. Essos laughs and gives his thanks to the poor waiter, whose hands are shaking.

"Because he raised concerns about the Calling. I kept it quiet longer than I should have. Once everyone decided to stay or go, I was supposed to notify the Council. Like the tattletale he is, he told the Council, which oversees the gods. As they're the entity that set the parameters of the Calling, including the restrictions, they assigned him to monitor things, to make sure I'm playing by the rules. He's here as a glorified pain in my ass." Essos swirls the wine in his glass, looking at me. "And I can't tell you much, I'm afraid. Though you shouldn't have to meet them until the ball. They're both married and tend to avoid my realm." He breaks the crust of the pie, letting the steam come through.

"You're a bit of a black sheep?" I ask, pushing the pie filling inside the crust. Around us, the bustle of the kitchen continues, despite it being after dinner. The clanking and humming sounds make excellent background noise, giving us time to talk and eat.

"Sort of. Xavier is a natural-born leader, making him the favorite of our parents. Helene is the only girl, so of course, she's beloved, and Galen is the baby. I am the mediator, willing to take the kingdom no one else wanted. I had one thing going for me."

I want to ask more about his siblings, but his last sentence gives me pause. "If I ask what that thing was, are you going to dodge me?" He takes a sip from his glass of wine, then nods. "Fine then, this is me not asking. What are your other siblings the god and goddess of?"

"Can you wait until the ball to find out?"

I leave my wine untouched, the dull pulsing in my head becoming more acute. It's been lingering since I came back to consciousness. I've been able to push past it, but it's getting more insistent.

"Do I have a choice?" I deadpan, already knowing the answer.

"No, not really. I've already told you about Galen, and I promise, Sybil will cover the others. We just hold it close to the chest. People have their own religious beliefs when they come to the Afterlife—finding out that there is a God of Gods and Weather or a Goddess of Stars and Victory tends to cause unnecessary disruption. We leave that information for the finalists." Essos gives me a coy wink when he lists a god and a goddess, and something in me breaks a little. I think it's my resolve to paint him as the bad guy. He's *trying*.

Essos doesn't seem bothered by my continued frustration. He must have dealt with this countless times during every iteration of the Calling. I wonder how it worked with each generation of women, who must have all been so different. A group of women from the 1800s had to be drastically different from the women here now. Although, invariably, there must have been some stubborn, pushy women like me.

"Then tell me what *isn't* off limits."

"You. You aren't off limits."

I roll my eyes at him and push away my empty plate. I rub my bloated belly, not caring how it makes me look to him. I think saving my life means I don't have to worry what he thinks about my food baby. "I think I *am* off limits."

He places his napkin on the table, pushing his plate away. "Then we've reached the end of our date." He reaches for my hand on the table.

"You call this a date?"

"Well, yes. I took you on a walk through some gardens, a horseback ride, and we had dinner. I think that's a damn good date. Swoon-worthy is what I believe your contemporaries call it."

"*And* you took me to work," I point out dryly.

Essos throws his hands in the air, looking exasperated and amused. I'm uncertain which emotion is winning at this moment.

"Only because you asked me to!"

I climb out of the seat without Essos's help. "I think the only thing missing from tonight then is a dance." I hold out a hand to him. I never understood when someone said eyes were smoldering, but that's the only way I can think to describe his eyes now. They're lit from somewhere within him, a fire burning that only I can put out.

Essos flicks his wrist, and soft music plays from nowhere. The lights around us dim, casting a sort of curtain to separate us from the kitchen. His hand slips into mine and pulls me against him.

This isn't the usual waltzing that we've been doing during our practice balls. He holds me close with one hand bracing my back and the other holding my hand tight. I rest my head against his chest, comforted by the thumping of his heart and the feeling of safety in his arms. I'm confused by this feeling, confused by how I'm being pulled in different directions.

I don't fight it now. I'm too tired. My head is pounding, but I'm not thinking about that pain. All I am thinking about is how he is holding me. How invincible he makes me feel despite my recent brushes with death, and how incredible he smells.

We sway for a few moments, my eyes growing heavier and heavier. I can hear Essos whispering in my ear, but I can't quite make out what he's saying as the weight of the day settles on me. My conversation with Galen feels like it was years ago, not this afternoon. Without me even realizing I'm drifting off, Essos scoops me up in his arms.

"I can walk on my own two feet, thank you very much," I mutter, wrapping my arms around his neck. Essos's nose nuzzles the curve of my neck. It's the most intimate move he's made.

"The lady doth protest too much, methinks," he whispers as he carries me off to bed.

21

When I wake up, Cat is sitting at my feet, petting Dave. I half smile, still in the grips of my dream.

I'm at my desk, reviewing figures of the mortal harvest above. Recent droughts are affecting what they will have in storage, and I'm less than thrilled. Someone is intervening, screwing with my work, and I'm mad about it. Everything about my desk and my office feels too harsh, too bright.

"Peony for your thoughts?" I lift my eyes to see Galen standing before my desk, a perfect red peony in his hand. He offers the flower to me, and I take it and inhale the scent. He pinches the pants of his light grey suit and perches on the edge of my desk.

"Nothing that can't be solved tomorrow. I think one of your brothers is playing with the mortal realm."

"Which one?" Concern causes a wrinkle between his brows. It's the

spot I've always reached for, as if I can smooth away his worries when it's there. I know it won't stop him from thinking too hard, but I can try.

"Does it matter?" I step out from behind my desk and walk into his waiting arms. His face is buried in the nape of my neck, dragging his nose from shoulder to my ear, which he tugs at gently.

"You smell of lavender. Is there anything I can do to help? Do you want me to intercede?"

I pull back and look at him. I know he means well, but I scowl. "I don't need you fighting my battles."

"What battles would you like me to fight then, wife?"

I step farther from his grip, making sure I'm out of his reach when I beckon my office door to open. Galen's brow furrows again, and I give him a wicked grin.

"Catch me and find out," I whisper, before I take off running through the halls of our new home to our bedroom, where we will have a different sort of encounter.

I TELL Cat about my dream. I try to hold on to that calm, comforting feeling that I had moments ago when I consider what today is going to bring. The memory of last night in the Underworld, hearing about the crimes committed, makes my skin crawl. It's one thing to know about the evils of man from afar, but to be faced with it so directly...I really get what Essos means about needing the right person by his side.

Not every case he had last night was simple. There were some, like the boy who accidentally started a forest fire that claimed eight lives, including his own, that had nuance. The urge to run from my chair and hug the boy and promise that it was okay was overwhelming, and Essos must have known it because, at that moment, it felt like I was bound to the chair. I found myself in agreement almost entirely with Essos on how he ruled, though there were a few people who I don't think faced enough punishment.

"So, you're still caught in a tug of war between them?" Cat's tone is light, but the look on her face tells me she doesn't approve. I realize that I haven't filled her in on what I learned from Galen the day before about the life we apparently shared. I tell her about Essos coming between us and trying to keep me away from Galen. The look on her face tells me she's not drinking the same Kool-Aid that I am.

"That just doesn't feel like Essos." Cat shakes her head. "If he had this master plan, then why would he let me stay?"

I gesture at her, my arms waving aggressively. "For this exact reason! You're on his side, pleading his case."

She looks offended and a little hurt at the suggestion. "I am on your side, and your side alone. I'm only stating that Essos has been good to us for the last month and a half, and you've known Galen for a grand total of..." Cat pretends to check her watch "... fifteen minutes. That's hardly enough time to base anything on."

"But we're supposed to know if we want to spend eternity with Essos in three months? That's a second compared to forever. I can't give you a good reason, but I have this strong compulsion to trust Galen. If these memories are real, I had a life with him— he was my husband—and maybe that's not who I am now, but I owe it to him and to that past self to figure it out, right? My feelings are so forceful when I'm around him, like there's nothing but the two of us." I throw the covers off the bed, startling Dave. He lifts his head and huffs at me in annoyance. I walk into the bathroom to wash my face.

"I'm not saying that either situation is ideal; I'm just saying that you need to slow your roll. There's still plenty of time left until the ball, and we don't want to rush it. Take your time to figure out what's going on before jumping in with both feet. You and Essos looked sweet together last night. You should really ask

Galen about those dreams you had about Essos. Maybe the simpler explanation is that you actually dated both brothers." Her words resonate with me, hitting every doubt that I have. My head starts pounding as I try to focus on the memories of Galen, trying to see if I can look past them. Are the dreams memories too? They feel real, as if I might be accessing something locked away deep inside me. I remember the dream after my nosebleed last night, of sitting on the boat with Essos—was that a memory? Was it Essos...or Galen? I try to focus on it, to see if I can call the memory to mind by force. There is something strange about the memories that I just can't put my finger on.

I grip the counter in the bathroom, my vision blurring. Holding on tight, I try to reach for the door to close it. I don't use enough force to close it all the way, but I don't care. I omitted the details about passing out, and I don't want Cat to worry. I feel hot all over, and like I'm going to be sick. I manage to get my sweatshirt off and toss it to the side, but that took so much more energy than I expected. Even the smooth silk of my sleepshirt feels like too much.

"I'm going to shower!" I try to shout to Cat. Using all the strength I have, I stumble into the stall and turn on the water. I sit on the basin floor with my head between my knees, still fully clothed, and let cold water run over my body, wanting nothing more than to lie down and sleep again. I open my eyes and see pink water circling the drain. I look up, squinting against the water to see if there's something wrong, and when nothing is, I gently touch my face. It's wet, which my brain explains to me makes sense because I'm in the shower, but when I pull my fingers away, it doesn't have a reason for why I'm bleeding.

Cat opens the door to find the shower curtain pushed wide open from when I climbed in. Noting the blood on my face, she frowns and springs into action. Always cool under pressure, she grabs a washcloth and holds it against my face, tilting my head back. I hear Dave whine behind her, his tail smacking the doorframe.

"I'm going to get help," she says, holding my head steady when I don't stop bleeding. "Do you think you can keep it together long enough for me to do that?"

Dave barks, and I nod my head. He barks a second time, and Sybil appears.

"I tried knocking, but you didn't answer. What in the world...?" Sybil squats down to get a better look at my face. Dave keeps barking, getting louder and louder, until he suddenly stops.

"What is happening?" a male voice says from the doorway, the sharp edge of unease breaking through my mental haze. I know that voice. Essos moves into my line of vision, and I sigh. There is a wrinkle between his brows again that looks so familiar, and once more I have to quell my urge to reach out and smooth it away. It's the same wrinkle from Galen's face in my dream. It must be a family trait, but I can't dwell any further on what it means. I just want everyone to be quiet. My mouth tries to move to shush everyone, but I don't think I make a sound.

Essos's face is otherwise blank, like he's fighting not to show just how worried he is. I could feel his frustration yesterday when he was shouting about it. Nothing about Essos screams loss of control the way it did then.

"Why is everyone shouting?" I mumble, loosening my grip on the washcloth. I'm so very tired and just want to close my eyes for a minute, then I'll pay attention. I'm not sure anyone actually heard me.

"Another nosebleed?" he asks, kneeling beside Sybil.

They lean forward to whisper in his ear, and he gives a small shake of his head, barely perceptible. Cat is still in the bathroom. She pulls the washcloth away, and it looks soaked in blood. I sense that she's trying to look supportive and not frightened out of her mind as she gets another.

"What do you mean, another nosebleed?" Cat and Galen say at the same time. Her head jerks around when she hears his voice. I know her, and I'm sure she's glaring daggers at him. I lean my head back, trying to lie down on the floor of the shower and close my eyes. I want to remind someone that the water is still on, but I can't get the words out.

Essos's hand covers my forehead. My hands feel like clubs as I try to reach up to grab it. I think that I close my hand around his wrist, but I'm not positive, because my hand drops, unable to hold on.

"I need you to open your eyes, Daphne." It's not a gentle request, but he's trying to keep his voice soft. I want to respond and tell him that I don't want to open my eyes, I want to go back to sleep, but my mouth stays shut as if my lips are glued together.

When I don't respond, he pleads with me. "Please, open your eyes for me, sweetheart." My eyes flutter open, and I find Essos sitting on the floor looking down at me. "I am so, *so* sorry, but this is going to hurt." He closes his eyes, his face scrunching up in concentration.

If I thought that my headache was bad before, this feels as though someone is pouring molten lava directly into my brain. I reach for something to hold, finding only Essos's hand on my forehead. I grab it and sit up suddenly, screaming and screaming and *screaming*, ceasing only to beg him to stop. His free hand grabs mine, so I have something to squeeze as the pain builds.

Then, abruptly, it's over. I slump back into the shower, my throat raw, soaked to the bone, the shower still running. Essos leans back against the glass wall of the shower, still gripping my hand. The water has run through his hair, ruining the combed-back look. I want to reach up and push it back, but I bury the urge. It takes a moment, but I realize that my head isn't pounding any longer.

Sybil falls to their knees beside Essos. "My lord!" they call, trying to get him to look at them. He's still holding my hand, and with the other, he waves them off, trying to get a good look at me. Cat finally has the good sense to turn off the shower, but now my lavender pajamas are see-through.

Essos doesn't seem to notice as he gets to his knees to look at me. His hand cups my face, his thumb gently rubbing warmth into my cheek as he studies me.

"Your eyes are clear now. Do you feel any better?" I nod, my throat too sore to find words. "Good. You know how I warned you about getting too much information too quickly and how there are consequences? I'm beginning to think that your mind is over-whelmed. I think we should postpone today." He looks away from me to find a towel, then he gently lifts me from the floor to wrap me in it, preserving what is left of my dignity.

"Please, don't." I croak, my hand touching my throat gently.

Essos reaches to touch it too, and I assume he is using his ability to heal it. "Do you have any shred of self-preservation whatsoever?" he breathes, sounding amazed. I'm sure it's not from pride, but in shock at my level of stubborn stupidity.

Galen steps into the room, crossing his arms. "I'm going to have to agree with my big brother on this one. You should rest."

Everyone in the room looks shocked at the agreement. I think Sybil falls over backwards because of it.

A shudder works through my body, not making my case, but I won't be cowed. It might take every shred of strength I have, but I'm going to do this. I stand carefully in the shower, forgetting the towel and my now see-through clothes. Essos presses his hand to the small of my back, sending warmth through my body. When I lean into the touch, Essos pushes against me to prevent me from falling.

Awareness prickles through me as I notice what this morning has done to him. He's soaked through, the way I am. Water is dripping from his hair onto his cheek while his suit is absolutely drenched. The white of his shirt is nearly transparent, and his chest is heaving.

My nipples are peaked as the fabric from my shirt brushes against them with each deep breath he takes, but not once do his eyes leave my face.

"I wish you would all stop treating me like some delicate flower. We're going to continue with the day as planned. If you would kindly leave so I can get ready, it would be greatly appreciated."

Essos steps away from me to help Sybil stand before bowing his head to me, relenting. This time when he looks at me, I think there might be pride in his eyes. Galen looks angry and like he wants to say more to me about this, but then he changes his mind. Before he goes, he sneaks an eyeful of my wet T-shirt, prompting a disgusted noise from Cat.

Essos watches his brother leave before looking at me. A towel appears in his hand, and he offers it to me. "*Please* tell me if you get any more headaches, even if you think it's just a hangover."

I nod. "Yes, of course." I reach out to grab his hand. "Thank you, for everything," I say, words not able to cover my gratitude.

"You can thank me by not dying." He turns and leaves quickly, probably to change, but at the very least, to speak with Sybil about what happened.

Cat goes to follow, but I grab her arm and pull her close into a wet hug. She returns it, holding me just as tight, both of us life-lines in the dark.

Before she goes, she turns to look at me. "For what it's worth, I'm not sure I trust Galen."

She leaves before I can respond. I don't know how to tell her that the memories feel so real, right there for me to grab on to. Is it because it's more information than I've had since getting here? Is it because he's filling a hole that I've been missing my entire life? Or is it just that I *want* to trust someone more than anything?

22

The schedule given to us by Sybil requires that we dress in all black, which fits my somber mood. I pour over my clothes, unsure what to wear, and find a black dress tucked deep into my closet. I pull it out, admiring it. It feels a bit formal, knowing what I do—that we're headed to judge souls seeking a reprieve, but I slide it on, and it feels right. The underlayer is a mini-dress in pure black that ends mid-thigh, with a top layer of black lace that makes the dress high neck and floor length. I don high heels, even though I'm unsteady on them, and tug on the sheer sleeves, making sure they're straight. Once my waves are swept back from my face, I look at my makeup and opt for heavy eyeliner and mascara and a dark red lip.

Today we are going to be standing beside the King of the Underworld, and we need to make an impression. It's more than just for Sybil and Essos—it's for the souls we'll be seeing today, and the souls we may see again.

I find Cat and Zara waiting at the foot of the stairs. Cat wears a conservative black dress that's form-fitting and falls to her knees, and Zara rocks a black bandage dress that hugs her every curve. Cat whistles at me, and Dave comes running, expecting a treat.

"Hot mamma! Who are you and what have you done with my best friend?" She takes my hand and makes me spin. She's trying to cover the edge of concern in her voice with humor. I don't want to discuss what happened earlier in front of anyone else, and I appreciate that she knows me well enough to leave it for a later conversation.

"You know that old saying, dress for the job you want? I figure if we're trying to become Queen of the Underworld, it's important to look the part."

Zara looks furious that she didn't think of it first. I don't admit that I have an unfair advantage after last night.

Our group will be the first to join Essos, and I hope for everyone's sake that what we see today isn't as horrifying as some of what I heard the night before.

"Ladies, Essos is waiting for you. I understand that we have not been forthcoming on details about today, but you will see firsthand some of the responsibilities that Essos has to attend to. No one will think any less of you if you feel the need to bow out afterward. This experience has stopped the journey for many girls. There are no wrong decisions, remember that." Sybil leads us toward Essos's office.

Galen is sitting on a couch when we walk by, and when he catches sight of me, he stands up. His gaze follows me closely.

We pass Essos's office and the gallery and walk down a flight of spiral stairs, each of us careful not to fall. Every day brings us new unexplored places in the house. I don't think a millennium in this house would be enough time to discover all the nooks and crannies.

We enter a room smaller than I was expecting. I had imagined another courthouse-like space with countless people waiting to be called. Instead, it is just us three girls, Essos and Sybil.

Essos gives us a cursory glance, as if to ensure we're in proper attire, and he does a double take when he sees me. He might not have taken advantage of the fact that my clothes were see-through earlier, but now he drinks in the sight of me. The obvious longing on his face makes me want to reach out and do something about it. Now is not the time, though. He clears his throat, the look gone suddenly, and straightens his suit.

"Today, I have been asked to adjudicate a man's life. You will hear the crimes he has committed during his lifetime and his defense for why he doesn't deserve to be punished for eternity in the worst of the afterlives. Cases like this are part of what you will be asked to oversee with me. You will need to be open-minded and unbiased before passing judgment. Before I administer my decision, I will ask each of you what your decision would be. You will hear only one case this session, but know that it is often many times more than one. I've sat in on as many as a thousand in one day, but doing so requires a certain level of emotional endurance, one I've built over thousands of years. As a new queen, you will not be expected to do nearly as much, but over time, you will. This is, of course, just one facet of what I do on a day-to-day basis. Most of the time it's endless paperwork."

Essos turns from us.

"Dell McMann," he calls, using the same detached voice from the day before. A man appears, and I'm surprised, because he's unlike the others yesterday who were bucking under the weight of their crimes, dirty with guilt. He's clean-shaven, standing tall in a polo and khakis, as if he were headed off to play a round of golf.

"Dell McMann," Essos repeats, confirming that the man before him is Dell. "You are disputing your punishment. Do you know your crime?"

I expect the man to nod; most of the people the day before were unable to speak, their shame preventing it.

"Yessir." Dell's hands are folded behind his back. "I killed a man with my car when I was 22 and fled the scene."

Zara's jaw drops in horror at this man's open confession. Cat looks uncomfortable, while I muse that this is much milder than the day before. Essos is going easy on us. I wonder what it means that he was willing to show me some of the more depraved situations.

"Were you ever caught?" Essos questions.

"No, sir."

Essos looks at the papers before him, flipping them and turning them over, pretending to study what is in them. The night before, I caught sight of what was on the pages—information about the person before him: their likes, their dislikes, their small crimes and their larger ones, the sum of a person in a folder for his judgment. Essos didn't show me these pages directly, but he held them in such a manner that I could easily read the content. Today, I sit tall, my back straight with my hands in my lap, so I might have a better view of them over his shoulder.

"Do you understand that you are to serve your punishment now? How did you come to hit this man with your car?" Essos continues with his relentless questioning. I was in awe, watching him work last night. He was quick with questions with very little time to prepare.

"I do understand, sir. It was an accident, sir. I looked at my phone, sir."

I can tell that Essos has already made his decision. This entire thing is a charade. I want to be angry with him for putting on a show, but I can't. If someone can't handle a case like this, how will they be able to handle someone like James Blane?

"And why did you look at your phone?"

These are all pointed questions that Essos already knows the answers to.

The man swallows. "My wife had called me earlier to say that our baby was sick and she needed me to get home so we could go to the doctor. I heard a *ping* on my phone, and I thought it might be her, but it wasn't. I saw lights coming toward me, so I swerved to avoid the car and hit something. I didn't know it was a person until I saw it on the news." Dell hangs his head, trying to fight tears.

"Knowing now what you do, that you hit a man, would you have stopped?"

Dell looks Essos dead in the eye, never wavering, "I would like to say that I would have stopped, that I would have been the better man and waited for the police or an ambulance, but I can't ascertain that. You see, we only had one car at the time. I can't say with confidence that I would have, though I wish with all my heart that I could."

"What do you know of the man you hit?"

"His name was Gideon Corrodino. He was a 67-year-old Navy vet. His car had broken down a few miles behind where I hit him. He was walking to get help. His wife passed away from lung cancer, and he lived alone with two Australian shepherds named Winnie and Church, named for Winston Churchill. Before retiring, he worked as a fisherman, taking tourists out to sea. He was planning to buy a boat and live out the rest of his days on the water."

The amount of detail that Dell knows about this man's life is astounding. He tells us that he and his wife found out their baby had a heart condition that night and, after he confessed to his wife, she told him he couldn't go to the police because it would tear their family apart. They would lose their insurance and their child would die. What man wouldn't succumb to that pressure?

"If you didn't confess to the police, what did you do to repent?" This line of questioning is purely for our benefit, meant to muddle the water.

"I adopted Winnie and Church and joined the Navy, because I didn't know what else to do at that age. I served for 20 years before retiring. I helped turn an empty plot of land into a memorial garden for Mr. Corrodino, with space for children to play and a dog park for them to run in."

I do my best to keep my face impassive as Dell continues to detail the good works he did to try to balance out the karmic wrong he had done.

Essos turns to face us. I catch sight of Zara out of the corner of my eye. She looks so uncomfortable. By his own telling, everything Dell did in his life was to make up for his crime. Even Cat is fidgeting in her seat.

"I put this case before you. Shall Mr. McMann be allowed to be reunited with his family or shall he serve out his term in the Deep as originally intended?"

"The Deep?" I blurt out, surprised that he would be sentenced to such a place for one mistake. It feels like it takes an eternity for Essos to face me.

"He took a life. This is why you are here—to determine if there are mitigating factors at play. Anyone can appeal where they are sent. Some situations have extenuating circumstances, some are just terrible people neglecting to admit to themselves and to others how truly heinous their actions were, regardless of the excuses they may have. As my consort, as my *queen*, you need to be able to make these calls."

Essos gives us time to think this over, but not much. I feel as though the Jeopardy theme song is playing behind me. The pressure is on to make not just a call, but the right one.

Zara shows that she would rule with an iron fist, denying Dell McMann's appeal.

"While nice that he adopted the dogs and joined the Navy, that does not change the fact that he took a life and must pay for that crime."

Cat sees that the good works he did with his life afterward

had a positive impact on the world and rules that he may see his family again.

"He took a life-changing moment and let it change his life. His punishment is that he has to carry this shame with him for eternity. For me, that is punishment enough," Cat declares.

Essos turns to me, his face impassive. After centuries of having to make decisions like this, he shows not a shred of emotion.

"I think that you have done a tremendous wrong to Mr. Corrodino, and you owe him an apology for your actions. I believe that he is in a better position to determine your destination, and we will take his decision under advisement." I try to adopt the same even tone as Essos. It takes everything in me to keep my voice from shaking.

Essos waves his hand, and another man appears. He's older, with silver hair and a strong jawline. For a moment, he's confused, then he sees Essos and Dell, and understanding seems to dawn on him.

"Gideon Corrodino?" Essos verifies.

"Yessir."

"Are you aware of why I have summoned you today?"

"No, sir," Gideon responds.

Essos gestures toward Dell, whose posture has deflated at the sight of Gideon. The guilt that he has felt from years of carrying this secret is nothing compared to being face to face with the man whose life he took.

"This is the man that hit you with his car and left you lying in a ditch for three hours while you bled out. He has been sentenced to live out his life in the Deep and never to see his family again. It was proposed that, since he took your life, you should help to determine how he lives in death. What do you have to say to him, Dell?"

Dell steps forward, his Adam's apple bobbing as he salutes

Gideon. "Sir, I imagined for my whole life what I would say to you if I ever had the chance. I never thought that I actually would. I know my words cannot express how sorry I am for what I did, but I hope my actions have shown it. Not one day went by where I didn't think about the hypocrite I was, telling my children to take responsibility for their actions while I was a coward. I am so deeply, deeply sorry."

Gideon is silent, considering the words he has just heard. His face is hard, angry. Then...

"I was mad for a good while after it happened, but my Cheryl reminded me that it brought us back together again. I was able to see the love and comfort your family gave to Winnie and Church for the rest of their lives and as they passed themselves. Same as you, I thought for a long time about what I would say to the careless bastard who killed me, but I'm not sure there's more that I can say to you that you haven't already said to yourself. I am *pissed*, stark raving mad about what you did. Some days are worse than others, but when I remember how long I was out there, I get mad again. I don't think I can accept your apology, not now, not yet. You've said your piece, and I won't stop you from being with your family again, but I don't forgive you."

The room is silent as Dell nods, accepting this, not pushing for forgiveness. Essos turns to me, waiting for me to decide what to do. It's no small thing, deciding if someone should go to their afterlife or the Deep, but it's a decision that needs to be made.

I stand and walk forward, not sure what possesses me to do so.

"You showed cowardice and carelessness, but from that, you found humility and bravery. For that, for the next one hundred years, you will wear a sixty-seven-pound backpack to represent each year of life Gideon lived before you took the rest of what he could have had. After those hundred, if Gideon still has not forgiven you, you shall bear it for another hundred years and another and another until he does forgive you. If he decides never to forgive you, then you shall bear that weight for the rest of eternity. You will do so in the Afterlife, with your family," I say firmly.

Essos watches me from his seat, not moving for a moment, before reaching for a gavel and slamming it on the table. "And so, it is decided."

Both men disappear, vanishing into what I have to assume is their afterlives. I stumble back and sit down, overwhelmed suddenly with the pressure of what just happened. I open my mouth to speak, but Essos holds up his hand.

"That was an easier case than many you will face. The true monsters usually don't try to appeal, but there are all kinds in the world. It is our responsibility to hear their plea before making a judgment. Your punishment was harsher than I would have handed out, but that is neither here nor there."

Essos dismisses us with a flick of his hand and turns to the papers in front of him.

Sybil rises to lead us from the basement, but I hesitate a moment, turning to Essos. "What would your punishment have been?"

Essos looks up at me, his eyes studying my face. "I would have let the bag come off after a certain amount of time. Dell isn't likely to ever be forgiven. But I've been wrong before. Regardless of how good his reason was, he still took something that was precious to Gideon. His soul was never destined for the Deep. He was to go to the Garden of Evil, but I find raising the stakes changes how people look at things." He dismisses me by looking down at his papers again, and I rush to catch up to everyone else.

As I think about the punishment I bestowed, each step I take feels heavier, as if the weight were on my shoulders. There is something so special, so important about this role, that I agree—not anyone can do this. But as I return to the main level, I start to feel lighter. This case was not at all like last night, where the situations seemed clear-cut, but it was almost uplifting to know that even in death, I can change people's afterlives. I want to think that I made Essos proud with what I decided.

I squint against the white marble of the upstairs as we emerge from the cavernous Underworld. Galen is where we left him.

I catch his eye as I sweep past, my dress skimming the ground as I walk, but I ignore him. There is too much going through my mind after last night and this morning. When I'm around Galen, there is a clarity that of course I should listen to him and believe him. That obviously I was once his wife, and that must mean something. But without those memories, I'm not the same woman. Without the pressure of Galen's presence, I'm able to look past the expectation to be someone I'm not. Around Essos, I feel his focus on who I am as a person now, even if he knows that I had this other life.

On the walk upstairs, Cat and I decide that the day should be spent at the beach in the sun, doing our nails and forgetting about Essos and what happened during the hearing. I don't want to talk about either of the men for the rest of the day, needing just to be with my friend.

I want to pretend we made it to Santa Monica and saw the stupid beach volleyball games. I want to pretend I don't have memories locked away about being married and in love. I want to pretend I'm still in college and have a future full of gardening and getting married and maybe having babies, and Cat becoming president.

I'm adding a shade called Petal Pink to my nails, about to say something about sea monsters, when I see that Cat is crying silently as she applies a red color to her own nails. It slowly builds into deeper sobs, her body shaking with the force of her anguish. I grab her and wrap my arms around her, holding her close as she cries.

I know how cathartic a good cry is, and I can only hope that it's having the same effect on my friend. Her cries slowly subside to a few sniffs. I pull away and brush a tear from her face, but she won't meet my eyes.

"I'm sorry. It's just...after watching what happened today with those men and how death can affect the people around them, I wonder what my parents are going through. Do they miss me? I know I miss them so much, and all I want to do is talk to them and tell them I'm okay, or check in to see how they're doing, and I don't know what I'm doing with myself. I just feel like you have so much going on with your own little love triangle, and sometimes I wonder if I should move on. But then something like today happens, and I thought you were going to die in the shower, and I can't stand the thought of leaving you and you being gone for all eternity." She peers at me out of the corner of her eye, watching how her concerns land.

It's hard to comfort your friend when you're part of the problem causing her pain.

I don't tell her that her leaving would be the worst thing for me. That's selfish, and I know it, but I don't want her to ever leave. But more importantly, I want her happy, and that is the only thing that matters.

"Whatever you decide to do, I will support. If moving on will make you happy, then you need to do it. You can't factor me into your decision. But do know that I will miss you deeply if you do decide to move on. You don't need to worry about me—today was a fluke. I'm perfectly fine now." And that's all we get to say about it, because Zara joins us on the beach.

Zara seems to have flourished, surrounded by all the pampering, and I wonder for a moment if that's her way of hiding her sadness. I don't know her history, her life story, if she had siblings or someone at home. I vaguely remember her talking about her grandpabby during her memorial toast before her glass exploded in her hand.

"What are we talking about?" she asks, dropping into a beach chair with a drink in her hand. I'm ready to cover for Cat if she doesn't want to fess up about crying or being sad, but my friend lays all her cards on the table.

"Home," she answers softly.

"I miss the rain. The weather is always so perfect here," I say, thinking of storms and the way the earth would rattle when thunder sounded directly overhead. I remember nights sitting on a porch, watching lightning flood the sky and rain pour until the sound carried me off to sleep.

"I miss TV," Zara says with a sigh, and we laugh, thinking of how we used to binge TV shows and not move from our couch. "Do you think we can get it here? I'm missing my *Real Housewives*."

"I'm sure Essos can do that. He seems to be very in the know with pop-culture references. I think the lack of TVs is more of an oversight than anything else," I muse.

I add it to my list of things to ask Essos when I see him later. While I know I won't be able to get any more out of him about our possible past, I do have other questions.

"Speaking of Essos, you seem to be awfully close with his brother and not him. Which is fine by me. Galen seems quite taken with you as well." Zara glances sideways at me.

I look at my nails and set to trying to fix them, not sure how to answer her question. "Galen was telling me more about them as brothers. Nothing more to it," I lie, and it comes so easy.

Cat glances between the two of us as we enter this shaky ground.

"Whatever's between them, all I know is that I heard Essos say to Sybil that he'll finally take back what his brother stole from him, and he seems awfully proud of it." Zara sighs.

"How did you hear that?" I ask, concerned. I wonder what Essos could have meant by that statement.

"Try being early for breakfast one day and you might learn a thing or two. At the ball the other night, Galen mentioned that his problem with Essos goes back to some tremendous wrong. He also said that because they're family, he wasn't allowed to do anything about it and has had to sit on his hands. Galen is at least interesting to talk to while you're fainting around Essos, begging for attention. Between the sea monster and the nosebleeds, Galen is very worried for you. It's simply not fair that you're getting the attention from both of them. If you want Galen, then let that be that."

I try to hold on to more than one thought as they fly through my brain. Is that why Galen has never done anything about us being separated? It's hard to tell if Zara seriously thinks that I'm leading both men on. She has no clue how important this information is. "I'll try and keep almost dying to a minimum until the ball, but I make no promises." I roll my eyes and add a topcoat to my nails. Her words about going off with Galen strike a chord. I'm risking going to my afterlife prematurely if I do that. There is something necessary about the ball, and I need to be patient and find out what it is.

"Please do. I'm trying to become Essos's queen," Zara says with a hair flip.

The thought of Zara at Essos's side leaves a sour taste in my mouth. I clench my teeth and look away from her to avoid saying something ugly.

"Shit!" Zara exclaims and I turn to find her dropping her drink.

"What?" Cat and I both ask.

Zara is still sputtering, spitting out her drink on the sand.

"It's gin. I know I watched them pour vodka," she says with disgust. Zara stands and marches inside to get a new drink. We laugh as she leaves us, calling out our own drink orders.

"She's hellbent on this," Cat says, watching her walk away. "I think she might be falling in love with him. After Tiffany left, she came to talk to me in my room. I think she's lonely."

I look up, trying to see Zara in another light—not like she's my competition for Essos's heart, but like I should have all along. She's another woman thrown into a scary, unfamiliar situation and given an impossible choice—try to become queen of this realm or move on to the unknown.

"May the best woman win," I say lifting my water in Zara's direction.

"I think you intimidated her today with your crushing win," Cat comments.

I raise an eyebrow at her. "It was hardly a win, if you think about it. Both those men are dead, and one caused the death of the other. It's only fair that there's some sort of punishment."

"Yeah, but you came at it like you had all the answers. Zara felt intimidated. She thought she knew what Essos was looking for, and that was to come down hard on the bad guy." Cat pauses. "I would really rather not talk about this." She seems desperate for a change in subject.

"You and Finn looked cozy," I say, having wanted to chat with her about it anyway.

"Finn kept me company while you were gone. It was nice having someone else to talk to."

Zara returns then with a small tray of drinks—a martini for her and margaritas for us. "Finn is a hot toddy on a cold day," she says as she sits down.

I can't help but nod in agreement, but her comment about Galen is still nagging at me.

"What would make you say that about me and Galen?" If Zara's noticed, there is no way that Essos hasn't, and yet he hasn't interfered. Questions swirl in my brain, and I'm almost disappointed to come to that realization. Is it because he knows I was once Galen's wife, and as much as having me in the Calling is complicated, maybe he doesn't want to stop that reunion? But then, there's how drawn I am to Essos—that chemistry isn't make-believe; it's very real. I down my drink in one gulp.

"Gosh, what could give me that impression? Every dance we have, he's always there, always watching you. It's like that creepy song from the 80s that everyone pretends is super romantic but actually normalizes stalking. But you seem to seek him out too, which...he's pretty and all, but he's like cubic zirconia, lacking any real substance."

"Drop the mic," Cat mutters into her own drink.

"Wow, okay." I pause, not sure how to move this away from the very awkward conversation it's become. "I'm sorry if I've been sort of a bitch since coming here," I say to Zara, trying to extend an olive branch. Regardless of how I feel about her, I know this has been a hard process, and we're stuck in it together.

"You've always been sort of a bitch." Zara huffs, pulling up her sunglasses. I want to shove them down her throat, but she continues. "To be fair, so have I. I'm not going to give up, though, just because you're in this weird relationship with two brothers. If you're into Galen, it's not fair to Essos or to the rest of us who want to be with him that you stay."

It's the closest I think she'll come to an apology. She's not wrong, though, the way I'm torn between the two brothers. It's exhausting, the emotional tug of war I feel when I'm around both of them. I feel an obligation to Galen based on what he's told me, what I've seen. But those memories sometimes don't feel real— it's like watching a movie; they happened to some other woman, not me. With Essos... Gods, with Essos, sometimes I look at him and I think my heart stops with longing. He's tied, bound to rules established by the Council, and I agreed to be here for him, though I decided that before I knew about Galen. Each thought sends me teetering like a seesaw on the end of the world.

We chat about the escorts and how excited we are to be

getting closer to the end. As Zara and Cat chatter, I zone out, thinking about Essos. I wonder what case he's showing the other group of girls and how they measure up.

I glance up at the house and see Galen lurking inside.

I try to recall the memories he's shown me, but they seem to lose their clarity when he's not around. Is this a part of the memory block?

I open my mouth to comment on him watching when Sybil walks down to the beach to let us know that there will be no ball that night. Some of the girls in the other group took their case harder than anticipated.

"Sybil," I call after them as they start to walk away. "Stay with us a little longer." Sybil, Cat, and Zara all seem surprised at my request. "That is, if you're not too busy."

Sybil smiles and walks back to us, then settles in their own lounge chair. "Are you all handling today well?"

I wave them off. "No talk of business; we're drinking. Can you conjure your own drink, or does someone need to get you one?" I ask.

They answer me by conjuring a drink, and I smile.

"Do you sit with Essos often?" Cat asks, and I frown at her immediate dismissal of my not wanting to talk business.

But Sybil seems happy to answer. "Mostly just in an administrative capacity. He has a lot of paperwork that comes with running the Afterlife, and I help streamline the process."

"Does that mean as queen, I'll have a lot of paperwork to do?" Zara asks, sounding disappointed.

Cat snorts into her drink.

"It's been a good many years since he had his consort. You will have some paperwork, I'm sure. It's not all balls and gowns. Being queen means having to entertain the citizens of Solarem. As a new arrival, the queen will be of particular interest." Sybil's answer seems to deepen Zara's disappointment.

"Have you ever wanted to do the Calling?" I can't help but ask, thinking about Galen's earlier warning.

"I don't think my girlfriend would like that very much. Essos also isn't my type—I prefer redheads," they tease, and we all laugh, though mine rings hollow to my own ears. If Sybil has a girlfriend, then why would they want to keep a queen away from the Underworld? Galen outright told me that they are comfortable having power and possibly want more of it.

"I'm sorry, but how do you manage to have a relationship in the middle of all of this?" Cat asks.

"It helps that she also works really hard. The Callings are so few and far between that it doesn't impact our relationship much," Sybil responds.

We play twenty questions with Sybil, teasing more and more information out about them and how long they've been working with Essos. It's hard for me to play along, and I wind up throwing in basic questions. Cat looks at me like I have seven heads when I ask Sybil what their favorite color is. It barely registers. My gut tells me that Sybil is exactly who they seem—kind, hardworking, and caring. Nothing about them screams that they're the mastermind behind a nefarious plot.

"Do you have your own magic, beyond the parlor tricks you've shown us?" I ask abruptly, cutting off some story about Dave nesting in Essos's suits.

"Rude," Cat mutters to me under her breath, but Sybil gives me a patient smile.

"Not much. I'm afraid I'm a failed seer. My visions were always wrong in some tragic way. A woman would come to me asking what the gender of her baby would be, and I would always be wrong. Or a man would ask if his husband was faithful. Trivial things, but after, well, I offended someone I shouldn't have with a false prediction regarding the color of the season, Essos offered me a job. He needed someone to help him. Essos said that everyone in his realm is already dead, so my predictions wouldn't matter."

"Hmm," I murmur, biting on my freshly painted thumbnail as I stare into the depths of the ocean.

To break the awkward silence, Cat stands and offers me her hand. "I think you can use some more practice. Finn said he's had at least two broken toes since this started." She laughs.

I scowl but jump up, bowing to her the way the men do. "I resemble that remark, and I don't like it," I say, prompting her to laugh.

Zara stands, offering her hand to Sybil, who seems confused but delighted by the inclusion. The four of us take turns dancing the rest of the day away in the surf. It gets my mind off of wondering if Galen has deliberately misled me about Sybil and Essos, and if there is anything more he could be keeping from me.

23

It takes me one week to follow Zara's advice and finally arrive early to breakfast. It's not for a lack of trying, because I really do try, it's just that every time my alarm goes off, Dave snuggles closer and looks so cute sleeping that I can't bear to wake him.

Essos had a busy week taking ten girls on one-on-one dates. Cat told me that they did her date to keep up the charade, and they ended up playing a distracted game of chess in Essos's office while he did some paperwork and she read between turns.

I almost think it's a shame, because she would make a great Queen of the Underworld.

When I come down, I find Essos sitting at the table with Spot and Shadow at his feet. He's looking over some documents and dropping pieces of bacon and sausage into their mouths.

"You really shouldn't feed them from the table," I say as I walk into the room, Dave trailing behind me.

I must have startled him, because he immediately stands, his chair almost tipping over. "I've been told that, but sometimes I just want to do what makes them happy, and bacon makes them happy. Is that so bad?" His cheeks are red, and for a second he seems to have a hard time meeting my eyes. An emotion flickers across his face in a blink, before his usual cool demeanor slips into place. He takes a moment, eyes surveying me for any telltale trauma. This morning, I'm in a cashmere beige sweater and snug jeans that fit perfectly but are never too tight. They are magic jeans and I love them.

I smile and scratch Dave behind his ears. "Do you think I could have a word with you alone?" I ask.

He gestures at the empty room.

"Yes, but anyone can come down, and I need to ask a favor of you."

His expression turns serious, and he wipes his hand on a napkin while nodding. "Let's go to the garden and talk there." He grabs his cup of coffee and hands me one too, waiting while I prepare it to my liking before we exit. We pass Galen as we head outside. The smile on his face is forced, but he winks, like he thinks this is all part of the charade. Sybil is coming down the hall from Essos's office but stills when they see us walking. Essos gives them a nod, and they return a knowing smile.

The walk to the gardens is long and silent. The flowers seem to brighten as we pass each hedge, waking in the presence of Essos's magic. Stepping outside into the morning chill makes me shiver. Essos reaches for me as if to rub my bare arms but thinks better of it, rolling his wrist instead and triggering that tidal wave of warmth. I have to admire his restraint, though I wish he wasn't always such a saint.

"You're making this a habit," I say.

"Only when you're cold." We get to a dead end and sit with the dahlias this time. I run my fingers over the gentle petals, the flowers not yet ready to bloom. Warmth spreads through me with each bud I touch. I blink as they unfurl, and when I glance at Essos's face, he's beaming. Doubt nags at me that it was actually he who did that. "What was it that you wanted to speak to me about?" he asks and takes a sip from his coffee.

"Cat is my best friend," I start.

"Of this I am aware."

I scowl. "Cat is my best friend, and she is devastated. She misses her family and wants to be with them again but understands why she can't. Is there any way that maybe she could look in on them? Just to see how they're doing? I know the hearing last week reminded her of all she left behind." I realize I'm rambling but can't stop myself. "Or if that's not possible, maybe, like, a photo of them for her room?"

Unbidden, the thought of what Galen lost pokes at me, along with the reminder that Essos may have had something to do with that. I've taken to avoiding Galen after what happened in the shower. I would really love to not feel like that again, and if that means being in the dark for just a little longer, I will.

"I see." Essos mulls over my words. "There is something I can do for Catalina." He takes a measured sip from his coffee. "I'll make sure that Sybil makes time for it in my schedule. You're a good friend, Daphne." He brushes a strand of hair out of my face, and I can't reconcile the version of Essos before me and the one that would go as far as stealing his brother's wife.

But it's already done, and Essos lowers his hand and stands abruptly. "I'll take care of it." He turns to go, leaving me sitting on the cold bench.

"Wait! There's one more thing." A rueful smile is on his face when he looks at me again. "Some of the girls wondered if TV might be a thing that we can have access to. Pop culture is sort of a big deal for my generation, and I think the girls might like it if we could have a movie night instead of a dance night."

I don't get a response to this question. Instead, he just nods and walks back toward the house. His lack of response makes me deflate.

Although he warmed me up with his magic, I feel a cold regret inside at his absence. Instead of going inside right away, I walk around the garden, touching flowers as I go. It seems as if in the week since I was last here, more flowers have appeared than the space knows what to do with. The gardens have exploded since my first visit.

I linger, picking a few flowers here and there to make bouquets for my and Cat's rooms. When I turn a corner, I'm startled to find Finn sitting alone among the irises.

"Fancy meeting you here," he snarks, eyeing my flowers. "Thieving around the garden?"

"I guess that depends on your definition of thieving. I was trying to make something nice for Cat."

"She's a grand girl, your Cat."

I nod and sit beside him.

"Is Galen still harassing you?" Finn prods gently. I wonder if Finn has made the connection between Galen and the onset of the headaches. I haven't told him about the headaches and the nosebleeds, not because I'm actively keeping it from him, but when we're dancing, I'm focused on trying to improve. It helps to keep my mind on the dance steps rather than who Essos is with. There's no way Finn doesn't know about the incident in the shower and any of the other times I've had a nosebleed. I may have known Essos for only a short time, but I know he would have told Finn—his close friend and my escort—to keep an eye out for any signs of trouble.

"He's actually kept his distance since Essos had us join him in the office for Take Your Concubines to Work Day. I've also been avoiding him a little."

"That's probably for the best."

I focus on rearranging the flowers to avoid Finn's gaze. I'm afraid that if I look at him, he'll know I'm keeping something from him.

"So, I know about the problem between Essos and Galen, but I don't understand the problem that *you* have with Galen." I'm hoping to get Finn to open up to me.

He chuckles and stands up, then looks down at me. "It's really not that hard to understand. I think you're just being daft, Daphne."

"Well, that's rude. It's also not an answer. I know that it has to do with a woman. I know that Galen *was* married, and that Essos had a woman in his life as well." I stand up too, offended. He's still taller than me, but the difference is less dramatic now at least.

Finn folds in half and pulls on his hair with an aggravated groan. "What *you're* doing is rude. You're hearing hoofbeats and thinking zebras. You need to be thinking horses." Once upright, Finn shoves his hands into his jeans.

"I am thinking horses! What am I supposed to think, with these dreams and flashes!" I shout back. I probably could have gotten away with the admission, but like any guilty person that just screamed something they didn't want someone else to know, I clap my hands over my mouth, eyes wide.

Finn prowls toward me with preternatural grace, and for the first time I consider he's not only a man but likely a god too. "Flashes?" he hisses, crowding my space.

I push Finn back, and he lets me. "Yeah, I mean, I had that whole meltdown with the nosebleed."

"Essos may have mentioned it. Go on."

"Right, and I've just been having these weird...flashes that I think, maybe, are memories." I test my theory on him, but Finn has a perfect poker face, because he lets nothing show.

"I am going to be as clear as I can within the boundaries of the Calling. Stop talking to Galen. Nothing good will come from you pushing this issue. You need to keep your eyes on the prize, which is the crown. Be the crown, Daphne. Get to the ball, and just ignore that fuckface. Not everything is what it looks like."

"You do realize that you're being just as cagey as Essos, and that makes it really hard to listen to you." I stand my ground. "If you would just *tell* me what's going on, maybe I would have a clue and be able to navigate it appropriately. Instead, you all continue to treat me like a child. It's bullshit."

Finn doesn't seem to like what he's hearing, because he sticks out his lower lip in a pout while pulling petals off a flower.

"Just accept that you can't always get what you want. Accept that you need to let this run its course. Usually, I admire your stubborn streak and willingness to fight for those you love and what you believe in, but right now? In this circumstance? It's making it *very* hard for me to like you. I can't help you if you don't talk to me." His words aim to hurt, but I don't let them.

"The feeling is mutual. But Finn, I can't talk to you about this. You've made it abundantly clear that regardless of what I tell you, you're not in a position to help."

We stare each other down for another moment before Finn throws his flower petals at me. I'm too far away from him for them to hit me, so they just flutter to the ground.

"My gods, woman, you are so *infuriating* sometimes."

"You act like I'm trying to spite you!" I say, walking toward him and the flowers he brutalized. I touch them gently, frowning at the damage he's done. Finn picks up the petals and presses them into my hands. Absently, I shove them into my pocket.

"I know you're not," he says sadly. "Can we stop fighting? It feels wrong."

I turn to face Finn. "I know it does, but I need you to respect that if you can't give me the answers I need, or even a straight answer in general, then I'm going to have to work with the information I do have. I am my own person, capable of making my own decisions."

Finn opens his mouth to speak, but he can only cough. This fit continues for a minute, and I approach him, my stomach clenching in concern. He bends over, putting his hands on his knees, and I press my hand to his back.

He clears his throat and straightens. "I'm your friend always, so you can count on me. But like any good friend, when I'm proven right that Galen is an untrustworthy swine, I'm going to say I told you so."

"Deal, but also, you're entitled to have your own conflicts with Galen that are separate from mine. Cat and Zara were also super close, despite Zara and I never getting along. Never did I expect Cat to alienate Zara because of me. I'm not going to let whatever conflict is between you and Galen color my impression of him. If you can ever give me context, maybe that will change." I lead the way into the house. "What are you even doing outside so early?" I ask, eyeing Finn suspiciously.

"I was in the neighborhood and wanted to talk to Essos about getting you some remedial dance classes."

I hit him, unamused.

Finn laughs, rubbing his arm. "Worth it. No, I was supposed to deliver a message, but I don't think I'm going to." He smirks.

"What are you? A messenger of some kind?"

"It's one of my many hats, yes, and make no mistake, there will be blood over disobeying, but it will be worth it." Finn's voice is soft, and he drags his knuckles over my cheek before tucking my hair behind my ear. "Stop underestimating yourself."

Finn gestures toward my pocket before he turns to leave.

"Where are you going?" I ask, confused. He came all the way here for a fight?

"I do have other work besides being your therapist." Finn walks away and is soon out of sight.

When I arrive in the dining room, Essos and Cat are missing and Sybil is seated with us instead of standing vigil at the back of the room. I don't ask where they are, hoping that he's found some way to ease her pain.

Essos returns alone shortly thereafter and pulls me to the side. I can feel Galen's gaze on me as we walk into the hall.

He bends his head close to my ear, whispering. "Catalina needs you in her room. She will explain. Take all the time she needs, and if *you* need anything, please ask."

I nod and move past him toward the stairs, my breakfast forgotten. Before climbing the stairs, I stop and turn toward him.

"Thank you," I whisper, before running upstairs to tend to my friend.

CAT IS SITTING on her bed holding Honey Bear while in her pajamas. Shadow has climbed into bed with her and is playing the part of little spoon. Her tail is wagging, head twisted in Cat's lap to look at the door. Dave follows me in and settles himself beside her.

"So, Essos pulled me aside this morning and took me to his office. He asked if I wanted to check in on my family." She sniffles and starts to cry, prompting both dogs to try to snuggle in closer to her.

I climb into bed and under the covers, waiting until she's ready to continue. I pass the tissue box to her and place a hand on her back, my full attention on her needs.

"They all seem pretty okay. Mom was seeing a therapist, talking about how much she missed me, and how she was trying to figure out how to start a scholarship in my name. My brother was in the batting cages hitting balls as hard as he could, and my dad was at work looking sad, like he was just going through the m-motions." Cat's voice breaks.

"I thought it would make me feel better to see them, but it

may have made it worse. How is my dad going to keep going? He looks like he can hardly keep his head above water. My mom is throwing all her energy into different events that she can host in my honor to build the scholarship that my dad has already endowed and ignoring him and my brother. My brother is pissed and is just hitting baseballs to try to get out his frustration, because that's the only way he knows how or can, with my parents so involved in other things.

"How do I do this?" she asks. "It's not as if it's going to get any easier when I move on. I'm still going to miss them. I'm still going to want to see them and what they're doing. And sure, it would be easier to keep tabs on them if I moved on, I think—I assume—but then that's all I would be doing. I would be obsessing, like my mom, and I just miss my mommy."

She starts to cry again, and I imagine this is what it's like to have a loving bond with a parent. To miss them so fiercely that it inhibits your own will to go on. I reason with myself that there really isn't a "going on" for Cat or me anymore; there will just be the Afterlife and what comes from that.

Before I can get into it, there's a knock at the door, and the dogs lift their heads. Cat calls out, allowing them access, and Essos walks in.

"I heard from a talking wallflower that you might miss your shows as well, so I wondered if this might help." With a wave of his hand, the mirror above her dresser turns into a TV. Essos tosses a remote in her direction. "I hope this brings you some comfort," he says, backing away. For the man in charge of the Underworld, he seems so uncomfortable with grief. I want to get up and hug him, thank him for not only listening to me, but really hearing me about how to help Cat.

Before the door can snick closed, Spot jumps on the bed, and Cat lets out a hiccupping giggle-sob. I hear Essos call from the other side of the door, "Traitors!" before his footfalls can be heard retreating down the hall.

"I think that your family will heal, the same way anyone does. I think that you are a shining light, and you were especially one for your family, and they need to learn to live without that light. That is going to be so, *so* hard, but they will get there—you have to have faith in that." I watch Cat listening to what I have to say as she fiddles with the remote.

Cat looks skeptical, as if she wants to believe me but isn't sure. I take the remote and start scrolling to see what our options are. Our brains need a serious break, so we decide on an old favorite. We spend the rest of the day curled up together watching *Grey's Anatomy* reruns as if this were a regular Saturday when we were hungover and tired and avoiding responsibilities like homework and tests.

Sybil pokes her head in with some food for us—a nice big bowl of popcorn and other snacks. They duck out of the room as silently as they came in, and I'm not even sure if Cat noticed. Cat cries intermittently, her tears leaving her eyes red-rimmed and glassy. We watch until our brains are fried, and once Cat falls asleep, I sneak back to my own room to get ready for bed.

It's not until I reach into my pocket that I remember the petals Finn gave me earlier in the day. Only, they're not just petals anymore, but a fully formed lush rose, all in one piece.

24

The next day, the rose that underwent its reverse transformation is crushed inside my bra. I'm grateful that the short stem is thornless so I can keep it close to me as a reminder. Part of me is afraid that it wasn't real, that it's somehow a trick, but I don't think that Finn would do that to me. I think it might have been his way of confirming what I've been asking, at least in some part. Little things start to click—the flowers wilting around Zara, her glass exploding, and I'm not sure, but maybe even her drink changing from a vodka martini to gin. Both are plant-based, after all.

I slept with the flower under my pillow and was surprised when it maintained its full shape in the morning. It's made me more desperate for answers.

Galen and I are alone in the dining room for the first time since he told me we used to be married. Since he told me Essos is trying to steal his wife. I'm done with my breakfast, so I rest my chin in my hand as I watch him eat cereal.

"Would you stop that?" He glances at me. "It's distracting."

"Distracting you from what? Eating?"

"Now that you mention it, yes." He shoves another spoonful into his mouth.

"I want another memory." I move to a chair closer to his.

His golden-brown eyes watch me closely as I continue to play musical chairs. "That's going to have to be a hard no. The last time we did it, you got nosebleeds. I'm not inclined to put you through that again."

I move another chair closer. "I don't think I'm going to give you a choice about this. They're my memories, and I want more. Especially if you want me to stay silent about them."

A dark look passes his eyes. "Fine, but I don't appreciate being blackmailed." He reaches out and grabs my wrist a little harder than necessary. Before I can really register the pain...the vision begins.

I'M PINNED AGAINST A WALL, *my bare breasts pressed against the window, moaning as Galen enters me.*

"Do you get off on the idea of them watching us together? I want you to scream my name, as you come around my cock. I want them to know how you like getting fucked." His hand fists in my hair, and he pulls back my head and bites hard on my neck.

"Oh, gods yes, I do, Galen." My voice doesn't sound right. It's guttural, but maybe that's just from the angle of my throat. As Galen thrusts into me from behind, it feels like it's happening to someone else.

THERE IS something different about this memory, and I don't like it. I can feel the pleasure in my body as it happens, but it's like I'm not actually there. Is that because I pushed him to give me the memory?

The scene cuts off suddenly, and I look at Galen, my heart pounding in my chest. He's released my wrist and is turning to his brother, who has just entered the room, with a smile. I pull back my hand and rest both in my lap. I keep my teeth clenched, trying to stop myself from being sick all over the table. For once, I'm grateful that Essos is more focused on glaring at Galen than he is on me. Essos's gaze does flick to me, and a slight narrowing is the only indication that he picked up on something even if he's not sure what it is.

"I do hope I'm not interrupting," Essos says coldly, glaring at his brother. I'm rubbing my wrist, looking from Galen to Essos.

"Not at all, brother. Daphne was simply wondering if she still had a pulse, and I offered to check for her," Galen answers. They are staring each other down, not willing to break eye contact.

"And does she?" Essos asks.

"She does, but I imagine you already knew that, being King of the Underworld and all." Galen smiles before shoving another spoonful of cereal into his mouth.

"You're correct in stating that, brother. I am the King of the Underworld, and I trust you won't forget it."

I sit awkwardly between them, hoping for something to break the tension. Thankfully, Cat walks in with a big yawn, followed by Zara.

Essos waits as the remaining women file into the room. Only nine of us are at the table, which is surprising—we were ten yesterday.

Once everyone is seated, Essos stands again. "There was an incident last night, and Madison was asked to leave," he says shortly. "It has been too long since we had a ball. I'm going to ask everyone to dress appropriately this evening. We have almost one month until the final ball, and I need you to be as prepared as possible for that evening."

We never get to ask what happened to Madison, because breakfast is interrupted.

"Oh, that's all right, brother, you don't have to have a ball in my honor," a smooth, accented female voice says from the doorway.

Essos fights a losing battle to hide his frustration. Galen, however, jumps up in glee.

"Sister!" he exclaims.

The woman leaning in the doorway is painfully chic in a green long-sleeve form-fitting dress that ends just below her knees. She's a willowy blonde who looks like she walked right off a magazine page with long, slender legs and a sharp, cunning face. Galen engulfs her in a hug then turns to Essos. Her reaction to Galen is frosty at best; she doesn't seem thrilled to see him here at all.

"Isn't it just lovely to see Helene?" Galen gloats as this new distraction joins the fray. Essos approaches her and leans down to kiss the cheek that she offers him.

"Of course, it is lovely to see our sister; I'm just unsure of what brings her here *now*." Essos's words are stiff as Helene walks into the room and surveys the nine of us. Her blue eyes scan us, as if she can see into our very essence. As she walks around the room, she pushes an imaginary stray hair back into place.

"I came to get a sneak peek at my future sister-in-law, whomever she may be. You know how terribly exciting this all is, and when I heard that Galen was already here looking to pick up a new wife for himself, I had to make sure that my brothers choose only the best of the best."

Helene approaches Olivia, who's always seemed like a quiet mousy girl, though very smart. She grabs Olivia's face and looks deep into her eyes. Her long nails dig into Olivia's cheeks, and Olivia looks absolutely petrified. Everyone in the room freezes.

"I'm sorry, dear, you're dismissed. Essos, send this one on to the Afterlife." She waves her hand, dismissing the girl, and Olivia vanishes.

"You can't do that," Essos protests, but it's half-hearted. I wonder if that's because he already knew that he didn't see Olivia in his future.

Helene continues around the room, eliminating women until only five of us remain—Zara, Cat, Ginny, Abigail, and myself.

"If you thought they were front runners, you would have stopped me," she points out with a simple lift of her shoulder. She surveys the rest of us, wiping her hands as if they were dirty. Essos has taken his seat, possibly knowing it's better to let her run amuck than to fight her. Galen looks positively gleeful over having another sibling around to run roughshod over Essos.

"Now, about this ball you are having tonight in my honor." Essos sighs at Helene's assumption. "You should invite Xavier. He'll be rather cross if you don't."

"Dear sister, were it in your honor, I would have invited Xavier, but given that the ball you three are supposed to attend is still weeks away, I would rather avoid the drama that you bring and let that be my problem then. Besides, he's your twin, you should speak with him yourself."

She rolls her eyes at him and summons a plate of food for herself. "We're not speaking for now." She picks at the crepe she conjured. "He's off gallivanting around the mortal realm with his son, and I, for one, am on Posey's side on this one."

Galen sits beside her, trying to take a piece of her crepe, but before he can get the food to his mouth, she slaps it out of his hand. "Naughty, naughty, baby brother." She wags a finger in his face. "So, aside from a ball tonight, what else have you got planned? I mean, we're in the final countdown. I like these five, and I think I would quite like that one." She points to Zara. "She has a lovely style."

Zara preens. The thought that someone other than herself can see her as queen must fill her with delight.

"Then again, this one has a heart of darkness that I think

would suit you well, brother." Helene's eyes flare on me, delight dancing in them.

I fight the urge to look at Galen but fail, before glancing back at Helene.

"Ohhh," she says, clapping her hands. "I have the best idea! I want to have a one on one with each girl to get to know her at her core. See who might be in your best interests. After all, who knows you best, big brother?" Her voice is saccharine sweet.

"Certainly not you," Essos says harshly, but seeing her expression reflect hurt, his face softens. "But if it will keep you out of my hair, then perhaps you can have the next two days to conduct your one on ones. I can use the time to get some work done."

"How about you give me five days, so I can have a day with each girl! Then we can have a practice ball, and *then* you'll be one month away from the Calling Ball—and maybe you'll have a fewer girls to worry about. Ah! Such a terrific plan. Thanks, brother!" She jumps out of her seat and gives him a kiss on the cheek.

Helene walks around the room tapping everyone on the head in a game of Duck, Duck, Goose. She passes around three times, before tapping Zara on the head.

"Peacock!" she exclaims. "Get dressed for a wonderful day, and we will get to know one another better." Helene exits the room, leaving Essos shaking his head as she goes. Zara jumps up, excusing herself to get ready for her day with Helene. The rest of us are stunned by what just happened.

"Is she always like that?" I ask, feeling naked after how quickly she narrowed in on me. The way that she tried to peer into my soul and pointed out that I had a heart of darkness felt like an attack on who I was. Then again, if she does know who I am, then maybe she knows my heart better than I do.

What does having a heart of darkness even mean?

I've always considered myself charitable and kind, but maybe I'm wrong? Maybe I'm not who I think I am. Thinking about how

Zara has been able to get under my skin, igniting my vindictive streak, maybe she's right.

"Unfortunately, yes," Essos says, turning to Sybil. They approach him, and he whispers in their ear briefly before they exit the room. "As you all heard, we will have a ball at the end of the week, after Helene has concluded her one on ones. I find it best to let her do things her way and do damage control after." Everyone starts to work their way out of the room, until it's only Essos and me.

"She was wrong," he says, looking up at me. "You don't have a heart of darkness. I'm sorry that she said that to you."

I stand up. "I appreciate the apology, but I'm pretty certain that she's right." I exit the room to await my turn with Helene. Perhaps I'll try the library again and revisit *The Princess and Her Guard.*

HELENE IS the master of building suspense. The girls that Helene took upon herself to dismiss were not actually sent to their after-lives, but rather to their rooms, allowing Essos to give them a chance to stay or go if they wanted. Essos also arranged for a final luncheon so everyone can say their goodbyes.

Helene makes a show of huffing about it but is scarce when they have the lunch. Knowing that the numbers are dwindling, I elect not to attend the lunch so Cat can devote her attention to her sorority sisters. Instead, I poke around the library, only to be disappointed when I try to remove certain books. Ones that look like they could have valuable information, such as the royal lineage of the gods of Solarem, won't budge from the shelf no matter what I do.

Helene makes me wait until the last day to meet, and I have nothing to go on from Cat, since Helene dismissed her from their time together, citing that she knew Cat wasn't actually a contender. Helene told Cat that she liked her well enough but was going to use the day to visit her husband and "bounce on him like a pogo stick." Cat didn't say how Helene knew, just that she did. Zara also wasn't able to share any details of her day with Helene —any time she tried, she had a coughing fit, spewing feathers. She stopped trying after it happened twice.

In a way, I'm grateful for Helene's arrival—it's given me a chance to put off what happened with Galen the morning she arrived. To push the memory further from my mind, I've been spending my free days reading *The Princess and Her Guard* and hiding in the garden, still toting that rose around. I'm torn while reading it, because I simultaneously want to binge read it as quickly as I can, but I also want to savor every page, hoping for some sort of insight into Solarem since it's set there. There isn't anything I can really glean, so while I try to pretend it's for scholarly pursuits, I'm reading it for the smut.

I wake on the last morning to a note that I am to meet Helene on the beach, ready to work up a sweat. I planned to arrive before her so I would have an idea of what to expect, but she's down there already in high-waisted leggings and a sports bra, her blond hair pulled into a high ponytail.

"Oh good! You're an early bird. And here I had been led to believe that you were chronically late to everything."

I stop in my tracks, wondering if I should be offended. "Good morning to you too, Helene."

She smiles at me. Our interactions at mealtimes have been limited because her focus all week was on mediating between her brothers while simultaneously getting under their skin. If they were irritated with her, it meant they weren't making jabs at each other.

"Please don't get me wrong. I'm excited to meet with you. You seem fascinating— do you want to tell me about yourself first, or shall I tell you what I have learned about you and you can fill in what I don't know?" She starts walking away, leading me toward the end of the beach where there are giant tires set out like in the CrossFit commercials Cat and I used to laugh at.

I'm suddenly wishing I stayed in bed.

"We aren't doing anything with those, are we?" I ask, incredulous at the thought of having to lift a tire and push it across the sand.

"Oh, we are. We're going to move these tires across the beach, go for a short run, then end with some light yoga." She dusts her hands on her pants and starts to lift her tire.

The commercials on TV always made it look so easy, the people who lifted them sprinting across the room. Helene is that type of person, but I am not.

I push out a deep breath of air, then try to pick mine up. She certainly made it look easy, but I'm not having the same luck.

"So, what will it be, shall I tell you what I know, or do you want to tell me?" When I can do nothing but gasp for air, she continues to talk. "Got it. So, I know that you're an orphan, your best friend is Catalina, and my brother is in love with you." By that point, I've managed to get my wheel upright and I freeze, looking at her, not sure which brother she's referring to. I'm framed by the wheel, a matching O on my lips.

"Have I got that right?" she says, leaning on her tire, waiting for me to catch up.

"Well, I can't speak for your brother, but I can confirm that yeah, I am an orphan and Cat is my best friend." I push the tire over, and it lands with a thud in the sand. Helene looks like she's hardly broken a sweat, and I can't even form a full sentence. Her tire is at least two full flips ahead of mine.

"That's really great that you got to go on this journey with your friend, I mean, it really blows that you both had to die, but still, very cool. Zara mentioned that her best friend Tiffany got to return to the world of the living. Which is cooler still—it appears that Essos has something resembling a heart in that ice block in his chest. I also heard that Dave has taken a liking to you." I start to lift the tire a second time, digging my feet into the sand as it slips away from me. If I didn't already know I was dead, I would think I was going to die again.

"So, I just want to make sure, but, like, are you planning on talking at all, or am I just going to have a conversation with myself?" Helene asks.

"Maybe...if...you hadn't decided...to make me lift a stupid tire a thousand times...I would be able...to talk to you...but you wanted...to do...*this*...instead." I huff, shoving my tire to the ground.

"There's that dark heart I was looking for!" She smiles and hops up to sit on her tire, then proceeds to watch me fall apart into a sweaty mess.

"Hating this...doesn't mean I have...a dark heart...and for what it's worth...this *sucks*." I spit the words out, trying to get as much strength as I can to push the tire over.

"No pain no gain, am I right?" She takes a sip from a water bottle she conjured. I stop, after having bent over to lift the tire again. I need to keep holding on to the tire, otherwise, I'm going to hit her. I stand up, trying to keep calm.

"That cliché is used by people who clearly have never had to work hard for anything in their lives." I lean down to grab the tire again and drive my feet harder into the sand so I can lift the damn thing. I manage to get it up and over in one move this time. When I look at Helene, she looks as if I hit her.

"Wow, tell me how you really feel." Her posh accent has thickened. I don't much care if I hit a nerve. I've seen all week how she pushes her own way on other people, making them feel shitty when they push back.

"Pretty sure I just did," I confirm.

I bend over again to keep going. We're silent for a time after that, just a lot of grunting from me as I try my hardest to get the tire moving. I am exhausted by the thirty minutes I have spent with her. I don't know how I can keep up the mental gymnastics required for dealing with this family at this level of exhaustion. Maybe that's the point—wear me down physically and get into my head. If I'm too focused on breathing, I can't focus on the questions she's asking.

"Stop," she says, and I flip the tire one last time then look at her. My muscles feel bruised and achy, so I'm glad to stop, but I don't want her to see that. "Look, I'm going to be frank with you, because you seem like the type of person who values honesty. My brother has had his heart shattered, and I would rather not see that happen again. I love him and won't let anyone hurt him. So, if you're not interested in Essos, get the fuck out."

I flinch at her words. "I am," I state simply. It's not a lie, but it's not the full truth, so it tastes sour in my mouth. The truth is, I'm confused. I feel drawn to Essos in a way that I can't explain, but the memories that Galen has shown me indicate the possibility of a different life.

She lets a long breath out of her nose, watching me carefully.

"Fine. I'm going to see what you're made of. Let's run." She takes off at a sprint down the beach and I curse, starting after her. A short run for Helene is just over six miles—three miles down and back. I trail behind her, of course, the wind pushing my hair back, my lungs pushed to the brink of exploding. I pump my legs and push into the sand as hard as I can, trying to keep up, but her strides are more gazelle than human.

When Helene has decided we've run far enough, she stops. I stumble to a halt, looking at her, furious that she still hasn't broken a sweat. I lean down with my hands on my knees, trying to suck in as much air as I can.

"Well, you certainly don't give up easily, and that's admirable. We'll take it easy with some yoga, and then maybe have a real conversation when you aren't gaping like a codfish." She walks to where there are two yoga mats waiting. She stands on one before conjuring a yoga instructor.

I consider that I need to stop being surprised by the abilities of these siblings. Their magic is a total mystery to me—how they wield it, what its purpose is. Is this just what it's like to be a god?

We're guided through an hour and a half of yoga by the instructor, which is a challenging feat after the tire and the run. Helene is doing arm stands and complicated poses while I can hardly stand on my own two feet. I want to murder her but decide that it won't win me any brownie points with either brother.

I glare at her, hoping that for once she'll fall and look less than perfect for even five minutes. I focus on doing my own birds of paradise, bending my arms and legs into positions that don't feel natural. As I try to straighten my leg next to my torso, I glance at Helene, and I watch as she wobbles and loses her balance.

Helene has to let go of her bind to avoid falling to the ground, and it makes her curse.

"Enough of this." She waves her arm. I am too relieved to protest. Perhaps the mighty Helene isn't as unflappable as she would like us to believe.

"Can all of you conjure people and things into existence?" I ask, following her to a pair of chairs.

She looks at me like I'm confused and am asking something exceedingly simple. "We're gods, sweetie. That comes with a lot of extra perks." She glances at me and catches sight of the unimpressed look on my face. "Yes, we all can. Essos is generally more conservative with his powers, and Galen uses them like they're beads to give away at Mardi Gras."

"I haven't seen him really use them," I comment.

"Just because you haven't seen it doesn't mean he isn't using them," Helene says forebodingly. I take a sip of the margarita that she's offered me. Not sure it's the sort of liquid I need after these intense workouts, but there are electrolytes in limes or something, right?

"What is the deal with Galen, anyway?" I ask, trying not to look too interested.

"Broken heart, blah blah, reign of fire, blah blah, retaliation, blah blah. He's terribly boring if you ask me. I love both my brothers, so I suggest you stop digging for information. Just because I like you doesn't mean that I'll betray my brothers." She gives me a warning stare.

"If this is what you do when you like someone, I would hate to see what happens when you don't."

She turns to me, lowering sunglasses I never saw her put on, so she can make eye contact. "I'm not sure if you're aware, but there are only four of you now." She looks back at the water, digging her toes in the sand. I was aware, having seen one less person at dinner. Abigail is no longer with us. To foster conversations, Essos had the dining room table reduced, so it was hard to miss that we were down another person, and with no explanation this time.

I think about another girl who left under mysterious circumstances. "Do you know what happened with Madison?" I ask, testing to see how free with information she is.

Helene nearly spits out her drink. "Right, so I'm not supposed to tell you, and Essos will probably be livid that I did, so I'm going to spell you so you *can't* tell anyone else, but it's too good to keep to myself. Apparently, she managed to locate his room and was waiting for him in his bed, completely naked, and said, 'Since we can't do hometowns, does that mean we get to fast forward to fantasy suites?' Poor Essos can't talk about it without turning scarlet." She cackles to herself, and I can imagine how mortified he would be at such a turn of events.

I feel mortified on his behalf. He's been so restrained around all of us, even as Zara continues to kiss him and try to tempt him into skinny dipping. Any jealousy that I might have had has cooled, knowing that not only did he send Madison away, but he can't even talk about it now.

Helene manages to get herself under control. "But remember, mum's the word, or I'll make you vomit frogs instead of feathers."

The threat of vomiting frogs is enough to keep me quiet. I'll find another way to tell Cat. "Essos mentioned you were married?" I try to turn the conversation to her, to see who she is as a person. I remember that Helene was supposedly my sister-in-law once upon a time, and I wonder if we were close.

"Yes, to some great big, gorgeous brute. He should be here for the ball."

"The one tomorrow?" I ask.

"Oh, honey, no. *The* Ball. Capital *T*, capital *B*. One month's time, and I'll have a new sister-in-law. Or sister-in-law-to-be—there's still the matter of a wedding." There's a hint of condescension in her tone as she says it. I'm surprised by this—not just the wedding, but her confidence in knowing that Essos will pick someone. Now that we're only four, it's down to Zara, Ginny, or myself, since Cat isn't really in the running. I don't know how Ginny managed to stick around, if she is here just as a filler or if Essos sees something in her. She's far more private than myself, opting out of movie nights in Cat's room even before our numbers diminished. She's poured over her notes, but even when it came to the sorority, Cat confessed that Ginny was more of a loner. She had joined the sorority freshman year with a roommate who dropped out during pledging. Ginny enjoyed everyone's company enough to stick with it.

"A wedding?"

"Of course. The Calling finds him a bride, and then eventually they're supposed to get married, only I wouldn't know, since he hasn't picked a girl in half a millennium." My eyebrows rise even higher into my forehead. "You did know that the purpose of the Calling is to get married at the end, right? Essos did tell you?" She sounds incredulous.

"Yes, he did. I guess I just didn't think it had been that long. Has the Underworld ever had a queen?" I know the answer to this, I know there was one, but I hope by asking a question as innocuous as that, she'll give up more details.

"It's obvious, isn't it, that this place has had a female touch. Sorry to say you're just going to have to wait for the ball." She shuts down that line of questioning the same way everyone else does—quickly. "I will warn you that Zara is your toughest competition. Catalina is your best friend, and she's only here for your benefit. I don't even remember the name of the other girl who's still here."

"Why are you telling me this?" I drain my drink and turn to set the cup aside, but Helene waves her hand, refilling it.

"Because I find that I like you best. Zara seems like she would be fun, but she hardly seems like Queen of the Underworld material, despite what she thinks. I know about the case you heard. That was a layup, and she missed the shot."

"I know. Essos took me to the Underworld to see others. They were...traumatic, and I don't mean for me. Watching some of these people relive the worst moments of their lives, like the father who forgot his kids were in the car. I felt awful for them. Some of them deserved worse, but it was comforting to see Essos rule fairly," I confide. I'm not sure why I feel like I can open up to her like this, but I do.

"Further proving my point. That same experience has sent lesser women begging to be sent on to their afterlife. It's fucked up." Helene reaches over and grabs the drink from my hand. "Enough. Go back to your room and recover. If you drink any more, you're going to pass out, and as much as I would love to see

Zara's face as Essos carries you back to your room *again,* I'm not in the mood for the drama that will come with that. So, scoot." She motions me to leave but gives no indication that she's going anywhere.

Before I can say anything more to her, she pulls a book from nowhere—*And Baby Makes Four*—and starts to read, leaving me to limp my way back to my room. When I get there, the rose is taunting me from beside the bed, reminding me that I have plenty of answers, I'm just too afraid to acknowledge them.

25

I soak in the tub, every muscle screaming at what I just put my body through. I let the tub water drain before filling it again as I soak in varying salts and soaps, hoping that something can erase the aches. I'm not even sure I'll be able to pull my act together for the ball the next day.

After showering, I decide to take a nap before dinner. With my lights still on, I close my eyes for just a second.

That second turns into hours, because when I open my eyes, the lights in my room have been dimmed, but the curtain outside is still wide open and I see that it's night. Something feels off, and I roll over to see Essos placing a tray on my nightstand.

He winces and straightens up. "So, I've been caught." He tugs down the bottom of his suit jacket.

"What are you doing?" I ask as the fog of sleep clears from my mind. It's obvious what he's doing here. I look at the tray next to me to find chicken with vegetables and roasted potatoes with steam rising off them.

"You slept through dinner. Helene mentioned that she might

have gone a little rough on you today, so I wanted to make sure that when you woke up, you had something to eat."

It occurs to me that this isn't the first time he has done this. "You left me food in the library, and another time," I state. I'm hungry, but my stomach sours. Each time food has been left for me, I thought it was Galen performing the good deed. Why would he let me think that? Galen even outright said it was him. If Essos is doing this now, I *know* he's done it those other times too, as surely as I know the sky is blue.

Awareness crackles through my body at how high my shorts have hiked and how twisted my tank top is. I actually might pop a boob, and while I know Essos would be a gentleman about it, a dark, twisted part of me wants it to happen in hopes that I could finally break his careful restraint. The muscle in his jaw ticks as he fights to keep his eyes on mine. I pull on my tank strap, trying to straighten it, and his gaze falters, slipping over my cleavage and between my thighs. He wets his lips, and I can imagine him pressing me down into the mattress, his body between my legs as he worships at the altar that is me. Desperation has me nearly pulling my strap down to force his hand, see what happens when he finally lets his leash snap.

What would his mouth feel like on my clit as he fucked me with his tongue? His chest is rising rapidly, as if he's thinking the same thing—how it would feel to capture my nipple between his teeth as he drove his body into mine.

Essos looks away first, rubbing the back of his neck. It's something else to watch him breathe in through his nose and out through his mouth while he tries to regain his control.

"You missed lunch too," he responds simply. "You should eat and then sleep. Tomorrow is a big day. If you thought today was tough with Helene, you don't know what tomorrow will bring."

I sit up in bed, putting the tray on my lap. To spare us both, I grab my sweatshirt, even though it causes my core physical pain to do so. I'm surprised but really shouldn't be when Essos helps to pull my sweatshirt over my head. His fingers graze my breast, so quick I might have imagined it, but I'm not imagining the flush on his cheeks. I have to bite back the words to beg him to do it again. Rather than call him out, I resituate myself, nestling into the sweatshirt.

"You're close with Helene?" I ask before putting a forkful of food in my mouth.

Essos, as if sensing that I'm not letting him leave that easily, perches on the corner of my bed. "She's my little sister, so she knows I'll do anything for her. Galen thinks being the baby of the family entitles him to whatever he wants, and Xavier is her twin brother, so their relationships are complicated at best." Essos grabs a stray piece of potato off my plate and pops it into his mouth. I stab at his hand with my fork, and he smiles.

"She's very lucky to have you looking out for her." I take a few more bites "Are you just going to watch me eat? Because I'm not a fan of that."

He rises. "I'll leave you to it."

"No!" I shout, surprised at my vehemence. As quickly as I can move, which given what Helene put me through that day isn't that fast, I set aside the tray and get out of bed. I wince, unsure of what body part hurts more. "I mean, it's nice talking to you—I just feel guilty eating in front of you."

"That's nothing to worry about. I only wanted to stop in to make sure that when you woke up, you had some sustenance beyond the margarita Helene gave you. We can talk more in the morning. For now, just eat and rest." He walks again toward the door. I move faster than I should in my desperation for him to not leave. My fingers graze his and I feel a shock of electricity when we touch. I choke down my moan of pain, but Essos turns to me, marking the agony I'm fighting.

I point my fork at him. "Don't heal me; I earned this soreness.

But I don't want you to go, if it's all the same to you," I say, not beating around the bush this time. I don't know why I'm panicking at the idea of him leaving, but my pulse is racing and my throat has tightened to the point that I can't draw a full breath.

Essos doesn't fight me on the healing front, he only tips his head to me in acknowledgment. "Then I guess I have no choice but to stay." He sits on the lounge at the foot of the bed and unbuttons his suit jacket. I imagine running my hands along his shoulders and pushing it off, then loosening his tie for him. I have to fight the urge to act on that impulse. When I'm with Essos, I find I have to constantly remind myself that I was once with Galen. I still don't have my memories unlocked, and until I do, I feel like I owe it to myself and to Galen to find out what was actually going on with us.

"It would make me feel better if you also had something to eat."

He laughs, then conjures a plate of food for himself.

"Why don't you use your abilities as much as Helene does?"

Essos starts to cut up his own food, which is balanced on the foot of my bed. "I'm old-fashioned like that. I don't see the point in using my power for things that I can easily do for myself. Managing the Underworld takes up enough of my time and energy that using my abilities on conjuring a dinner when I have other means available to me doesn't make sense. I like to get my hands dirty, anyway. When there's no Calling, I cook for myself."

"What's your best dish?" I ask, setting the remainder of my food aside on my nightstand. I readjust so I can pull my covers over myself, hiding my bare legs.

"Pasta carbonara."

"Funny you should say that—that happens to be one of my favorite dishes!" I lean toward him with a smile.

"I thought that was mac and cheese and chicken nuggets."

"I love those too, obviously, but carbonara is probably my favorite grown-up meal. There was this Italian place near campus that used to make it with tortellini and pancetta and peas and onions. I gained like, the freshman forty-five eating their food all the time because they would deliver until two in the morning. It was too easy to call them when I got back to my dorm, trashed." I lean back on my pillows and pat my stomach with fond memories

"We will have to test if mine holds up to this place."

"Doubtful. What's your favorite food?" I want to know more about him. I feel guilty, wondering if my involvement with Essos would be considered cheating on Galen, or maybe it would be the other way around, since I'm unexclusively dating Essos? If I was married to Galen, am I still considered married to Galen? Questions circle my mind. I'm a completely new person with different experiences; I grew up with no magic or abilities, no memories of this past life I had. The whole thing blows my mind and confuses me to no end, because there's no clear definition when it comes to emotional cheating. Whatever it is, I feel like I'm toeing the line.

"I love a good seafood risotto. I go to Italy just for that."

I laugh. He's unbelievable. "You go to Italy just for risotto? That's absurd. Wait—can you go to the mortal realm whenever you want?" I realize I still know so little about how this world works.

"I'm a god," he points out simply. "I'm free to cross between realms with ease, because so much of what I do is grounded in the mortal realm."

The idea gives me butterflies. Going to Italy and seeing the world with Essos sounds like a dream, and for a moment, I imagine it: sitting on the coast of Positano, enjoying seafood risotto before popping over to Germany for some pretzels and beer. Then, in my mind, I see Galen dressed in lederhosen in the background, waving his hands as if to say, *What about me?!*

"That would be amazing," I say, subdued.

Essos seems to sense a change in my mood. With a wave of his hand, the dirty dishes are gone.

"It's after midnight." He stands and rebuttons his suit. "I'll leave you to rest. Until tomorrow..." He walks over to me like he wants to kiss me, but instead he tucks a stray lock of hair behind my ear. My head lowers in a movement that probably looks coy but is meant to hide my disappointment.

"Essos?" I call before he leaves.

He's at my side in one stride. "Change your mind about the healing?"

"No, I...I pulled this from your garden, and I want you to have it." I press my magic rose into his hand. When he lifts it to his nose, it brushes against his lips first before he breathes in the scent.

"*Thank you*," he whispers, holding it carefully. "Rest now," he orders before he leaves me wanting more.

"So, how was the queen bee?" Cat asks, thumbing through *Between Two Lovers,* the book that follows *The Princess and Her Guard.* It would seem that the prince Lorelei was married to was not as opposed to her guard as they thought he would be.

"Brutal."

I'm sitting at my vanity, wondering if I truly need to comb my hair. My shower yesterday was easy, it's that second-day soreness that makes it impossible to move. I skipped breakfast because I just couldn't find the strength to physically get out of bed.

It certainly didn't help that I was in the fugue of a genuine sex dream. The memory dreams I've been having feel different. They

303

grab me and won't let me go until they've shown me what they want me to see.

My dream last night was unadulterated lust. It didn't have any of the hallmark strangeness of my prior dreams that were memories. It picked up right where Essos had left me. In my dream, he turned around and gave in to the temptation between us, pressing his lips against mine, until the memory of pain from working out was gone. Our coupling was everything I imagined it would be, since it was my fantasy, after all. His lips were soft and full as he worked from my mouth to between my legs before I felt the generous length of him slide into me.

It was fantasy fodder for the shower that had me almost falling to my knees with release.

"She seems like a good sister, and like she would be a good sister-in-law."

I make a noncommittal noise and focus on my breathing to lift my hands so I can comb my hair.

"I think she's fiercely protective of those she loves, and that anyone who can count themselves among those numbers is lucky."

Cat bites her lip. "She doesn't seem very partial to Galen."

"From what Essos told me, he's their baby brother, and it sounds like he has golden child syndrome."

"And you would really be okay with that?"

Her question is poking at a bruise I've been ignoring. Everyone just wants me to get to the Calling Ball, and I want to. I need to know what secrets my memories hold. Yet, the last memory imparted to me from Galen's touch left me feeling itchy all over. It felt all wrong, like my skin was too tight, and I was grateful that Helene's arrival served as a distraction.

"I guess it depends. If these memories are mine, which we're assuming they are because it makes the most sense, will regaining all my memories erase who I am now? Will I merge with my former self? What if I was a total bitch? What if I was this terrible goddess? I want answers, but at the same time, I don't."

"What are you going to do about Essos?"

She stands and takes my comb from my hand so she can get at the back. I sag with relief.

"What else is there to do? This me—Daphne Marie Hale— wants to know him better, but knowing that he knows who I am, that he could maybe, I don't know, make the Calling stop and help me but doesn't, feels wrong. Then again, if I was his brother's wife, what purpose is there for keeping me around, if not to fuck with Galen? Essos *has* to know who I am, right? He's King of the Dead; this feels like something he would know. If Essos dismisses me, will I get my memories back? Methinks not, otherwise, he would have just done that. I want to put my full faith in Essos, but these secrets are a huge problem."

Cat finishes the last of the knots and rests her hands on my shoulders. "You already know I think that, if it comes down to the two of them, Essos is the right call, but it's super easy for me to have that opinion, being the one with no past life, and Galen doesn't give me the warm fuzzies the way he does you."

"You should feel these memories—there was such chemistry. My need for him was so extreme, and it wasn't one-sided."

"I hate to be the parrot here, but I guess we just have to wait for the Calling Ball."

I HARDLY SEE Essos the next day, as Helene has him tied up with preparations for this teaser ball that she's throwing. Each time someone approaches him, she shoos them away, including Sybil when they come with paperwork for him. I disappear to the gardens with a book, trying to find another world to disappear into that doesn't involve being torn between these two brothers. I've been avoiding Galen because I hate these big feelings and the confusion that comes with him. He hasn't said it, but I can feel his expectation that I'll go along with him. I can't blame him—he wants his wife back—but without my memories, I don't feel like that person. It's like he wants a version of me that doesn't exist anymore.

When I return to my room in the afternoon to get ready, there's a large box with a note on top. I open the envelope and find a gold notecard inside.

Please find your attire for tonight inside this box. Defy me and pay.
    —Helene

I snort, but when I open the box, my amusement dies immediately. Resting on top of the tissue paper is a golden mask. One half is gold with some black scrollwork around the eye, while the other half is a full butterfly wing, grand and open with five different gems on the wings—three on top and two on the bottom. The weight of the mask presses on my hands, and I can hardly imagine what it's going to be like to wear it. Gingerly, I put it on and turn toward my mirror to see how it looks.

I shouldn't be surprised when it's weightless on my face, but I am.

I set the mask aside and pull out the dress. I have to remind myself how to breathe while I admire it. It's hard to believe that it fit inside the box. If I know anything about Helene, it's magic.

There is so much skirt to the dress, I have no idea where to even begin to get into it. It's lower-cut than anything I would have chosen for myself, with off-the-shoulder sleeves. The bodice is a shiny gold fabric, and the skirt is covered in gold sparkles and sequins, starting with more at the top and getting fewer and fewer as they travel down to the bottom of the dress. I look closer and realize that they aren't sequins at all, but instead what I hope are only rhinestones, covering the tulle of the skirt. The dress is heavy in my hands, but I suspect that, like the mask, it will be weightless on my body. I set it aside and take my shower, almost wanting to take the dress with me so it's never out of sight.

When I come back out, there's another box on my bed, smaller this time, with another gold note.

Oops! I almost forgot!
—H

I open the box to find a simple drop necklace—a sapphire surrounded by tiny diamonds—and Art Deco chandelier earrings covered in diamonds and a solitary sapphire at the bottom of each. I pull shoes out of the box next and place them on the bed, just staring at them. They look like they're solid gold with beautiful gold scrolls and laurels around the heels.

I pinch myself, because I must be dreaming. When that fails to wake me, I do the only thing I can, and get ready for the ball. I can only hope that I don't suffer the same fate as Cinderella, and that I get to see this night play out.

26

To maintain the mystique of the masquerade ball, we're all given different times to arrive at the party that only we know. It's not like it's hard to figure out who is who when I get downstairs, but I like the idea behind it. I'm not even allowed to *see* Cat while we get ready, let alone know what her dress looks like.

When I walk downstairs, I see Helene first. She's easy to make out, bossing everyone around in her white dress. Calling it a white dress is too simple, though, because the back is covered in peacock feathers twisting up her skirt to the bottom half of her strapless bodice. The sweetheart neckline has feathers extending over her shoulder, and her mask is black with a peacock curling around the right eye, the feathers sticking out to the side. She's stunning as she points and directs people toward the food, waving away the staff who come to take her place. From what I've come to know about Helene, I'm hardly surprised that she's micromanaging to this degree.

A man approaches me and holds out his hand, a grey mask on his face. I smile at Finn.

"May I have this dance?" he asks, faking a deeper voice, and sweeps me onto the dance floor. I let him lead me around in a waltz. We don't last long together before we're interrupted by Galen asking for the next dance. Finn looks like he would rather eat rocks than say yes, but I nod my head, accepting.

We're all supposed to pretend we don't know who's behind the mask, and I'm okay with that, enjoying the pretend mystery. I know that dancing with Galen means I'll get a memory. I side my hand into his, and he pulls my body close as we start dancing.

WE'RE DANCING CLOSER *than we are now, at another masquerade ball. Around me, the colors of the dresses swirl past, and everything is so sharp, it's almost painful to look at. Galen whispers something in my ear, sending chills down my spine, offering to get me a drink, asking me to follow him. I nod, letting him lead me off the dance floor into a side room.*

No sooner are we in the room than he's kissing my neck and reaching up to untie my mask. I stop him, catching his hand in mine.

"Sir, a lady must maintain her mystery. How could I face anyone if I let you tarnish my honor while everyone dances in the next room?"

He acquiesces, kissing down my chest. The dress is low-cut and tight, pressing my breasts up. His mouth traces the swell of my breasts. My skirt is voluminous, meant to make me look like a virtuous princess, not to encourage illicit trysts in side rooms. A laugh bubbles out of me as Galen struggles to the point that he gets on his knees just to find my ankles.

His hands are rough against my bare skin, sliding up and up and up. Galen is swift—once he finds the soft spot between my legs, he doesn't tease, he doesn't play. I grip the door frame, biting down on my lip, full of wanting. He kisses me as he thrusts himself inside me with the same need. I let out a soft moan, burying my head in his shoulder as he moves in a fevered tempo. I hold on to him, barely able to hook my ankles together around him because of the damn dress and its layers between us. Unlike when we were dancing in the 1920s, we both go to great lengths to stay quiet this time, his hand staying firm against my mouth as I try to fight the power behind my orgasm. I want to scream and let my magic explode from my body, but instead, I bite hard on my lip, tasting blood as his body shudders with his own release.

My cheeks are burning red with embarrassment on the dance floor. Galen is smiling at me, a smirk on his lips. This is a game to him, and it pisses me off. He spins me, holding my hand tight. The lights from the room reflect off the gems on my gown, casting light everywhere. I feel like I'm lighting up the room like a disco ball.

When he spins me back into his arms, I whisper in his ear, "Are you capable of showing me something other than us having sex?"

He frowns. "Of course," he grits out, and squeezes my hand.

We're seated in the library, a book in my lap, my legs curled beneath me. Galen is seated across the room, looking over papers before him. There's that same worry wrinkle between his brows, only I don't have the time to obsess over it, because I have other things on my mind, things I'm desperate to talk to him about. I don't know if it's the mood, but the room feels shrouded in shadows.

"Your brother won't leave me alone, and it worries me," I say casually, not wanting to alarm him needlessly. I don't want him to have his focus split—his work ethic is something I love about him. Except, if I admit the truth to myself, I do want him alarmed. I need him to focus on me.

He looks up, watching my face. "He's throwing a tantrum because he's gotten his way always as a prince, but he can't have you. He thinks that you have been denied to him and that you are the solution to making him happy after his wife left. What he fails to realize is that taking you isn't going to make him happy." Galen looks back down at what he's doing, as if trying to put me at ease.

He doesn't sound convinced, and I fight to keep my expression as neutral as my voice. "It makes me uncomfortable. He's your brother, and I would rather not come between you two."

Galen places his papers down and gives me his undivided attention. "I, too, would rather not have my brother come between us. But, love, you're the only thing that matters. I'll burn all of Solarem down for you, my brothers be damned." He rises, and I think he's going to take his papers and leave, not wanting to do the same song and dance we've been doing for months. The ottoman scratches the floor as he pulls it closer to me. Galen places his hands on my knees and slides them to my ankles. His touch always electrifies me, and now is no exception. I shift so I can uncurl as he wants me to. My legs rest on his lap, and his fingers massage my feet and calves.

"My love," I say leaning toward him. "I would sooner die than let that happen." I kiss him gently on the lips, but Galen is unconvinced.

"After everything that has happened, I can't lose you."

I kiss him again, harder this time.

"You never will," I whisper in his ear, pulling him closer to me.

"BETTER?" Galen's voice is tight. His breath tickles the baby hairs on my neck. I nod, but my mouth is dry, and I feel sick. I look up at him, trying to find the words I want.

"How long was that before...?" I choke out.

"Three months. I had three more months with you before he took you."

I think about that span of time and how that's almost as long as this whole process. The Calling.

"And how did he 'take' me?" I ask, not sure I want the answer.

I'm not stupid; I had to die, but I don't understand what that has to do with Essos. Does it have something to do with him being God of the Dead? My gaze searches the room for Essos, but I'm unable to spot him. I think I might throw up.

"He..." Galen chokes up. "I can't tell you what he did to you before I got there, but when I came home..." He pauses again. "The knife was still in your chest, and you were cold." As if reacting to his words, coldness spreads through my body. I am barely aware that the song has ended. My muscles remember what to do, because I step away from him in the silence. Galen goes deathly still in front of me.

"May I have this dance?" Essos says from behind me, and my stomach churns. Galen looks at me as if asking if this is okay, and I give a small nod and turn. Essos has a vested interest in ensuring that I make it through the Calling, for better or worse. I give a small curtsey and take his hand, startled by the shaking of my own. When Essos sweeps me into his arms, my knees nearly buckle, and I lean into him for support as my body trembles.

"Cold again?" he asks, his body pressed against mine. There is a hint of concern not only in his voice also in how he looks at me. I nod, still unable to find words for what's going through my head. My body starts to warm, but it doesn't fix the underlying confusion caused by dancing with my alleged murderer. I should be repelled by Essos. My brain is telling me *danger*, that this isn't safe, but my heart and body haven't gotten the memo.

I see Galen watching us with visible concern beneath his mask.

How can this man who has shown me nothing but kindness be the man who stabbed a knife into my chest? I struggle to reconcile the Essos I know with the Essos Galen has told me about. My mind is so preoccupied trying to reconcile the two that I stumble and step on Essos's toes. He recovers easily, adjusting his grip on my back to compensate for my obvious distraction.

There is so much that Galen has told me that is at odds with what I have seen exhibited in Essos. He's been kind and sweet, making sure that I have food and am tended to. These are not the actions of a man who's trying to one-up his brother—these are the actions of a man in love. Even my interactions with him go further than base desire or attraction. There is no denying how my body, even now, on the heels of being told that he murdered me, wants to stay connected to him and only him. But I've seen the mask he wears while judging souls—maybe the way he's acting with me is another mask. How do I balance this man who has done his best to protect me with the man who allegedly killed me?

"I've been speaking with Catalina, and it got me thinking. I have a surprise for you tomorrow that I hope you'll like." Essos is speaking, and I turn my attention back to him. "I know that emotions have been running high since Helene dismissed so many girls, so I plan on letting everyone have a sort of spa day. That's not the surprise, though. Come to breakfast dressed for the day."

My chest constricts at yet another kindness from Essos. It shouldn't be surprising that he thinks of me like that, but I still feel tears prick the back of my eyes at the idea that he's going out of his way for me. Unable to control my response, I say, "Yes, of course, I'll come to breakfast dressed. If you'll excuse me, I want to make sure I thank your sister for all the generous gifts that she's given me." I pull out of his grip mid-dance and walk to Helene.

Helene grabs my wrist as I walk toward her. "What are you doing?" she hisses in my ear, pulling me toward her.

I rip my arm out of her grip. "I am getting some fresh air," I say, trying to hold on to the calm that is leaking away like a balloon with a hole.

I notice that Zara has swooped into Essos's arms, looking all too happy to fill the gap I've left behind. She's wearing all black, the see-through corset designed with black flower appliques worked strategically around her chest, and a black lace mask covering her face.

"You're *also* letting Zara shove her tits in my brother's face. I spent this entire night trying to get you and Essos on the same damned page. If you don't get your head in the game, one word about how Catalina isn't here for Essos, and she's gone." Fury burns behind Helene's eyes. "What did you and Galen talk about?"

Her threat stokes my own rage. "You better think twice about threatening me or Cat. You may be a goddess, but I will salt and burn this realm for her," I snap and instantly regret it. I could have done less damage if I slapped her. She gives me a dirty look. I planned to thank her for the gift, but the damage is done, so instead, I flee outside.

I try to take a calming breath, but it feels insufficient. I try again, inhaling slower, then exhaling on a count of ten. If I am unable to get my breathing under control, I know that I will start to hyperventilate.

Cat follows me outside. Her silver gown and rhinestone mask glitter in the light of a full moon. "You look like you're about to vomit."

I rush to the edge of the deck and do that just, throwing up the champagne and strawberries that are all I've had this evening. Cat rushes to me, placing one hand gently on my back. I vomit again, thinking of Essos's hands on my skin and the possibility that he could be playing me. I've hated to admit it to myself, but it's more than just attraction to Essos, I like him. I *want* to spend time with him, and to think that he could be manipulating me is unfathomable.

I feel Cat's hand leave my back and the door close before she comes back a moment later with napkins and a glass of water.

Once I feel like I'm not going to throw up anymore, I turn to face her, dabbing under my eyes to collect the tears streaming down my face with a clean napkin. I take a sip of water, meeting her eyes.

"Aside from Helene basically threatening you if I don't choose Essos, Galen showed me a conversation that we had where I told him I was afraid of his brother, and then I asked how exactly Essos took me from him, and he told me that Essos murdered me."

Cat gasps, backing up until she finds a chair to sit down and digest this information. She's too far away from me, but I don't have the energy to move closer to her.

"I just find that so unbelievable." She's trying to process what I've said. I take another small sip of water. "But, like, actually, he's so into you. I really shouldn't be saying so, but he's got this whole surprise planned for you and everything."

"Galen thinks Essos is acting that way because he's trying to win me over so he can get me away from Galen. I just don't think he counted on Galen being able to open up my memories." A waiter steps outside to offer us glasses of champagne and I take one, knocking it back before grabbing a second for myself.

Cat jumps out of her seat suddenly and crosses the porch to me, pressing a napkin to my nose. I don't have to question why she's doing this; it only means one thing—I have another nosebleed. I take the napkin from her hand and squeeze my nose, tilting my head back, a headache starting to form between my eyes.

"Maybe you're getting these nosebleeds because Galen isn't supposed to be opening these memories."

She's right; I know she's right. Essos and Finn and Sybil have all warned me about learning too much too fast. I doubt there's anything permanent anyone can do about my nosebleeds and headaches, if that's the case. And we've been told that a Calling or two was canceled because other women learned too much too fast.

"The thought has crossed my mind, but I feel so in the dark. I hate that I don't know myself, and that I don't know who to trust. I feel so drawn to Essos, and so safe with him, but now I'm wondering if he's been taking advantage of my lack of memory. And I just feel so, *so* confused." I pull the napkin away from my nose to see if I'm still bleeding. Catalina is quick to thrust another napkin in my face, so I assume that I am.

The door opens, and I turn my head to see Finn. He approaches and places his hand on my back. It's a gentle touch, and I can almost feel the concern radiating off him.

"I know I'm a pain in the ass, but you don't have to turn your nose up at my existence."

I glare at him from the corner of my eye. "Hardy har har," I say, sarcasm dripping in my nasally tone. He chuckles, handing me another new napkin. I swap them out, finding the second one redder than the first.

"Any idea why you're still getting these awful nosebleeds, dear?" His question is a test. I can see it in how his eyes flick toward Cat to see just how much she already knows.

"I think all the classical music is melting my brain." I switch the napkins, but the bleeding has slowed enough that I can hold my head regularly. The next napkin reveals that it's stopped. I toss them in the trash, but they burst into flame before making it into the can.

"That shit is gross," Finn says with a shrug.

"You have *powers*? We've been friends for how long, and I'm just learning this now?"

"You have your secrets and I have mine," he quips. "But they won't be secret for much longer. One more month, and this nonsense will be over and I will be an open book." Finn sips his champagne, and I take a chance.

"Like, I'll get my memories back in one month, sort of an open book?" I ask.

Cat raises an eyebrow at me but goes with it.

He's slow in taking his mask off to really look me in the face. I admitted I was having flashes and tested out the idea that they were memories, and he brushed me off, giving me the same company line that I needed to *wait*. He was more controlled in his response then. Now he's less so.

His reaction tells me I'm right.

"What would make you say a silly thing like that? You know all that you know. Look, we'll be missed if we don't head inside— let's hit the dance floor and see if we can get rid of these grandiose ideas that you have." He gives a fake little chuckle and tries to drag me into the ballroom.

"Finn, if I ask you a direct question can you answer it?" I push.

He eyes me warily. "Depends on the question."

"Did Essos's wife leave him?"

Cat gasps, and Finn grits his teeth, "Yes, but th—" He coughs hard.

"There's more to it and you just can't say?" Cat jumps in.

Finn's eyes flick from her to me before he blinks rapidly, even his head unable to move.

"And Galen?"

Finn's body relaxes, like this is an avenue he can answer. "Same."

"Same she left or same you can't answer?" Cat presses.

Finn tenses again, gritting his teeth, "Yes."

"That's what I thought." I shake my head as I push off from the railing of the deck. We're getting exactly what I expected, a whole lot of nothing.

Finn stops before he opens the door and looks me dead in the eye. "*No one* can know that you know *any* of what you just said to me. This whole thing ends if anyone finds out that you know, and we're all back to square one, including you. This is how the Council set up the Calling. Please...sit tight on this for one more month. That's it, just 30 measly days." His voice is more serious than I have ever heard it. "And stay away from Galen," he adds. Finn doesn't wait for my agreement before opening the door. The sounds of the party filter through the brief opening.

I decide that after I see whatever surprise Essos has for me, I'll reject it in favor of some solitude. I need to do some serious thinking about the emotional tug of war I'm engaged in between Galen and Essos—a battle I'm not sure Essos even realizes he's in. Galen has opened my eyes and helped me see that Essos is trying to take advantage of my naivety of being in the Calling and not remembering.

I put on the performance of a lifetime that night, dancing with Finn, and then Essos again, and a few of the other escorts in attendance, pretending I don't know that Essos murdered me. Every easy smile from Essos makes my heart dip at the deception —not only his, but mine.

Galen watches from the corner of the room, mostly just drinking, but occasionally chatting with Zara. His mouth is close to her ear as he whispers to her, and I expect to feel the same spike of jealousy I do when she's with Essos, but it never comes. Helene swoops into their conversation and clearly scolds him for taking his mask off.

Before the night is over, I see Helene relax and embrace the party, spinning around the floor with Finn. She seems to float as she dances then eventually collapses into a chair with a drink in her hand. While I'm standing off to the side with Zara, Essos takes his sister onto the dance floor for the last dance. I watch them glide across the room, hand in hand, each with a smile on their face.

"Those two are apparently closer than she is with her twin brother," Zara whispers to me, I glance at her and take a sip of my drink. "I heard that since they were little, he's always covered for her when she's done something wrong, so in turn, she covers for him. I even heard that there was this awful coverup a long time ago and someone *died.*"

Goosebumps break out over my skin.

"She covered it up?" I try to keep my tone light, curious.

"Yeah. Apparently, there was some sort of inquest by the Council, and she helped craft the details of the cover-up so he got away without any sort of punishment."

She must have been asking Galen all sorts of different questions to get these answers.

I hold my glass tight, knowing she's talking about me. I have no idea how I'm going to survive the next 30 days without breaking down. In my effort to avoid dropping the glass, I clench it so hard that it shatters in my hand. Thankfully, the song ends at that moment, the round of applause covering up the sound. No one notices except for Finn and a passing waiter, who swiftly cleans it up. Even Zara doesn't notice until the waiter comes over. Finn pulls a handkerchief from his pocket and checks my palm for glass, then squeezes my hand to stop the bleeding.

"If you keep this up, you're going to become anemic and die, again. And that would suck worse than the first time." He tries to keep his tone light, but mutters under his breath, "I swear, you're going to be the death of me. You're not going to make it through the next thirty days, are you?"

Finn studies me too closely for my own liking, seeing the truth of my impatience written on my soul. I take the handkerchief and press it to my wound, deciding that I'm not going to let it heal. Instead, I'm going to pick at it, never letting the scab stick. I'm going to use it to remind myself of this moment. How it felt finding out that Essos killed me, and that his sister, who was so kind to my face, helped cover it up.

27

I do as I am asked the next day. I show up to breakfast ready for the day in black tights, a red pencil skirt, and an off-white blouse. I have a hard time finding my appetite as I dig my thumb into the cut on my hand. I opt for plain toast with butter, my stomach turning at the thought of the French toast sticks on Cat's plate or the runny eggs on Zara's.

Helene walks into the room in a black dress and a large-brimmed sun hat, sunglasses on.

"Kisses, everyone. I have to go make sure my husband hasn't flooded our house in the week I've been gone. I'll be back in one month to see you all one last time. Behave, brothers of mine, or I'll call Mom. Also—" she turns to Ginny, who has a book beside her "—bye." With a wave of her hand, Ginny vanishes, as if she was never there. Just as quickly as hurricane Helene swept into our lives, she is gone, just a wisp of air, the smell of apples faint in her absence.

Essos clears his throat and stands.

"Daphne, if you would be so kind as to join me today, I have something I would like to discuss with you."

Zara wiggles her eyebrows at me, and I stand, knees shaking, to follow Essos into the hall. We walk side by side to his office, and he opens the door to let me in.

"I had wanted to surprise you with this, but Finn counseled me that I should probably talk to you about it first." He gestures for me to sit on the couch. Instead of sitting in the nearby chair, he sits beside me. My body slides closer to his, and I don't fight it, even though my brain keeps trying to tell me to move away. I stay silent, letting him continue.

"Do you want to meet your parents?" he blurts out, watching my face carefully. For a second, I forget to breathe. The world goes hazy before narrowing into a pinprick. Essos's hand is on the back of my neck, guiding me to hunch over. "Breathe, love, breathe," he orders softly. His grip grounds me. Essos's other hand rests on my knee, giving it a firm squeeze to keep me present.

His hand slides down my back, rubbing small circles as I keep my mind on the action that is air in and out of my lungs. I've never considered what it means to have to think about breathing, but right now, I think I could just stop again. I grab his hand and choke down a sob.

Essos leans into me, his forehead pressing to the side of my head. "I'm sorry," he whispers, and he sounds genuinely pained. I lean into him, needing him to be my rock. Cat has been that for me for so long, but right now, he is the one I want, no, *need*, holding my hand.

Meeting my parents is not something that even occurred to me to ask Essos about. They've been out of my life for so long that my mind goes blank even thinking about it now.

Of course, when I was younger, I would think of them. When all my classmates were making gifts for their parents for Mother's Day and Father's Day, I made filler gifts or something for my social worker. Or that one year, a gift for that troll of a foster mom who demanded it. My teachers and social workers telling me that my parents would be so proud of me if they could see me became a mantra.

Now I could find out if they actually were proud of me.

Do I want to find out? Do they count as my parents if I had a prior life? Were they just placeholder parents, meant to bring me into the world just so I could die? My brain moves a mile a minute, considering the possibilities. Would they want to know me? Did they watch me grow up, or did they know that I was something more—a sojourner, passing through on my way from one life to the next?

I sit up abruptly, nearly taking out Essos. He stays silent, waiting as I filter through each scenario in my head. Meeting them and them being proud, meeting them and them being disappointed, not meeting them, not meeting them and regretting it. Would I be able to have a relationship with them?

"I...I don't know." I glance at him for guidance, so lost in the question that I forget to be wary of him. I feel that familiar tug toward him, the same one I've been feeling through this entire process. I want to open my heart to him and lay myself bare at his feet, but I can't do that, knowing what I know about him. I start to lean into him, but then pull back, so I can search his face for an answer. Essos reaches out and takes my other hand, further linking us and prompting my heart to summersault, knowing that I have someone sitting beside me who understands me. I stare where our hands are connected, wanting to dig my nails into my cut again to remind myself he's supposed to be the bad guy. His fingertips graze the indent on my palm. He turns it over, giving me a questioning look. I can't talk about this with him. I close my hand and pull it back.

"Well, I'm glad that Finn talked me into asking you first. I'm pretty sure you would have kicked my ass with that giant tire if I had just surprised you like I planned to."

I guffaw, looking away, into the fireplace. I'm grateful that he

THE KING'S GAME

doesn't ask about the cut on my hand. "That would have been a terrible idea. I'll have to thank Finn the next time I see him. Can I think about it, or do you need an answer right now?" I face him.

He surprises me by resting his palm on my cheek. It's such a familiar gesture, and I want to lean into the warmth, into the comfort he's offering. "The option will be open to you whenever you choose to use it. I'm just sorry I didn't think of it sooner."

"What did make you think of it?" I lean away from him. He looks hurt for a second but recovers quickly.

"Catalina said something about looking in on her parents again, and I told her that we could work something out. She mentioned how thankful she is that she got to see them, even if they will never know she's watching. It got the wheels spinning, even if they do move slowly sometimes."

I stand up, and he stands up quickly too.

"I'd like time to think about it, if that's all right with you. Alone," I emphasize.

He puts his hands in his pockets and nods, looking chastened. "My door is open once you make your decision either way."

I quickly walk to the door and pause. I take a breath and face him. He's still watching me. "Can I go to the gardens? I know you said—"

"I know what I said. You are welcome in the gardens whenever you like. I know you dreamed of being a florist. I hope you start to see the space as a safe one for you."

Words of thanks get stuck in my throat, so I just nod and walk out. I lean against the door, closing my eyes, wondering if I can handle being alone with him again. I head toward the stairs and my room, Dave following faithfully behind me, but then I change my mind and go straight outside to sit in the garden.

I stumble across a bucket with tools, and I take a small hedge cutter and use it to trim a few spots that are starting to be overgrown. I gather bouquets to put in my and Cat's rooms. I feel at home here, gazing at the flowers and walking the paths as Dave shadows me.

The busywork distracts me from the problem at hand. But as soon as I think about how distracting this work has been, it stops being distracting, and my worries come flooding back.

When I grew up in foster care, I thought I would never have to worry about parental approval. Then Phil and Melinda adopted me. I felt pressure to live up to their expectations, but I don't think it's fair to compare the expectations my living parents set versus the ones imagined in my head that my birth parents might have had. I thought I was done trying to live up to some unknown ideal, but here I am, wondering again if I will measure up to the person they hoped I would become. I sit on the ground, not caring if I tear my tights or dirty my skirt, and curl my feet under me. I drop my head into my hands, all the flowers I painstakingly picked discarded at my side.

It's been so long since I cried about my parents and all the things they would never be there for, but now that they're in my grasp, I'm scared. Scared of not being good enough. I let the tears start flowing and ride the emotional waves as they rock me. The hard sobs that make me think I'm going to break a rib are no help for the headache that has plagued me since the ball last night.

Dave sits beside me, licking my tears as they stream down my face. I'm still in that position when Cat finds me, maybe an hour later. She says nothing, just sits down on the other side of me, arm around my shoulders.

My relationship with Cat strikes the perfect balance for support. Since freshman year, when we were on our own for the first time, the first few months were rough on her, being away from her family. I was there for her, and that was what brought us together and bonded us as friends. There would be days or nights when she would climb into my bed, knowing that I was the one in need of TLC.

Today is the day that I need her comfort, and in a way that we never thought I would.

"You could have warned me, you know." I look at her through puffy eyes.

She shakes her head. "Essos was so excited to have come up with some grand plan. I didn't know what it was until he came to tell me after you left his office. I wanted to give you some time to properly digest before bombarding you. He seemed worried." She sounds like she's all in for trusting him, and I want to be mad at her but can't manage to get past feeling sorry for myself.

"I don't want to talk about Essos right now. I want to think about what I'm going to do. I mean, I never really thought about what it would be like to meet them."

"Never ever?" She starts to rub my arms soothingly.

"Okay, maybe *never* isn't strictly true. When I was young, I had this fantasy that it was all a big mistake and that they got stuck on vacation because of the plane crash and found their way back to me. But I was, like, nine and never thought much further than them hugging me and loving me and getting me out of foster care."

"Well, now's your chance," Catalina says encouragingly.

I sigh. "Is it my chance, though? What will it mean? Will they be back in my life? Will I get to see them all the time? Are they even actually my parents, given my reincarnation?"

"I think *you* get to decide what they are to you. But had they not died, then they one hundred percent would be your parents, and you one hundred percent would be missing them right now. You're letting this reincarnation part get into your head—they are your parents no matter what." Cat hands me a tissue, and I blow my nose. On the other side of me, Dave whimpers. I know she's right, but thinking about this is just one more thing that I want nothing to do with.

Or rather, it's not that I don't want to think about it, but my head is already crammed with memories and dreams and feelings and *questions*. I didn't ask for any of this, but here I am, deciding if I want to meet my long-dead parents while being the apparent frontrunner for Queen of the Underworld.

"So, I gather you think I should meet them?" I ask.

"I can go with you, if you want. It might help to have a friendly face in the room," she offers.

I nod my head, liking this idea so much more. "Okay. I'll talk to Essos in a few days. I don't want to be around him for a little while. It messes with my head. I almost forget that he murdered me, and I should say no to the Calling and him and being queen, but my body has a very different opinion. It's so frustrating that my heart and mind aren't on the same page."

"I'm still not convinced that you're getting the whole story. You might as well take advantage of the perks, like him being able to summon the dead so you can meet your parents. I know I'm going to ask if I can see my parents a few more times before this is all over."

In all my self-pity, I failed to realize the implications for Cat. Some best friend I am. I never even considered what our world will look like after the ball. What will be Cat's fate? I have to assume that if I reject Essos and chose Galen at the ball, I risk losing Cat forever. I could probably live with never getting to meet my parents, but the thought of losing Cat is something I'm not sure I can handle. Even the subtle threats to her have been too much.

"I need more time to think on my own. I spent all my alone time crying, and I haven't truly given this idea a chance."

Cat nods and stands, dusting off her pants. "I hear there are mud baths to be had, anyway." She holds out a hand and helps me up. Once I'm up, I give her the handful of flowers I cut for her room. We embrace one last time, and then she departs.

Since I have actually made my decision about meeting my

parents, I use my time alone in the garden to weigh what I know about these two men. I think about how I felt when I met Essos, and how everything he has done has been carefully crafted. From his initial lies about why we were here to how secretive he is with information, everything has been a subtle manipulation. The Council has tied his hands with so much of what he can and cannot reveal, but Galen was motivated enough to figure out a way around it.

And yet...my heart seems to sing when I'm around Essos, and I catch myself turning toward him whenever he's around. My heart associates him with safety and comfort, ever since he offered shelter immediately following our crash.

I want to hold on to my anger, but he's been so tender and sweet with me. The thrill I get when he touches me brings a smile to my face. I remember the warmth of his breath on my neck and the sensation of his fingers grazing my skin. I think of how patient he has been, and how these actions would look without knowing about that malice.

Galen though...when I'm near him, I don't get the same warm feeling Essos gives me, but at the same time, there is a change in me. There is a need to be close to him, but it's like I need to know what he's doing, what's going to come next. He opened my eyes in a way that Essos has tried to keep them covered. My draw toward Galen is strongest when I'm around him. The memories that he has shown me have allowed me to see what I had before with him.

My relationship with Essos evolved as we got to know each other. Galen, on the other hand, has shown me so much of our former relationship, but I can't *feel* anything past the memory. I try to hold on to the emotions, the sense of rightness, and hope that, maybe once I have all my memories back, those feelings will return and stay with me. Is that an empty hope, or will it materialize?

What I do know is that the Calling Ball cannot come soon enough.

I press my eyelids together and allow myself one last cry before I go back to my room. This time, I don't bury my face in my hands. I let the tears flow freely down my face onto the ground in front of me. The burden slowly eases off my shoulders as the catharsis of crying takes root.

When I open my eyes, I see that I've cried a river of flowers.

28

I tell Essos at dinner that I would like a few days to prepare to meet my parents. I need to get used to the idea of meeting them and come up with questions that I want to ask.

He agrees, telling me that I can change my mind anytime. I almost change my mind immediately and a hundred times over the course of those days. A few times, I stop Essos to tell him I've changed my mind, only to change it again and just walk away from him. Every time I stop him and open my mouth to tell him, he waits patiently, understanding that this is not easy. He never gets frustrated and he never ignores me.

I take until the last minute to decide if I want Cat there when I meet them, but I ultimately elect against it. It'll be hard enough for me to keep it together in front of the King of the Underworld. If Cat is with me, I'll have a much easier time falling apart, and I don't want to show Essos that weakness.

I spend the morning of the meeting pulling every piece of clothing out of my closet and drawers, changing thirty times, unable to decide what I want to wear. Do I wear an ultra-conservative dress and cardigan with neutral pumps? What about nice slacks and a button-down? Should I wear my usual leggings and a shirt or jeans? Should I wear neutral colors? What about bright colors? Is red a no go? I ask this every time I grab a piece of clothing hoping that something sticks out. Dave keeps his opinions to himself, sensing that I need to make this decision for myself.

Cat sits on my bed, calmly letting me freak out while petting Dave. To start, she lets me spiral out of control, asking her for advice on each thing I consider. She offers some gentle advice—too short, too dark, too dour, too much cleavage, until I throw what I have in my hands up in the air.

"Maybe I should just go naked," I say.

She stands and grabs my shoulders, looking me in the eye. "Daphne Marie Hale. Relax." She draws the word out as if it's that easy. "If you find nothing in the closet, see if Sybil can conjure you a purple dress like cartoon Daphne, and have Essos wear an ascot to be your Fred." I try to laugh at her sad excuse for humor, but it sounds brittle and harsh instead.

"I just have no idea what to wear. The last time they saw me, I was in diapers and a onesie." I drop the black ball gown I'm holding onto the floor. It's the same one I wore when adjudicating over Dell McMann.

"What would you wear if you were meeting your boyfriend's parents for the first time? An interview is too formal, but I think that's the right sort of scenario. You want to look cute and sensible, and bright, but not showy."

When I give her a look that says that I'm still just as lost, she pushes me onto the bed and turns into my closet, rummaging through what remains.

Dave crawls over to me and sets his head on my lap. I run my finger from his snout to his ears, taking the comfort where I can find it.

Cat emerges from my closet holding a sleeveless lavender

blouse and a white pencil skirt with black music notes on it. "Flats or wedges, not pumps." She hands the clothing to me.

I get dressed as she picks through the jewelry, first pulling out a simple strand of pearls with studs. I try them on, and we take in the whole look before nixing the pearls.

I take a peek and find a necklace with a sun pendant, an opal at the center and ironwork scrolls twisting as the rays. Catalina steps back and moves my loose curls first behind my shoulder, then in front before brushing them back again.

She's nervous for me, and it's evident as she tries to clean imaginary lint off my skirt. I pull her into a tight hug. This would not be possible without her in any way shape or form.

"You'll be waiting outside?" I confirm.

She nods. "The whole time." Although I decided not to have her in the room with me, I still want her nearby as my safety net.

My hands are sweaty, and I'm glad I opted to skip breakfast when nausea churns in my stomach as I walk with Cat to Essos's office. Every step has me second guessing if I should do this, if I should keep going. The only option in my head is catastrophe; I don't—I can't—leave hope in my heart for anything good. If I'm prepared for rejection, then it won't hurt as badly if it happens.

Cat holds my hand as we descend the main stairs. The hallway we walk feels darker than usual, as if shrouded in shadows. I know my mind is playing tricks on me, because in truth it's the same as it always is.

When we reach his office, Essos's expression is grim, his mouth set in a hard line.

"Why the long face?" I ask weakly. Maybe something came up and we can't do this.

"Had I known this was going to cause you so much strife, I don't know if I would have offered it. I never want to cause you pain like this," he responds with a solemn shake of his head.

My brows pull in, and I almost, *almost* step into his embrace to reassure him that I wouldn't change anything. But my throat feels swollen around letting any words of gratitude out.

Cat looks at me to make sure it's okay to release my hand. I loosen my grip, and she takes a seat on a bench outside his door. Out of the corner of my eye, I see her shake her hand to get the blood flowing before she pulls out a book.

I follow Essos into his office, and he shuts the door gently behind me. He keeps glancing at me, as if expecting me to change my mind. When I meet his eye, I realize that he wants me to know I *can* change my mind. For the last three days, he has watched me war with myself over this decision, and he wants me to know that it's never too late to walk it back.

My heart keeps leaping into my throat, trying to claw its way out and away from getting hurt. I expect to sit on the couch again, but instead, he walks past me toward a door behind his desk that I don't remember seeing before. He opens the door and watches as my brain processes what I am seeing.

Beyond the door is a wide-open meadow with green rolling hills in the distance. Sunlight pours in through the doorframe, illuminating the room. I can feel its heat from where I stand. Essos waits for me to pass through the door first before following me into the light.

The sun is warm on my skin. A gentle breeze blows across my face, pulling strands of hair along with it.

I glance at Essos confused. "Is this real?"

"As real as you or I. It's part of the Afterlife, which is part of the Underworld, so it is part of my domain."

I squat down and run my hands over the blades of grass, confirming that they are real. I glance around and see a picnic table laid out with glasses and plates, but only for three.

I turn to Essos. "You're leaving me here?" I don't see the door we came through, and my panic rises. For being in such an open space, I suddenly feel trapped, like a mouse cornered by a cat.

Essos crosses the space to me. I reach for him as soon as he's close enough, my hands gripping his forearms. His hands close on my elbows, and calm spreads through my body. Part of my brain is trying to remind me that he murdered me, but the other part, the louder part, is insisting that I need him right now. The thought that this is one of his parlor tricks dances around in my head but is quickly followed by wondering if I care.

"I won't go unless you want me to. I thought you would want some alone time."

"*No!*" I shout at him. His eyebrows quirk. I clear my throat. "I mean, no. I think you should stay, at least at first."

He nods, understanding in his eyes, and another place setting appears at the table. I need a familiar face, and I think he can see that. He's had millennia of reading people, of being able to look at them and in a moment know if they are inherently bad or victims of circumstance.

"And do you think you could bring back the door?" I ask, watching the space we just came through.

He chuckles and conjures the door, and I'm grateful, regardless of how out of place it looks.

"When do they get here?" I glance around for another door they would be coming through. I can't contain my nervous energy. I wish I had something to hold on to and squeeze.

"Whenever you're ready," Essos responds. "I cleared my schedule to be available for this."

My heart skips a beat as I stare into his eyes. I'm still holding him, my fingers digging into his suit. He won't release me until I let him go first. I draw in a deep, shuddering breath, taking the leap before I chicken out again.

"I'm ready," I whisper, closing my eyes.

Essos slides his hands down my arms and slips his fingers in the spaces between mine. He waits until my eyes reopen to make a second door appear.

Two people walk through it, and I wonder if they know what's about to happen. Did Essos tell them we were going to meet? Are they prepared for this? Do they know I died? It doesn't appear that they need to be told their purpose for being in this strange place. The woman rushes toward me but stops short when I flinch.

"Daphne." She breathes my name like a prayer. She reaches out a shaky hand to tuck my hair behind my ears. She's petite, shorter than me, but has the same green eyes that I do. With that one motion, I'm a kid again. I'm the same little girl with my hair in braided pigtails standing beside my grandmother's grave, holding the hand of my social worker.

"Hi," I manage to croak out, my mouth dry and throat raw. I squeeze Essos's hand for all the strength he can lend me. He gives me a reassuring squeeze back.

"Can I hug you?" she asks, her voice thick with emotion, sensing, like any good mother, that this is overwhelming for me.

I nod, and she envelops me in a hug, holding me close to her. I release Essos's hand after a moment and wrap my arms around her, rigid at first, before melting into her embrace.

As much as I don't want to, I cry. I cry for the mother who never got to see her daughter grow up. I cry for five-year-old me, who didn't understand what was happening when her grandma died, leaving her alone in the world. I cry for ten-year-old me, getting my period for the first time in gym class, needing the school nurse to explain that I was becoming a woman. I cry for fifteen-year-old me, when I lost my virginity to a boy who pushed too hard when I didn't know how to say no. I cry for the missed milestones, the dances my parents never got to send me to, boyfriends they couldn't interrogate, and for never getting grounded after missing curfew. I cry for my father, who never got daddy-daughter dances and never got to scream my name, embarrassing me at graduations. I cry because my dad never got to press on an imaginary brake pedal while teaching me how to drive or take me out for milkshakes after my heart was broken for the first time.

I cry for the life that was stolen from us and for this blessing of a second chance to know them. My mother is running her fingers through my hair, soothing me, murmuring that she loves me the way I imagine she would have if I had woken up from a nightmare. She tells me she loves me over and over again, and that she is so proud of the young woman I became.

I manage to pull myself together, slowly extracting myself from her only to find my father openly weeping behind her. He isn't as cautious as she was. He just pulls me into his arms, crying into my hair. He pulls my mother in, too, so it's the three of us huddled together, the way it was supposed to be.

This gets my tears started again. I never realized how safe I could feel, and I never want this moment to end. The tears continue, the three of us crying together, both of them fighting for control over who gets to hold me closest.

Once we are able to control ourselves, my father turns to Essos, holding out his hand. Essos gladly takes it and gives it a firm shake.

"I don't think I can find sufficient words to thank you for giving me a second chance to hold my baby girl."

"It is my pleasure, sir," Essos responds with a smile. The man is a god, and yet he speaks to my father with deference. He gestures toward the table, and we four sit, Essos waiting to see where my parents chose before picking a seat for himself.

My mother sits next to me and my father directly across so they can both look at me as fully as possible while also being within touching distance.

"I was so relieved when you wound up with my mother, but when we could see her health was declining, we felt so helpless. We never expected you to be alone in the world." My mother sniffs, holding back more tears. My father reaches across the table and grabs her hand. If she starts crying again, I know the water-works will start for me all over again too. "I was just so glad we got to watch you grow up."

"It's not what we would have wanted for you, but it was like we were there for every moment. It was great getting to watch you graduate from fifth grade with your cute little song about moving up, all the way to getting into college." My father clears his throat then takes a sip from the water glass in front of him.

"People get to see their loved ones in their afterlife?" I ask Essos.

Solemnly, he nods, squeezing my knee under the table. "It's like watching TV—they can watch whenever, though intimate moments are never shared. They're also able to watch highlights that they would have missed. I can't tell you any more, though," Essos warns, and I nod, grabbing his hand under the table and squeezing it.

Every question I wanted to ask vanishes from my mind. I just want to spend my time staring at my parents.

"Do you get to see Grandma?" I ask, thinking of the woman who raised me, even if it was only for a short time.

"Of course. She feels so bad for leaving you so abruptly. She just missed me too much, and her heart couldn't take losing me and then my dad. When you're a mom, you'll understand that bond with your child. It's not that she didn't love you, it was just that it was a lot all at once."

"I'm not sure—" I look to Essos. I'm not sure of a lot of things. Can I have children? More importantly, do I even want a child? I search Essos's face, but he won't meet my eye for a moment. When he finally does, I get a short flash, imagining him talking to my swollen belly, his hands rubbing circles on my bare skin as I lie in bed, laughing as it tickles.

Was that a memory, or something else? A vision put there by

Essos? It felt nothing like the memories from Galen, where emotion was like a flash of heat, gone as soon as the memory ended. There is still lingering hope clinging to me, though it feels far away as the memory of it drifts, set loose in my mind as I muse on it. Essos cants his head, his brow furrowing before smoothing out, as if he's asking me a question.

"You have time, ladybug. Plenty of time before making any sort of a decision," my father says sternly with a pointed look at Essos.

I look sharply at Essos before turning my whole body toward my mother, taking her hands in mine. "I don't know if you saw this or know this already..." I pause, unsure of how to continue. "But...I died." My mother laughs, and it sounds like wind chimes tinkling in the breeze.

"We do know that, but the Afterworld is a magical place. I can't wait to show you what's in store for you. You'll get to see it all soon enough."

But she's wrong. I probably won't ever get to see it, because choosing Galen at the ball will mean severing ties with Essos, who has the power over my parents' souls. I worry for a moment that he will retaliate against them or Cat. I don't know if I could live with myself if I didn't do everything I could to protect them from the fallout.

No. Essos wouldn't—at least, not the Essos I've come to know. I might not know who he was when Galen says he killed me, but I know who he is now.

"What's it like?" I ask, trying to push away the weight that has appeared on my chest. That line of thinking isn't going to get me anywhere, and I need to enjoy this time with them while I can.

"It's like a Utopia. The sun is shining, and you get to be with the people you love who have moved on. If they haven't moved on yet, you get to watch them and see—"

Essos holds out a hand to stop my father from going any further. "I'm afraid that's enough detail for now."

It hits me then, when Essos cuts off the conversation, that I've spent all this time in the Underworld and I never considered being able to see what the Afterlife has in store. Here I am, sitting with the answer to life's biggest question—what comes next—and I've allowed myself to be distracted by dresses and boys. It makes me want to kick myself.

Essos moves the conversation along with the appearance of food before us, but it's hardly touched except for a piece here and there. We start talking about the cheese and how my parents fell in love over how to set up a charcuterie board.

"It was a little like fate, I think, getting to meet this beautiful creature," my father says. "We both happened to be in London for different reasons. I had a work thing, and your mom was visiting friends, and we both wound up getting invited to a masquerade party. Someone called my name, and when I looked in that direction, I saw your mom, and it was over for me. I almost didn't talk to her, either."

"No, I got lucky, someone bumped into me, and I spilled my drink all over his white tux. Red wine, too. It wasn't a great combination."

"There I was, trying to work up the nerve to say hi, and this knockout is standing next to me, glancing at me from the corner of her eyes. Then some woman in what I think was a peacock mask bumps her without an apology before walking off with her own drink. Never could figure out who it was, but I still need to send her a thank you card."

I'm soaking in every word, trying not to let my mind dredge up questions, because I want to hear them tell their story the way they would have when I was a kid.

Mostly, Essos and I sit there while they reminisce, making comments about how they've seen me do certain things, proving that nature plays a huge role in who you become. Dad points out that my love of 80s hair bands is thanks to my mother, and my sarcasm is definitely from him. My parents tell me about their parents and how they grew up, and I just lean against the table, my head in my hand, listening to all the tales I wanted to hear growing up.

They tell me how they fell in love and how to know that I'm with the right person. That I'll feel safe and at home in that person's arms, man or woman. They tell me that no mess is too big to fix and to never go to bed angry.

"Don't wait for your ship to come in—row out and meet it," my dad says, as if this is the ultimate advice he can pass on. I cherish it like every other word we have shared this day.

The sun never gets low in the sky, so it's not until my mother stands up and pulls me into a hug that I realize the day must be ending. I look around and, at first glance, Essos is nowhere to be found. My father steps in behind me so he's holding my mother and me at the same time.

"This was so special, ladybug." My mom cups my face after we break apart. A tear must be rolling down my cheek because she wipes it away with her thumb. "We love you and are *so* proud of you."

"And you picked a real winner here—steady job, reliable. You could certainly do worse," my father says, nudging me with his elbow, nodding at where Essos is now standing near the door. I see a flush creep up his cheeks as he pretends to fiddle with his watch.

They both hug me one last time, then open the door they came through and step back into their Afterlife.

I stand there, watching as the door disappears, and I'm left in this beautiful meadow on what feels like the perfect summer day, feeling emptier than I ever have before.

Essos watches me for a moment before walking to me and

wrapping his arms around me, pulling me into a tight hug. I start to pound on his chest, to push him away, but it's a halfhearted attempt at best, and soon I'm clinging to him, crying until I can't cry anymore.

WE STEP INTO HIS OFFICE, and he hands me a handkerchief. A glance out his window shows just how much time has passed. I don't remember noticing a window the first time I was in his office... I pause. Actually, there was a shelf of books there before. Now, there's a large window with a bench underneath it covered in pillows and a cozy throw. It's not something I would have expected from the God of the Dead, but maybe having a houseful of women has opened him up to changing his view.

It's twilight, casting the gardens in a romantic light. I didn't think his office would have a view of the gardens, but I can't think over those logistics right now. I sit on his couch for a moment, drawing my knees into my chest. The fire roars to life, and Essos sits next to me and hands me a drink. I take it and knock it back in one gulp, then shudder.

"What was that?" I ask, making a face as I hand the glass back to him.

"Very fine aged whiskey, meant to be sipped, not shot," he says with a laugh.

"Then why did you hand it to me now? I'm hardly in the mental state to appreciate fine liquor." I set my head on my knees and stare at the fire before me, watching the flames lick up the chimney. I sigh. "That was both wonderful and awful. Thank you."

I glance at him. He has one arm slung over the back of the

couch, facing me, but he's not looking at me. He's staring into the flames.

"I'm glad I could give you this gift. It's unfair that they were taken from you when you were so young." He takes a sip from his glass.

"It wasn't fair, but life rarely is." I pause, then reach over and take his glass. I sip from it and hand it back to him, this time experiencing the warmth and bite of the fine liquor. It's smokey with a sweet undertone of caramel. It's how I imagine Essos would taste. "Is what my mom said possible? For me to have children?" I never thought much about having them before that moment, beyond the vague notion that I would someday. For some reason, this is the thing I'm most hung up on. There's nothing like having the possibility stripped from you to make you want something.

Essos stands and goes to the bar cart, complete with a crystal decanter and matching glasses. He refills his glass and stills with his back to me before he drains it. There is a tension in his shoulders that remains there as he refills it a second time before refilling mine.

"It's a complicated question with a complicated answer. To keep it simple—as my consort, yes, you can. In the Afterlife, it's much more difficult." He turns to me, holding up a hand. "Before you ask why, it's because you are dead, a shadow of your former self, and new life isn't possible in the world of the dead. There are, however, other ways to become a parent in the Afterlife. Very sad ways that someone else came up with. It was something I had overlooked until my eyes were opened." It doesn't feel like he's talking to me, but I wait for him to continue. Essos remembers himself and finally meets my eye. "It's an atrocity, which is why I never thought of it. Children who are unwanted in life are often unwanted in death as well. The solution was for families that wanted children but could not have them to welcome them into their homes. I'm surprised I was able to tell you this much without triggering a nosebleed. You haven't had any more of them, have you?"

"Nosebleed free. How would it be possible as your consort?"

"Because any mortal woman chosen to be my queen will be getting a new life as a goddess. It also involves my brother, and I've put the whole thing off because asking him for favors makes him unbearable."

I suck in my lip, thinking on this.

Essos must understand the look on my face, because he continues. "It involves bestowing divinity on my queen, but it's still accomplished through the usual means." He coughs, unable to meet my eye.

Essos returns to the couch with my drink but pulls it back when I reach for it. He squints at me dramatically, as if checking on my mental well-being, before handing it to me.

I glance around his office, looking for photos of anyone—Helene or her twin or Galen or their parents—and, unsurprisingly, I find none. On his desk, though, I spy the rose I gave him, still pristine.

"Do your siblings have children?"

Essos laughs, and I lower my feet from the couch. "Another complicated question. The short answer is, yes, they do, but we have been alive for millennia, which means they're all adults with children of their own and so on and so forth. If you're imagining family reunions where everyone is happy and we all get together for a barbeque, you would be very wrong. Fidelity has been a problem for most of my siblings. Helene might be the only faithful one, but even I can't say for sure. She wouldn't let me know about such an indiscretion. Galen, well, no one has seen his wife in centuries. He might have an offspring, but if he does, they're not hers. It's hard to keep track of my brothers' progeny when so often my brothers themselves are unaware of their existence."

The glass in my hand shatters, startling both of us. I wasn't gripping it particularly hard. Perhaps I should handle only plastic cups from now on if I'm going to keep doing this. The idea that my powers could have caused the breakage momentarily distracts me from the reason it happened.

Of course, it wouldn't be shocking to hear that Galen had a wife—I would presume that Essos is talking about me. It's not even shocking that Galen might have children. He's existed for millennia. What shocked me is the insinuation that Galen's wife is still alive, and out there somewhere when he's made it clear that I was killed.

Could this be part of the cover-up that Zara overheard?

Essos springs into action, grabbing a towel from his bar cart and gently pressing it to my thighs after making the shards of glass disappear. Once he's done, he checks my hands to see if I cut myself, and there's another wound over the scab I've been picking it.

"You're bleeding," he says, voice barely more than a whisper.

Essos becomes stock still as he stares at the blood on my hand. There is a faint tremor in his hand as he holds mine. The cut isn't particularly deep, but blood is welling along the slit. I start to pull my hand back, but he holds fast to it, jolting into action. He dabs gently at the blood with his cloth. Once the blood is gone, he lifts my hand to his mouth, gently pressing his lips to the opening. Warmth suffuses the injury. I start to lean toward him, and for just a second, he moves toward me too, nearly closing the distance between us before his head hangs, breaking the moment. It's for the best, because my heart is hammering in my chest and I don't know how to feel. Straddling him right now to kiss the daylights out of him is not an appropriate thing to do, no matter how the desire to do so drives me to shift infinitesimally closer to him on the couch.

We sit quietly for a moment. I hope that Essos will feel obligated to fill in the silence, but instead, he seems to enjoy it. I suspect it's where he is most comfortable. I imagine that living in the Underworld doesn't give him much reason for entertaining.

"Do you have children?" I ask, deciding to fill the silence myself.

"I almost did," he whispers, staring into the fire. He seems to fall deep down the well of memories, and he looks like he might drown. It's like watching a timelapse video as he deflates, causing an ache in my chest. To lose a child is unimaginable. I don't fight the urge to embrace him, as my own heart breaks. My hand slides to the nape of his neck as I enfold him into my arms. He fights it for a fraction of a second before he melts into me, giving up any pretense of resistance. His arms slide around my waist as we twist toward each other. He leveled me out when my own pain was blinding; maybe this time I can do the same for him.

Essos presses his face into the crook of my neck, breathing in deeply. I stroke his hair, hoping that what little of myself I can give him is enough. Maybe someday, I'll know Essos's story, but today is not it.

Abruptly, Essos releases me. He won't meet my gaze, looking instead at the fireplace, but I think I see a glassy sheen to his eyes. Blinking rapidly, he turns to face me with what I have come to think of as his official mask slipping into place.

I take this as a dismissal and finish my drink, then set it aside. I pushed the wrong buttons, and he shut down, as he's right to. I'm not sure why I think I am entitled to his secrets, given I haven't been forthcoming with information either. "Thank you again for today. It meant everything to me."

He stands up, shaken from his reverie. "Do you want me to have food sent to your room? Or we can go to the kitchens together and I can whip something up for you. Maybe we can finally put my carbonara to the test?"

I consider his offer, imagining him cooking for me. If I didn't know about Galen or my murder, it would be so easy to fall in love with this man, but I can't. I *can't* let him keep doing these kind things for me. I shake my head and walk toward the door. "No, thank you. I'm actually not even a little bit hungry."

Essos follows me, slowing to set his glass on his desk.

I open the door to find someone standing on the other side, and I jerk back in surprise, bumping into Essos's chest. Essos's hands catch my hips and pull me closer to him, and he takes a step back, like he's trying to widen the distance between me and this stranger. The man looms there, looking down at his phone.

He looks past me at Essos. "It's good that you're not hungry. I need to have a long conversation with my brother." His accent isn't posh like that of Helene and Essos. Instead, his voice is smooth and almost American. This man is just as formal as Essos in his manner of dress, and the familial resemblance is strong, with the dark curls and strong jaw. His hair is swept back, and he seems to have a minor receding hairline. His cheeks are sunken, further enhancing the strong lines of his high cheekbones and square jaw.

"Xavier," Essos says coolly. My eyebrows shoot up at this confirmation. The similarities between Essos and Xavier are much stronger than Essos and Helene or Galen. If I didn't know better, I would think Galen and Helene were the twins, with their similar golden coloring.

This is hardly the warm welcome I would expect toward a brother, but it's certainly warmer than when he greeted Galen.

"Essos. We need to chat." When I don't move, he looks at me pointedly. "Alone."

I match his stare. "I would go, but you're blocking the door-way." I give him a blank look until he takes a step back and lets me pass. I don't look back as I walk down the hallway, but I do pause as I hear the start of their conversation.

"Someone has filed a formal complaint, and you know my hands are tied on this. Since we're already so close to the end, we're moving up the Calling Ball before the complaint makes it into the papers. You have enough of an image problem as the aloof King of Death."

This is the last thing I hear as the door clicks shut. *King of the Underworld, God of the Dead*, I silently correct, irrationally mad that his own brother can't get Essos's titles right.

Grimacing, I flip the bird at the door and the abrupt dismissal. Cat is nowhere to be found, despite promising that she would wait outside. Even her chair is gone. I want to linger, see if I can hear anything, but my whole body is pushed away as if by some outside force. Fighting against it, I take one, then two steps back toward Essos's office until the effort is too exhausting on top of the emotional turmoil of the day. These gods and their secrets are godsdamned annoying.

I didn't do anything nearly as physically strenuous as the day Helene and I worked out, but I feel that same level of exhaustion. I understand so much better now why Essos and Sybil have kept the details of the Afterlife so locked down. If I had known that's what it would be like, I would have wanted to spend all my time with my parents, learning all the things I was robbed of.

I'm left with so many thoughts and emotions and questions that when I get back to my room, I almost miss the box sitting on my bed that seems to be moving. I don't have a chance to open it before the top pops open and a card flutters to the floor.

Inside the box is a ginger cat, who looks up at me, the crisscross pattern on his fur a dead giveaway of just who this is. A gasp strangles my throat, and the dam that had been holding in my tears breaks. When I walk closer to him, an angry but recognizable chirp breaks the silence, and I scoop him up, hugging him close. I forget about the card for a moment, hugging Waffles to my chest. My foot crushes it, and I plop onto my bed and bend over to pick it up. Waffles cries again under my crushing hug, trying to squirm away and explore, and I finally let him after pressing a hard kiss to his head. The desire to know how he came to be here is squashed quickly because I really don't want to know if he died and now lives in this realm eternally. This is a question I am better off not knowing the answer to. I pick up the card and tear it open.

Thought you might need this after today.
  -E

I curl around the note, tracing my fingers over his script that is so familiar. My heart has grown three sizes from his monumental level of consideration today. Tears once more streaking my cheeks, I struggle again to reconcile the man Galen has warned me about with the man before me, who has made some of the grandest gestures possible.

29

Since breakfast has somehow become everyone's introduction meal, I'm not surprised the next morning to find Xavier sitting at the table, reading a newspaper over an egg white omelet.

"Good morning," I greet, taking my usual seat. I opted for a simple cornflower blue sundress and flats today.

Xavier's eyes track me over the top of his paper, but he says nothing in return. Cat is the next to filter in with the dogs at her heels. I woke to Dave whining at my door, and when I tried to introduce him to Waffles, Dave got a sharp swipe to the nose. First blood to Waffles.

Xavier sits up a little taller, watching as Cat takes her seat next to me.

"I tried to stay last night but was shooed away." Her gaze flicks to Xavier, then to me in apology.

I squeeze her hand. I didn't leave my room after getting Waffles, taking the time to cuddle with him and then falling into an exhausted sleep, but now I can't wait to tell her all about meeting my parents.

Zara arrives next, coming up the stairs from the kitchen in a candy-apple-red satin tank top with lace trim and matching short shorts. I catch the way she sways her hips as Essos follows her. In their hands they each have two plates piled high with pancakes. Zara and Essos set them in the center of the table, and I watch as Xavier takes in an eyeful of Zara's bottom.

Zara turns to Essos to wipe some of the pancake mix off his face and gives him a kiss. I can't bury the hot flush of jealousy that courses through me, no matter how hard I try. I want to take my eyes off them but find I'm unable to as Zara presses herself against him, pretending to clear a smudge that's already gone. I should be happier about this. Maybe Essos will be happy with Zara, and he won't feel the urge to murder me again when I pick his brother. Maybe that *is* the best possible solution—Zara and Essos, me and Galen.

The thought doesn't sit right with me. Actually, it makes me want to throw up, as the image of Zara and Essos entwined naked rises unbidden in my mind.

One of the glasses on the table next to them shatters, not unlike last night, drawing everyone's attention. While glancing around the room to see what caused it, I catch Xavier and Essos sharing a look before Essos clears the broken glass from the table. If that was me, if that was my powers, I need to get a handle on what is causing the outburst. It seems to happen randomly. It must be from being in the Underworld for so long.

Pretending it didn't happen, Zara barrels on as Galen enters the room and seats himself on the other side of me so I'm sandwiched between him and Cat.

"We made pancakes for everyone!" Zara announces cheerfully, starting to put pancakes on everyone's plates. She goes to drop one on Xavier's plate, and the look he gives her would wither the sun. She turns and drops that one on my plate.

"Big brother!" Galen exclaims, dropping his napkin on his lap.

"Have you been working out lately?" Xavier looks pleased at the comment, but Galen doesn't stop there. "Because it doesn't look like you have. You must be slacking."

Galen tries to laugh at his own joke but finds that his mouth has been sealed shut. Essos laughs but covers it with a cough. Galen glares at Xavier, but Xavier just picks up his newspaper and hides his face behind it. The paper is called the *Solarem Times*, and one of the top-of-the-fold articles mentions Essos and the Calling, but I'm unable to read more before Xavier shifts the paper to read a different section. From the few headlines I'm able to catch, I'm starting to realize that Sybil hasn't covered nearly as much as we need to be ready for the ball. There are pop culture headlines about Solarem media, and even a gossip column wondering who Xavier's flavor of the week is.

When asked about it, Sybil gives the same explanation—that we need to be prepared to be grilled about the type of wood used for the Trojan Horse, and not the anniversary of Posey's lost diadem. I'm not sure what a Posey is other than a flower, or why we'd care about this diadem. They also haven't told us about Xavier and Helene, but I'm sure one copy of the *Times* would give us a ton of insight.

We're all seated and silently enjoying our breakfasts except for Galen, whose arms are crossed like a petulant child.

Xavier folds up his newspaper and stands. "Some of you in this room don't know who I am, so allow me to introduce myself. I am Xavier, Lord of Solarem, King of the Gods. There has been a change of plans, but I trust you are all capable of making adjustments."

Everyone in the room tenses except for me, since I know what is coming.

"A complaint has been made regarding the Calling. To avoid being forced to cancel this late into the process, the timeline has been..." he pauses for dramatic effect "...modified. One week from tonight, you will need to be ready to dazzle the lords and ladies of Solarem." Xavier and Essos share a significant look. "The complaint itself has nothing to do with you ladies, but rather that the timeline is too long, and with interested parties lingering about, there is a risk of interference."

Cat and Zara exchange worried glances, but I just stick a bite of pancake in my mouth, waiting to see if there's anything more. Galen is unmuted and able to start eating, but he keeps shooting dirty looks at his brother.

Cat raises her hand like she's in grade school. "King of the Gods?" she asks. If I know Cat, and I do, she's mentally cursing Sybil for promising to teach us closer to the ball so the information would be closer in our minds. It certainly doesn't help that our lessons also keep getting cut short for one reason or another. When Helene was here, we didn't have any.

"Someone needs to rule these miserable bastards," Xavier says. He turns to Sybil, who is standing at the back of the room. "Have you taught them nothing?"

"They have had lessons, but I've been busy. Your siblings dropping in unannounced also hasn't helped." Sybil doesn't cower under his gaze. Essos is watching closely from behind his tower of pancakes.

"Impertinent. What could possibly be more important?" Xavier demands.

"Running this realm while someone dated twenty coeds."

Galen spits out his coffee as Essos coughs and Xavier glares. Sybil remains unapologetic.

"I've been doing my job, thank you very much," Essos snaps, standing up. "Speaking of, I have matters to attend to." He leaves the room.

Xavier sighs, turning his sights on us. "Then I suppose you are all in luck. After breakfast, we will meet in the library. Be prompt." He sweeps out of the room.

Galen jumps up to follow him, leaving we final three alone.

"Damn, do they all have to be so good-looking and well dressed?" Cat says into the void.

WE DO as asked and meet in the library after breakfast, ready for anything. Zara had to get changed, so for once I am not the last to arrive. Cat is the only one of us with a notebook, which Xavier observes with disdain. He leads us to a table and gestures for us to sit. Cat sets down her notebook, pen at the ready.

"Clearly, they have done you a disservice by not educating you well enough on what is to come. The purpose of today is to fill your tiny mortal brains with the information you need about the people you are going to meet in one week's time. The vacation of having parties every night is over. Now comes the hard part."

Xavier spends the next three hours telling us an abbreviated family history, a who's who of the Solarem gods. Some of what we've learned is covered again, namely minor gods like Dion and Luminara. I'm thankful to Sybil for covering some of what we needed. We learn that Helene and Xavier were to be married until her husband literally sprang out of the sea and swept her off her feet to his seabed. Xavier casually mentions that he has several children who won't be in attendance as his wife, Posey, will be there.

"So, you're a philandering narcissist? Does that make you the God of Infidelity?" Cat asks pointedly.

"Only on weekends," he snaps back, but through the rest of the lesson, his eyes keep returning to Cat.

Noticeably absent from the discussion is anything about Essos.

"Helene mentioned that Essos had his heart broken, but you haven't said anything about him," I remark, and I see Xavier grind his teeth. We've heard little tidbits about his consort, but nothing handed to us the way he could now.

"This petty gossip is beneath me. Who hasn't had their heart broken in several millennia of existence? I don't care how Kai claimed Helene, or if I wooed my wife, or if she likes any of my children. Helene should learn to keep her big mouth shut," Xavier says before turning back to the family tree.

I notice that Galen also has two leaves attached to his name.

I don't have to think hard to know that Galen has never mentioned his children to me. I assume they aren't mine, because that is something he would have shown me himself.

I think about the visual of Essos rubbing my pregnant belly. Yet another oddly shaped puzzle piece that doesn't clearly fit. The vision could have been my overactive imagination, or maybe something more. I won't find out until the fucking ball.

"Who are they?" I point to the leaves.

"My nasty little niece and nephew, who won't show up if they know what's good for them. Goddess of Strife and God of Murder." A shadow crosses Xavier's face, and thunder clatters in the distance. His tone tells me that's the end of that discussion.

I refuse to let it go. "Galen never mentioned any children." I hope I'm not being obvious, but with the way Xavier looks at me, I think maybe I am.

"He's not proud of his extramarital misfits. They're usually off causing problems in some other part of the world."

"Are any of Essos's former flames or wives or something going to be at the ball?" Zara asks casually, prompting Xavier to roll his eyes.

"In a manner of speaking, yes. His side piece should be there."

The world narrows to a pinprick, and I try to remember to breathe even as the world drops out from under me.

Cat reaches out and grabs my wrist. "*Breathe*," she whispers, intentionally digging her nails into my skin, grounding me. I focus on the half-moon crescents before looking back at Xavier.

When it comes to Essos, Xavier is light on the details. "You three understand that this is beneath me, right? Your petty questions about my brothers' love lives are demeaning and vapid. This is hardly an episode of *Gossip Girl*."

Cat and I share a look.

"What do you do as the King of the Gods?" she asks him, probably to boost his ego after tearing him down before.

"Now *that* is a question worth my time." Xavier preens like a peacock. "I keep the lesser gods in line and monitor their goings-on. I make sure that everyone is doing their part to combat the mortal stupidity that we have to deal with."

"You wouldn't mean the mortal stupidity that gods have been instigating since they discovered worship? Sybil did cover that in our lessons." I bat my eyes innocently at Xavier.

"But, of course, they taught you *that*. Let me guess, they wanted to make sure you knew—"

Cat cuts him off. "But you don't work in the Underworld?"

"No. Dead people creep me out. Of course, you three are caught somewhere in the middle. Not quite dead, but not quite mortal anymore. That's why Essos was able to pull off sending your friend home without any great cosmic disturbance. The realm of the dead plays by its own rules."

"Tiffany made it?" Zara's voice is small and hopeful. Essos and Sybil have been tightlipped whenever approached about it, to the point that Cat and I stopped asking. I'm not sure Zara ever did.

Xavier is unsympathetic. "Yes, though she now lives with crushing survivor's guilt for the missed calls and snoozed alarm." Zara looks destroyed. "Steve is there to help her through it, though, if that makes it any better." He doesn't look like he cares either way. If Xavier knows that much about it, my guess is he has the heart of a romantic in there somewhere.

Cat grabs Zara's hand and gives it a squeeze. We'll help her through this later. For now, it looks like if a single tear is shed, Xavier will level the place.

"And whoever controls the realm of the dead, controls the dead? Can they control the influx of the dead? Create zombies? Does the God of the Dead change? Can there be a different King of the Underworld?" Catalina is scribbling in her notebook as she fires off these questions until Xavier makes her notebook and pen disappear mid-word.

"The King of the Underworld, or as some know him, the Lord of the Underworld, has, is and always will be, Essos. Removing him from power would be like a monarch executing another monarch, a precedent no one wants to set. If you want to get specific about it, if a ruler is shown to be ineffective, someone *could* put forth a vote of no confidence. If there is enough support among the gods, that person could be removed, but it is unlikely. Short of a riot, I'm stuck with my job, and Kai and Essos are stuck with theirs, no matter how much the latter would love to walk away. And there is no such thing as zombies." Xavier seems to think on this, but shakes his head as if realizing he doesn't want to venture down that path. "At least, I don't think so—you'll have to ask Essos."

He conjures an apple and takes a bite. "Gods, this teaching thing is exhausting. No wonder Sybil was going to leave you all to be fed to the wolves. I can see it now—you not showing my wife the deference she commands, and then all of a sudden, BAM, it's World War III. In case you were wondering what set off the powder keg for World War I, it was my wife." When he looks at our appalled faces, he laughs. "I'm joking. Someone else started World War I—my wife helped kickstart the French Revolution." He stands as we remain silent. "Well then, tough crowd."

Sybil enters the room as Xavier begins to tell us about his parents, the God and Goddess Supreme. Sybil touched on them during an earlier lesson, but it was one during which I struggled to focus, naturally. I'm curious to learn more, but he stops talking as they approach.

"That will be all for today," Sybil says curtly, their long legs carrying them quickly toward us.

"I'll be the one to decide that." He towers over them. Distantly, I think I hear the roll of thunder.

"Yes, you would be, but I've been informed that you missed an important meeting this morning with your brother-in-law, and he is quite displeased. He's demanding you contact him immediately."

"Displeased with me? I'll make sure that barnacle-covered fish fucker knows who can demand what." Xavier pushes past them, static crackling in the air, causing my hair to rise. "I am *the* God of Gods. No one gets to be displeased with me." He pushes his way out the door, still cursing under his breath.

"Now that he's gone, Helene would like you all to change into workout attire in order to—and I'm quoting her—'sweat the mortal off' at the beach." Sybil lets out a sigh after dropping this information.

"Helene is back?" I asked, confused.

"Yes, and she hates to be kept waiting. Off you go. Oh, and ladies, don't mention this to any of her brothers."

The three of us scurry off to get changed.

I'm the first one on the beach, really on a roll for being punctual today. I'm lucky Helene greets me with a smile after the way we left things at the ball. I never got a chance to thank her or apologize. The beach is covered in various workout items—more tires, dumbbells, cones, and yoga mats. I can't imagine what she's going to have us do.

"Helene?" I start, hoping to gauge her mood.

"Daphne."

"I just wanted to—"

"I'm going to stop you right there. I don't have the time or the patience to listen to you craft some sort of half-assed apology about why you thought it was appropriate to yell at me, a goddess, someone who could smite you without skipping a step. I said you had a heart of darkness; don't go and ruin it by backing down now."

Cat isn't far behind me and gasps when she sees the layout. Zara is the last to arrive, and she runs to Helene and gives her a hug. Helene frowns and pats Zara on the shoulder before disentangling from her grip.

"So, I heard that the Calling Ball has been moved up, which means that I need to kick your sorry asses into shape. There's going to be an expectation for you to be able to keep up with everyone, and if you're getting winded by the fourth dance, that's going to reflect poorly on all of us. I'm not interested in that. We're creatures of grace. If one of you were to become a goddess and you, say, struggle with letting someone else lead—" she looks at me pointedly, and it makes me want to kick Finn in the shins "—that problem will likely only become a larger problem when you descend into godhood. Though I'm not positive about that— this will be the first time a mortal has been allowed such a gift. As it stands, I'm not willing to take the chance, so, chop fucking chop."

HELENE SPENDS the week before the Calling Ball breaking us down and building us up with details we need to know to survive it.

357

Such as, Xavier's wife, Posey, is a stickler for protocol, including us curtseying to her.

"No one curtseys anymore, but she demands it," Helene imparts as we toss a 15-pound medicine ball around between us. Cat nearly topples over when Helene lobs it to her.

Helene focuses on me and Zara, trying to get us into shape. She mostly ignores Cat, which Zara finds strange. Zara is the only person out of all of us who doesn't know Cat isn't really in the running. Helene is hardest on me, at one point pushing me over during yoga while I'm balancing in Tree Pose.

I collapse on the ground and stare up at her with fury in my eyes.

"Do better, Daphne. You should be as sturdy as a tree, that's the fucking point of the pose." The next time she tries it, I close my eyes and try to brace myself, envisioning I am rooted to the ground, and I don't fall.

The hierarchy of the gods is the most important thing she drills into us. Xavier is at the top, the God of Gods, as he calls himself. On the same level, though Xavier hates to admit it, are Helene's husband, Kai, and Essos. In the court hierarchy, they are the three kings, and not even the God Supreme ranks above them. The God Supreme has more raw power than them but would bow to his sons and son-in-law. Galen, the baby, falls into the fodder with all the other gods, only given a distinction as a brother of kings.

"Don't get me wrong, I love my daddy, and I do mean that literally and not as a cute nickname for my husband, but that deadbeat can't be trusted to brush his own teeth, let alone govern a kingdom," she says between blowing a whistle for box jumps.

While Helene is harder on me, Zara seems to be the one more in need of help, so Cat tries to aid her when Helene is focused on bullying me. A hateful, jealous part of me gets a little thrill at seeing Zara winded. We have patched our relationship, but it doesn't change that she's my chief competition. I want to question that angry little voice in my head—what does it matter if Essos picks her if I want Galen?—but it fights back, refusing to let go of the way he looks at her.

Helene lets us know that Xavier hates her husband. "He thinks that as King of the Gods, anything and everything should want to screw him. I'm his twin, not his concubine. Besides, my husband is a god in his own right, and a total babe."

As much as she is willing to gossip about Xavier and Posey and their marital problems, she offers us nothing about Essos or Galen. She rebuffs Zara when she pushes for more information about Essos's love life.

"As I told Daphne, you have to ask Essos." She is immovable on this point, the way she has been since we first met her.

She focuses more on the interpersonal rather than grander-scale details. She does confirm that a family member started each of the world wars over a petty disagreement, and that many of the large worldly disagreements can be traced back to their family or offshoots.

Helene works with us and beside us, making sure that we are prepared in ways that Xavier and Sybil didn't. We are coming away armed with information we will need. Cat is rightfully annoyed that we spent the first few months learning none of this. Our time was wasted parading around in dresses, ignorant of all the things that mattered.

On the last day, Helene relents for several relaxing hours of yoga and massages. We sit in a mud bath she conjures for us on the beach, unable to move, not just from the mud but also from the pure exhaustion.

"Since I have your full and undivided attention... What I really have to say is, don't fuck up tomorrow. It was nice knowing you all and nice to see us finally get to this point for once. You each make my brother happy, and I am hoping to see this through to completion." She gives me a wink. "I actually have my own prepa-rations to make for tomorrow, so I'll get out of your hair. Relax for the rest of the day, just the three of you, because after tomorrow, you may never see each other again. Toodles!"

She skips off into the house, leaving us sitting there with her words sinking in. I meet Cat's eyes across the mud bath, mad that most of our final month was stripped from us. Helene worked us so hard that each night, we didn't even want to chitchat—we just passed out.

"What do you think she meant by never see each other again? You don't think Essos will let you stay?" Zara tries to lift her arm, but it's stuck in the mud.

I cast a sympathetic look in her direction. I don't have a plan, but if things wind up the way Galen wants, I don't know what will happen. I exist in Essos's world, stuck between life and death. If the ball will unlock my memories, will that return me to my former state of life? If I reject him, I assume that means he will ask Zara to be his partner. I like to think Essos would indulge his new queen and let Cat stick around for emotional support. They're still good friends, if not in the same way Cat and I are.

Would Cat want to stay? She's here for me, but if I'm not here, will she pass on? I haven't been able to see Galen alone all week to ask him what to expect from the ball, and what comes next.

I'll never be able to get back the nights this complaint stripped us of, so I plan to make our last night together time just for us girls.

30

That night, we are exhausted. Essos and Xavier are working hard on arranging the menus and tables and making the house ready for an influx of gods. I overheard Essos trying to put it off, but Xavier insisted, saying that his wife demanded it since he doesn't do anything anyway. Because of the sheer amount of people who will be in attendance, some of the prep work is being done the mortal way. The dining room is being prepared for the ball, so we eat on plates in the living room, sitting on the couches and on the floor.

Galen stops by and observes us from the doorway as the three of us struggle to lift our arms to eat. "What has gotten into you three?" he asks. While Essos and Xavier have had their heads bent over seating charts, he's been noticeably absent. I don't know where Galen went each day; we never saw him on the beach, but he always returned at mealtimes.

"Helene has—" Zara begins.

"Left us with grueling exercise routines that we've been doing, and it's exhausting," I cut her off, throwing her a look.

Essos and Xavier walk in together in time for the end of my complaint. Essos catches my eye, but I pretend not to notice.

"Good," Xavier says, sipping from his glass tumbler. "My wife is going to eat you all alive." There's a vicious gleam in his eyes.

I narrow my eyes at him, mentally noting that, in the library, he didn't tell us his wife would want us to curtsey to her and address her by her formal title—Her Royal Majesty, Lady Posey, Queen of the Gods, Goddess of Mothers. Hardly seems sporting that he set us up to fail.

I heft myself up and go into the deserted kitchen to refill my drink. With everyone preparing for the ball, I don't want to disturb the staff. We have a separate section set up exclusively where we can serve ourselves away from the bustle of their preparations.

Galen follows me into the kitchen and grabs my hand, spinning me around to face him. He brings his hands to my face, cupping it gently. For a moment, I think he's going to kiss me, but instead, I get another memory.

WE'RE PANTING, *our bodies molded together as he thrusts deep inside me. My orgasm is already tearing through my body, his name falling from my lips as I play out a million lifetimes between us. I'm grateful for our immortality, because it means never having to lose time with the man I love.*

He shouts his release into the hollow of my neck. The movement of his hips becomes jerky and uneven before he slides out of me. I watch Galen as he rolls to his side pulling me snug against him.

"Perhaps this time next year we will have a little prince or princess roaming our halls," Galen teases, brushing his nose, then his lips across my brow.

"Perhaps if the Goddess of Motherhood chooses to bless us this time. Do we know her? I'm drawing a blank." My tone is dryer than his, less

hopeful. Instead, I cross my legs, twisting closer to my husband, planting a kiss on his chest.

FOR THE FIRST TIME, I feel Galen's hands outside the memory tense on my face. Is this not what he wanted me to see?

GALEN WALKS *his fingers over my abdomen. "Maybe she is yet to be born. Maybe you're to be the mother of such a goddess, one who will be worshiped by all. And you know what? Even if they become the god or goddess of birds or grain or nightmares, we will still love them. They will be our child, our prince or princess, and we will love them because you will be their mother, and they will inherit your wit and charm and that clever, wicked mouth of yours. The Fates might see fit to test us, but I will never tire of trying. I will never tire of us."*

I push him back down onto the mattress and reach between us, hoping to hide my tears. I feel him hardening under my ministrations until I slide down onto him. For a moment, I think I get away with the empty feeling growing in me despite how Galen fills me now. That is, until he rolls me over so I'm on my back, and he stills to kiss each tear away.

THE MEMORY ENDS THERE, and I feel tears on my face. Galen wipes them from my cheeks, and I smack his hand away, not interested in his comfort.

"What happened?" I demand. "What changed from then to here? You want me to be patient until tomorrow, but I've done my waiting, weeks of it, in fact. These memories are teases, and I'm tired of it."

Galen steps away from me, giving me my space to be angry. "After you were...taken from me—"

"Murdered. Just say it out loud," I interrupt.

He swallows, not meeting my eyes. "After you were murdered —by Essos," he finally says, his voice cracking, "I tried to get you back, bring your soul back, but the weapon he used locked it away. He kept your soul from me. I don't know what changed, why he released your soul, but he is King of the Underworld, and he alone has power over souls."

"I just don't understand any of this." I shake my head, moving to the other side of the kitchen, away from him. I am too confused by what I'm feeling versus what I'm seeing. They don't match, and I don't have time to figure out how to get them to line up. I have too many questions to even know where to begin.

"Tomorrow night, during the ball, Essos will choose his next bride, and I think he intends to pick you." I look up, surprised. A part of me always wondered if maybe I was here to tease and taunt Galen, and that he would ultimately pick Zara. "Oh, don't look shocked. This is his way of taking you from me forever. If he chooses you to be his queen, then we can never be together. Tomorrow, he's going to announce it in front of everyone."

I turn away from Galen, my hand covering my mouth. He's right. On some level, I did know that Essos would choose me, but I held on to the hope that I could avoid being forced to choose between him and Galen by having Essos pick Zara. How am I supposed to know what to do and who to choose? With the knowledge I have, it seems as though Galen is the choice I'm supposed to make. But what about the magnetism I feel toward Essos? Is he somehow influencing my attraction as part of his charade? To make me love him?

"So, what am I supposed to do instead?" I ask, my back still turned to him.

"Pick me. When the time comes, I need you to choose me. I know you haven't yet, but when you remember, you will love me.

I suspect it's the only way you'll get your memories back. Your mortal fairytales have it covered quite well with true love's kiss."

I spin around to him. "Are you *actually* trying to sway me using a *Grey's Anatomy* quote? That moment didn't work out so well for Meredith," I say, completely befuddled.

"I know it's your favorite." He tries to move into my space but I back away.

"What about Cat and Zara? What happens to them when I pick you?" I worry my bottom lip between my teeth.

"They will be fine. Essos will have to pick his runner-up, and he'll probably let the other girl stay to help his new bride. Once your memories are back, you'll be caught up in trying to learn about all that you missed, and your friend will be so busy adjusting to being queen, she won't have time for you."

His words leave a sour taste in my mouth. "I need to sleep on this." I go to walk around him.

Galen slams his fist on the countertop, cracking the marble. "I won't lose you to him again, *damn it*," he hisses, looking at me, eyes flashing red. There are warning bells going off. This level of vehemence is startling, and it feels wrong.

I take another step back. "I want you to know, and remember, that I will *not* be bullied into making any decisions. What I decide tomorrow will be *my* decision. If you love me the way you claim to, then you will respect that. Now. Step. *Aside*," I say, not breaking eye contact.

He reaches for me again, and once again I step back.

"I'm sorry. I just—I'm terrified of losing you again, forever. It would break me to know that you are just out of reach, and I think that, once you remember, it would break you too." His voice sounds feeble now, a drastic difference from moments ago.

"I don't appreciate feeling like you're pushing me into a decision, and if you keep pushing me, you won't like the decision I make." My voice is low and lethal.

Galen holds his hands up and steps aside. "I'm sorry. You're caught in the middle of a centuries-long sibling rivalry, and I'm terrified to lose you again now that I've found you."

I opt to let him have the final word, shaking my head and leaving him behind in the kitchen to wonder if he's pushed me too hard.

I am shaking from this interaction, and I don't say anything to anyone as I walk straight past the group laughing in the living room. Sybil passes me on the stairs. Their small hand reaches out to stop me, but I need to get into my room and away from people. I dodge deftly out of their grip and take the rest of the stairs two at a time.

I get into my room and close the door, then lean against it. Waffles winds himself around my legs, rubbing his face on my calves and marking me as his while Dave is absent. I hold my hands in front of me and watch how they tremble.

I scoop up my cat and squeeze him to my chest. Waffles lets out an angry yelp and claws his way out of my grip. I try to think about how Galen must feel, how fear of losing me all over again must be making him act like that. Is he right? If I don't choose him, will I regret my response once I get my memories back?

If I don't trust Galen...will I find myself bound to my murderer?

31

The morning of the ball, I feel like death warmed over. The entire night, I couldn't sleep, my grand plans of having one last night with Zara and Cat evaporating in my hazy worry about today. After the confrontation with Galen, I didn't want to talk to anyone, not even Cat. When she came to my room, knocking to see if I was up, I stayed silent, holding my breath, until she went to her own room.

I took a long, hot bath before bed, with Dave sitting beside me on the floor. Waffles and Dave seem to have come to some sort of an accord. At night, they cuddle close on either side of me, both staking a claim. My legs act as a divider, giving them each a separate half of the bed. Since they started sleeping like this, it's kept their nighttime battles to a minimum. They're not exactly getting along or tolerating each other, but at least they let me have my sleep.

As the hot water burned my skin, I wondered what I should do next. Galen's behavior was concerning, and I wondered if the pressure was getting to him. Did he not believe that I would pick him? It was true we hadn't seen much of each other in the past few weeks, but he knew the reason I was *here* was because of Essos. I would have thought him above jealousy, after what he'd helped me see. Something as everlasting as love between gods should transcend death.

But on the flip side, *should* he believe it? I still felt that I had a deeper connection with Essos than what was on the surface. Perhaps being murdered led to a special bond with your murderer. Was that why I felt so magnetically drawn to him? Maybe it wasn't sexual energy but something else.

What would come next with Essos at the ball if I picked his brother? Would we just leave? No goodbye to Zara and Cat? Would Essos rain his fury down upon us? Would my parents be punished for my decision? Every time I thought I was out of questions and would start to drift off, a flash of silver behind my eyelids jolted me awake.

When I go down for breakfast and Zara gasps, I know it isn't a good look.

"What happened to you? Are you sick?" she asks, reaching over to take my hand.

"Wow, I must look pretty bad if you're asking me that."

Finn, who I haven't seen in weeks, waltzes in. I'm sure Essos has work for him to do this morning in preparation for tonight. "Daphne, I'm surprised by the makeup this morning, but the smokey eye looks good on you." I shoot him a glare, only to see that Finn is serious.

"I'm not wearing makeup, Finn. Glad to know I look as tired as I feel. Where have you been anyway?" I'm grouchy, but I can't be mad. I'm exhausted; I can't even deny it. Cat puts her hand over my other one.

Finn looks like he wants to melt into the wallpaper. "I do have an actual job. Much as I would have loved to continue to drink wine with you and talk about how dreamy Essos is, I've been busy." He edges closer to me, effectively caging me in from behind by placing a hand on the table on either side of me. I turn my head, knowing he has more to say. When it comes to Finn, there is always something more.

"Yes?" I ask.

"Tonight is going to be epic. Please, just—all you have to do is follow along, and everything—*everything*—will be made clear."

He plants a kiss on my cheek before he skips out.

"You disappeared halfway through last night, and you didn't answer when I knocked," Cat says sadly. Right then, I wish more than anything that I had opened the door to her. The confrontation with Galen was the only thing on my mind—I was too overwhelmed for company. I probably needed Cat last night more than anything to help me sort through what I'm feeling.

"I just wanted to get some sleep, which I wasn't very successful at," I say weakly.

"Clearly," Zara adds helpfully.

I have no patience this morning for her snark. "What is your problem?" I snap.

"What is *my* problem?" she echoes. "You and Cat are so close, you won't even entertain the idea of letting someone else in. Well, my best friend left to go back to her life, and I've been all alone, so screw you guys." She starts crying softly. I scrub my hand over my face, realizing I have only a few hours to start to make amends for how unfair I've been to her. Cat and I share a guilty look. We tried to include her, but after three years as roommates, we don't always need words to communicate. Maybe we were leaving her out without even meaning to.

"I'm sorry." My words are insignificant, given where we are at in this process, but I can't go back and change things. I can and do move closer to her, resting a hand on her forearm. Cat sits on her other side and starts rubbing Zara's back.

"I'm sorry, too," Cat says, and takes Zara's hand with her free one.

"I know we're all supposed to be romantic rivals, but I was hoping to have more of a sisterhood with you both."

My guilt thickens as I reach forward and envelop her in a hug, prompting Cat to do the same.

"Is it so bad that I just want to be included?" she asks between sniffs.

"No!" Cat and I say in unison. I contemplate trusting her with the whole Galen fiasco and decide that, at this point, it can't do any more harm. I need a sounding board.

I suggest that we move our conversation to my room, away from prying ears, so we can speak freely. Cat, sensing that I have more information to share, agrees, and we get up to leave without breakfast, confusing Zara, who follows along anyway.

Once in my room, I close the door and turn on the sound machine that came in all our rooms. Cat scoops up Waffles, who rubs his head against her chin. I fill in Zara on everything about Galen, from the touching to the memories we shared to the details that I know of my past life. I give her fewer details than I gave Cat, but I do catch them both up about last night and the latest memory. I omit the part where Galen broke the counter and tried to block my exit. Cat is already skeptical of Galen, and that will only solidify her against him.

"Did you have any dreams of Essos?" Cat asks Zara, biting her lip

"No—well, yes. I had plenty of dreams where Essos and I are at a Zeta Tau Beta party, and we're in the hot tub, right? And he just whispers in my ear that no one is going to know as he impales me on his dick and—"

I bring my hand to my mouth as if I'm thinking, but I'm biting down on my finger to fight the stoked flames of anger that grow in my belly at the thought of Essos and Zara together. Cat squeezes my knee, and I realize my entire body tensed up as Zara spoke.

"My dreams of Essos—or who I assume was Essos—weren't like that. When I told Galen about them, he warned me that Essos could be planting memories in my head, but they seem so close to the memories I've seen with Galen."

Cat rolls her eyes and pinches her lips, but says nothing, giving Zara a chance to impart her opinion.

"That makes so much more sense!" Zara exclaims, and Cat and I give her confused looks. "Well, I went to get a midnight snack, and I saw Essos talking to someone who was standing in the shadows, and he was all 'she's in my grasp now.' I'm paraphrasing here, but it was to that effect. Ugh! I was going to say now this is great, I can have Essos and you can have Galen, but it doesn't sound like Essos was going to pick me anyway." Zara pauses, letting that really sink in. "But, if he murdered you...I don't think I want to be involved with someone who would do that. Then again, he murdered you, not me..."

I let her finish rambling. Her eavesdropping abilities proved useful once before, and I wonder if she knows anything else.

"First of all, you make your own choices—if you don't want to be with him, don't. It's your life. Second of all, you sneak, what else have you heard?" I push.

"But that's just it, isn't it? I don't have a life, just an afterlife and being dead. This is my only shot at living—choosing to be with him. That said, I'm glad you asked what else I know, because I did also hear him say something about locking Galen away. I thought he just meant lock him out of the ball, but maybe he meant like *away*, away—for good."

"So that's it?" Cat stands up abruptly and crosses her arms. "You're going to choose Galen? I just don't feel like any of this fits what we know about Essos."

"What sort of proof do you need?" I ask her. "I'm serious. What can I get you that will prove it?"

"I think Galen should show you when you died," she states.

"That should show that it was in fact Essos who killed you. Or can he only show you memories that he's part of?"

"Wow, talk about traumatic." Eyes wide, Zara places her hand on my arm. "I think this goes without saying, but you do *not* need to relive that."

I'm anxious about the idea, but maybe Cat is right—maybe it would help banish my uncertainties about Essos. Seeing him plunge a knife in my chest will suck, but at least I'll have no qualms about my decision and this agonizing need to be near him.

"No, she's right, I do. You two can hide in my closet. I'm sure I can get Galen to come here. I just need to ask him." I tell them to sit tight while I find him. Thankfully, he's right where he usually is, sitting in the dining room, eating. Essos is nowhere to be seen.

Galen seems confused by my request but follows me to my room. The wariness that was in his eyes after what happened last night is still visible. Regardless of how tonight goes, he can't behave that way and blame fear. He's a god and should be in better control of his temper.

I assume Cat and Zara are sitting silently in the closet when I open the door to Galen. Wisely, they let Waffles roam free, so he won't paw at the closet door to be free. He's settled back in his usual spot on my pillow, eyes closed, tail flicking.

"What's this about?" Galen asks, sounding guarded.

"I need you to show me one last memory." I don't meet his eye for a moment, then finally, I do. "I need you to show me when Essos killed me."

He looks crestfallen and moves away from me toward the door. "I really don't think I should." He scratches the back of his neck as he shakes his head.

I get his hesitation, but it's not his decision to make.

"I need you to show me. I need to know what kind of monster I'm dealing with."

Galen answers me by slipping his hands into my outstretched ones.

Essos is in my house, and I'm frustrated, fury pounding through my veins. He looks just as flustered and angry. There is smoke clearing from a small device that Essos is standing in front of. He's unaffected as I cough. A chill runs down my spine, and when I try to dematerialize to the safety of our apartment in Solarem, I can't.

When I look at my surroundings, it all feels wrong *somehow. The flooring is half carpet, half marble. When I look at Essos, his coloring flickers from full color to black and white and back again. Maybe I was wrong to try to push for this memory, the trauma of trying to relive it is too much for my mind to handle.*

"I need you to leave," I tell him this firmly through my coughing fit and point at the front door. "I need you to GET OUT," I scream, the sound scraping my throat. "You're not welcome here, and you know it."

"Why won't you see, Daphne, that you're not meant for my brother? You are meant for me, and I will stop at nothing until you realize that." Essos sounds hysterical as he pleads with me. Galen isn't home, and Essos is moving closer and closer to me. I draw vines up from the ground, shattering the floor so he's held in place. I don't have a deep well of abilities to pull on, but I will draw on that well until I can't anymore.

"I am not meant for you. I belong with Galen, and if you won't leave, then you'll stay there until he can make you go." I don't waste any time. I start to run toward my bedroom to lock him out, but the vines I drew up have already withered and died. I cast a glance over my shoulder and see Essos is free again, the angry glint in his eyes telling me he's going to make me pay for the crime of using my powers against him. I can hear the heavy tread of feet as he takes the stairs two at a time, calmly rushing toward me. That he's not even bothering to rush

sends a spike of terror through me. His height is his advantage as he chases me down the hall to my bedroom.

"I promise you, there will come a day when you realize it. I will have to bide my time, but I have been waiting for you since the first moment I saw you, and I will wait until you come back into this world. You alone can bring balance to my world. You will help me be a better god. I saw you first, and I am here to take what belongs to me."

I am petrified about what he will do. I've been keeping my distance from him as much as possible for the last several months. Every time I saw him, he was more and more deranged, more vehement that I don't belong with Galen, that I belong to him.

Once I get through my bedroom door, I try to close it, but the attempt is futile. He's a god; he has the ability to move things with his mind. Essos pushes the door back and, by extension, me. The weightlessness I feel before I slam into one of the bedposts doesn't fit what is happening. It cracks and breaks, sending me crashing to the ground. Essos steps into the room, picking at invisible lint. He can do this all day; as one of the kings, the well he has to pull from is bottomless. The power Galen has to pull from is bottomless too, but he's not here to defend me. I am on my own.

I remind myself that I am a goddess in my own right. I have my own abilities to use against him, and I have to. Now is not the time to be conservative with my powers. I dive deep into that fear and anger, causing more roots to climb through my house to hold him. I scramble off the floor as he is encased in vines again. I add another layer for protection.

Essos laughs from inside the case I'm building around him, and the sound chills my blood. He laughs as he burns away the cage with half a thought. My powers are no match for a king.

I see it then, the glint of steel in his hand.

"You will be mine," he says with finality, grabbing my wrist. I try to yank it away from him. I will throw myself from the window before I let him take me. Knowing that I might have lost does not pull the fight

from me, and I still struggle against him. I make thorns grow from my wrist, and he just laughs as they pierce his skin. "Even if it takes centuries for it to happen. She promised me."

Essos pulls my body against his, and I spit in his face, out of options. He raises his arm, needing a high angle because of how close I am to him.

Then Essos plunges the knife into my chest.

The air whooshes out of my lungs as he drives it in deep, twisting it for effect. My battle changes from the fight against Essos to the fight to stay alive. My only hope is Galen. That he comes home and can save me.

"Shh, my love," Essos says as he lays me back on the bed. "If you struggle, you will only bleed out faster." Once I'm on my back, he kneels over me, his face red and dripping with sweat as he pulls the knife out and slides it into my chest, lower this time. With each stab, he says my name, my sheets chaffing under my back. His movement over me is almost intimate with each forceful drive of the knife into my skin, six times in total.

He is careful, posing me on the bed, smoothing my hair, leaving streaks of my own blood on my face. I cough, blood droplets landing on my chin and his face. Essos leans his face close to mine before he licks my cheek, capturing my blood and tears on his tongue. I can imagine how the blood is spreading on my dress. I don't have the energy to fight him anymore. My well is dry; there are no more powers that I can call on. Essos stands on the bed over my body, triumphant while we both wait to see how my husband will respond to my prone form. The dagger is still protruding from my chest, the crystal at the top of the hilt swirling with smoke and silver. The weaker I feel, the brighter the silver grows.

THE MEMORY ENDS THERE.

I reach my hand to my chest, touching the spot where the dagger entered my skin. I don't know what I expect to find, but I don't find it. I come out of the memory crying, first slowly, from shock more than anything, before it gives away to total devastation. I was wrong—that was more traumatic than I was prepared for. I thought it would be like watching a movie, but it was so, *so* much worse. I cannot stop crying long enough to form words. Instead, I cling to Galen, my safe harbor in the storm. He holds me close as I battle through this wave of emotions, moving to the chair in the corner and pulling me onto his lap.

"That's where it ends?" I manage to ask between sobs.

"Yes," he says, his own voice choked with emotion.

"Why couldn't I fight him off?" I ask, pulling back from him. I get up and start pacing, needing to move, but my legs are shaking so much more than I expected. I plop onto the bench at the foot of the bed. Galen doesn't seem to sense that I need my space, because he gets up and follows me, sitting beside me, too close.

"He's the King of the Underworld. He's in a power class I can't match. Xavier maybe, but I'm not as strong as him. I can't hold my own against him." Galen sounds like he regrets that he's not strong enough to fight Essos. I imagine finding your brother standing over your wife's body would have that effect.

I put my head in my hands. One thought breaks through the haze of my anguish.

"Every other memory you've helped me see, you were in. How could you show me this if you weren't there?"

Galen shuffles his feet. "I'm able to pull up long-forgotten memories. Everyone assumes that I use the power for ill, but I used to use it when you would forget where you left something." He reaches forward to tuck my hair behind my ear, much the way Essos has done so many times, and I *flinch*. I'm not sure where the reaction comes from. I feel like I should be leaning into his touch, not flinching away. An ugly twist flickers over Galen's mouth, and the brief expression almost feels like scorn, but it clears just as quickly. I draw back, acting like it was all part of me drawing my feet under me. There is no reason for that reaction from a man who loves me, who just helped me watch my own murder. I feel compelled to apologize, explain my reaction away, but he should be understanding. I just relived my own murder.

"And you're sure I have to go through with tonight?" I look at him, eyes wide with pleading. I reach forward to try to soothe that anger I think I saw, but I'm careful to touch his shoulder and not his hand or arm. I don't want any more memories right now.

Galen nods. "We need to show him that you're not a prize to be won and that you know the game he's been playing."

"How did he keep me from you for all this time? I didn't realize that gods could be killed." My voice trembles.

"Anything can be killed if you try hard enough. The dagger was unusual—it trapped your soul inside it. He kept it until he thought he could release you without me noticing and win you over. But please, wait for tonight. Tonight is when we will have our revenge. I am so sorry—I never wanted you to have to see that or relive it."

"It's important that I did." I stand up shakily. "You should go before anyone starts looking for one of us. I need to pull myself together before tonight." I usher him to the door without giving him a chance to respond and shove him out. Once he's on the other side, I lean against it and slide to the ground.

I put my head between my knees, trying to take deep breaths. I was able to get myself under control in front of Galen, briefly, but the brave front isn't enough anymore. A fresh wave of tears rises, and I stagger to my feet.

Zara and Cat emerge from the closet with trepidation. I push past them into the bathroom, where I throw up bile. There's nothing in my system to purge, but my body is rejecting every-thing that just happened. I start crying again, collapsing on the floor next to the toilet.

They approach slowly, unsure of what I learned. Cat sits next to me and hands me a glass of water while Zara perches on the tub, her fingers grazing my shoulder to let me know that she is there as support, too.

I explain to them through my tears what happened in the memory, but I start to hyperventilate and hiccup through the story. I can barely manage more than two consecutive words. How it felt being pursued by Essos. The fear and the terror of my life flashing before my eyes. I don't know how much of the story they actually get.

They let me cry it out for what feels like hours. At some point, Cat places a hot cup of tea in my hands. After taking a few sips, I begin to calm down.

"I am more sorry than you'll know. I never should have—" Cat chokes, tears brimming in her eyes. She grabs my free hand, squeezing it.

"Don't be. It's something I had to see. It helped to solidify what I need to do." I take a deep, shuddering breath.

"So, what *are* you going to do?" Zara asks, glancing between me and Cat.

"Go through with tonight. Follow Galen's lead. What Essos did..." I rub my chest again, feeling for the spot where the blade pierced my chest. I keep expecting to feel the pucker of a scar, but it's not there, just smooth skin.

"Why not talk to Essos?" Zara suggests, and I shake my head.

"He murdered me once. I can't imagine he'll hesitate to do it again. What are the chances that he would be honest if I confronted him, anyway? This whole Calling has been based on rules of him not being able to tell us anything."

There's a moment of silence as my words sink in.

"So, we'll be ready for the backlash," Cat says, Zara nodding beside her. "I guess we need to put on our battle gear."

32

After we shower in our own spaces, we get ready in my room. We want to spend as much time together as we can after the morning we had. As we spend our possibly last hours together, I realize that I'm mad. We've been robbed of so much time together. We all could have used those additional two weeks to get closer instead of focusing on the drama with Galen and Essos.

I don't want my time with Zara and Cat to be over. I want to explore a friendship with Zara, get to know her better. I regret that it's only during our last day together that I open up to her.

The more she chats to fill the tense air, the more I find out about her. The guy who started our whole rivalry in the first place was talking shit and had spent weeks leading Zara on while getting her to tutor him, only to ask me out instead. She told me she'd spent the entire semester trying to get a date with this asshat, and she couldn't help but feel hurt. We share a good laugh when I mention that he was a groper and a shitty kisser, and she admits to having the professor flunk him because she knew he plagiarized a paper.

I zip Zara into a sequined emerald mermaid-style gown that hugs her curves. She admires herself in the mirror. She has her hair swept to one side and pinned so the curls cascade over her bare right shoulder.

Cat wears a strapless crimson dress with a full skirt that she needs no help getting into. Her shoes, on the other hand, are another matter. She's lying on my bed, skirt pulled up as far as she can, struggling to strap on her heels. Every time she gets close, her balance is thrown off, and she falls backwards onto the bed.

Zara and I are doubled over with laughter, unable to contain it as Cat flounders. Waffles is mad at our rambunctiousness and glares at us from the pillow. I haven't seen Dave since this morning, and I assume he's sequestered away from guests. It weighs on me, not to have him here when I want sloppy puppy kisses, even if it does ruin my makeup.

"Guys!" Cat whines, lying there until we can get it together enough to help her with her shoes. While they settle in and do their makeup, I step into the closet to put on my own amethyst satin floor-length dress. I settle the garment around my waist and zip it up as far as I can.

I glance at myself in the mirror. I'm not sure I recognize the person that I've become. Will I feel different once this night is over? Will I still be me? Will I ever get my memories back? Am I Daphne, the once-mortal woman, or am I Daphne, the goddess with powers?

I step back into my room as Cat and Zara are putting on their jewelry. They don't need any more gemstones—we are the gems. We're dressed in coordinating jewel tones, and I wish I had a camera to lock this moment in time before our worlds explode. Melancholy has its claws sunk deep in me, and I fight hard to shake the feeling. The back of my dress is still gaping open while I apply my makeup. Cat comes up behind me to start doing my hair, but I shake my head.

"Leave it down," I say, pushing my loose curls over my shoulders. Cat nods, zipping up my dress instead.

I look at the jewelry and opt for a teardrop diamond necklace and chandelier earrings.

"Some battle armor," Cat says, looking at the three of us in the mirror.

"Time to take on the Big Bad Wolf," I say. My dress has small, off-the-shoulder drape sleeves, and I distract myself fussing with them.

We were instructed by Sybil to wait to be summoned, like we're dogs. We can hear people arriving downstairs, their laughter and clinking glasses indicating that they're greeting one another with drinks in their hands.

Finn pops into my room, looking sharp in black tie. It makes what he's been wearing to all the balls seem like his casual look. Tonight, he cuts a striking figure, ready to impress people. He does have to play my escort for most of the night.

"I cannot believe Essos has three smart, beautiful women fawning over him, and I can hardly get a date."

I consider standing to give him a hug but can't find it in me to go to him. When none of us really react to him, he puts his hands in his pockets. "If things don't work out with Essos, I'm happy to take any of you ladies out," he says with a wink. His attempts to soften the room are admirable, but we can't laugh, no matter how hard we try.

"Wow, do we maybe need to pregame to loosen you all up?" he says when none of us laugh.

"Nerves," Cat says, tossing him a bone, but she keeps clenching and unclenching her fists, watching the door. We're all waiting for Sybil to call us forward. None of us know what tonight is going to bring, not only because of Essos picking his new queen, but because I don't know what will happen when I openly reject him in front of the crowd.

"It will all be over tonight. You'll see. Everything will work out. You are the crown; you will be the crown," he says to me. "No offense, you two." Finn gives a nod to Cat and Zara. "You need to trust the system," Finn then says ominously, just to me.

"It's totally fine. I wouldn't want Essos anyway after—*oof!*"

Cat elbows Zara in the ribs, shutting her up.

Finn narrows his eyes. "You want to drop out now and make this easier on my girl? Go right ahead, but I'm not sure why you wouldn't want Essos."

"Um, well..." Perfectly poised Zara stammers. This whole situation seems to have affected her deeply. "If you're so confident that he would want Daphne over us all, why would I want to be someone's second choice?"

"Second choice?"

This line of questioning is shut down when Sybil slips through the door to put us out of our misery. Their usually long braid is gathered into a bun at the nape of their neck, and they're still dressed in their customary black, only this time, the dress is more elegant with a fuller skirt and long lace sleeves.

"Ladies, I just want to say how lovely you all look tonight." Sybil nods in each of our directions. "I will have each of you introduced, and you will be led in with your escort, who should be waiting for you at the foot of the stairs." Their grey eyes shoot to Finn, who takes the hint and slips away, giving me a wink as he closes the door. Before he goes, I notice the firm set to his mouth.

"Zara, Catalina, and then Daphne, that is your order. You will each hear your name, and then you will descend the stairs to your escort. He will lead you to Essos, and then you two will have a dance. You will wait for each girl to follow until Daphne is there, at which point you will join the dance floor with your escorts. After that dance, you will be expected to mingle with the rest of the party guests. During the party, topics of conversation will include the subjects which you have been learning about over the last few weeks. As much as this is Essos's decision, the queen will need to interact closely with the citizens of Solarem. This is your chance to impress them and set the stage for your relationship.

"Again, that order is Zara, Catalina and then Daphne. Is this understood?" They don't wait for our response, just clap their hands twice.

I retained absolutely nothing from that exchange and feel more lost than before.

"Zara, if you will follow me—you will wait at the top of the stairs, out of sight until you hear your name." I grab one of Zara's hands and Cat grabs the other, and we squeeze, a silent understanding of strength shared between us. Zara pulls her hand away and follows Sybil, leaving Cat and me behind.

"I'm scared," I whisper my confession to her, and she looks at me. "I'm scared of what happens to you when I pick Galen."

She pushes my hair over my shoulder. "I don't *think* that Essos will do anything to me. Before today, I would have said he won't with absolute confidence, but after the last few hours, I'm less sure."

I understand what she's saying. I'm sorry to have shared this burden with her. "What if this is goodbye?" I ask, tears stinging the backs of my eyes.

She bites down on her lower lip. "You know it's never goodbye with us. It's always 'catch you later.'" Her voice is thick with emotion. "Stop it now. I can't ruin my eye makeup." She fans her eyes with her hand, and I choke out a laugh.

I hear Zara's name called, and the swell of music drowns out the sound of her shoes on the stairs. We have one more song together alone. We don't fill it with idle chatter, or thoughts of what we will miss. We just enjoy it, our time together, hands held and heads on shoulders. The song comes to an end, and we both rise. I don't let go of her hand until she pulls it out and heads to the door.

"You're my best friend. Nothing can change that." She slips out the door and away.

I'm left alone with my thoughts, and all the nasty ones rise to the forefront. Galen's behavior last night, and Essos murdering me are the first to sink their teeth into me. I sit at the foot of my bed, trying to wrap my head around it all.

I will never forget the look on his face, the pure glee as the dagger plunged between my ribs and toward my heart. I know he was careful not to puncture it, because he wanted his brother to see me take my last breaths and know that he had won. It would have been too fast otherwise. He was sadistic, wanting to extract the maximum amount of suffering from us both.

I let the anger build in my chest as I think of the injustice done to me. As I think of the life that was stolen from me, how happy I could have been with Galen, and I let it wrap itself around me like a warm coat on a bitter cold night.

I let this anger hold me as Cat's song comes to an end, and I rise.

33

I stand poised at the top of the stairs, waiting for my name to be called. When Sybil does call it, a hush falls over the crowd, and I wonder if they all know my real identity. Do they know how Galen loved me? Do they know how my life was robbed? Do they support Essos and his rule? Galen recognized me right away—do I look the same?

I take the stairs slowly, my face searching the crowd for Cat, then Galen. Each of them gives me a reassuring nod. I force a fake smile to my lips as my eyes find Essos. He beams at me, studying all of me. He thinks he's won. There is almost hope on his face, and I want to tell myself that I should be happy about this. I should be glad to rip the rug out from under him for the years of my life he stole, but it only makes me want to fall to my knees and weep.

As instructed, Finn is waiting at the foot of the stairs. His smile is an equally wide but genuine one as he offers me his arm. I hit the bottom of the stairs and slide my arm into his.

The crowd parts for us, and we make our way toward Essos, who is now alone in the center of the dance floor. Finn offers him my hand, and he takes it with a bow in my direction. I give the required curtsey. I am amazed at myself for remembering this much.

Essos draws me toward him, holding my hand in his, the other hand at my waist. My body trembles as I settle into his arms, and then, unbelievably, I relax. Heat radiates from his hand, and he offers me a timid smile. We wait for the music to start, and then the dancing begins. I don't meet his eye as we dance, keeping my head turned away from him, focusing on my steps. I've gotten better, so much better, but I know that if I'm ever going to mess up, it's now. It's as though the magnetic bond between us has been broken by that memory.

"You look amazing tonight," he whispers in my ear. His breath on my skin makes me shudder. He sends me out on a spin, and I catch sight of the concern on his face.

"I just don't feel up to this tonight, Essos," I say, glancing around the room. Zara is trying very poorly to hide her concern, one of her nails in her mouth as she gnaws on it. Cat is watching closely too, with Finn at her elbow. I can see them whispering to each other as we waltz around the room.

"This will all be over tonight. I know you're nervous, but you have no reason to be," he reassures me, and I try to take it as comforting, but I can't find it in me. I should want to ruin him. I should want to wipe the floor with his happiness, but the thought of it sets my nerves on fire. If I had a dollar for every time I considered that getting close to him might be a mistake, I'd be wealthy enough to buy a country and then some. At this moment, his touch feels right, but my brain is telling me that this is wrong, wrong, wrong. Wrong not because he's not Galen, but wrong because he murdered me. I watched it. I saw it through my own eyes.

Something nags at me, and my face must be a storm. Essos ducks his face closer to me, so he can whisper in my ear. "Daphne,

I know this isn't easy. I know that all I have are pretty words to reassure you...but trust me. There will be light again in this dark world." Essos's hand rises to my shoulder, his fingers very gently rubbing my bare skin. He searches my face, trying to see if anything registered with me, but I'm so focused on the music and my steps that his words don't click. I hear the final notes of the song, and I step away from him as soon as it's over, giving him a curtsey before seeking out Finn for the next dance.

Essos looks lost until Zara steps into my place, distracting him. I grab a glass of champagne from a waiter and barely have time to take a sip before a young woman approaches me with a smile.

"Daphne?" she asks. She seems sweet, with a round face and long, black hair. Her features are dramatized by her dark black eye makeup. If I didn't know better, I would think that she was in the Calling. She's wearing a black dress with a plunging neckline and gems lining the edge, drawing attention to her cleavage.

"Hi, yes." I give a curtsey, unsure of what I am supposed to do. She doesn't look familiar from Sybil's lessons.

"Oh, I'm so delighted to meet you. You look stunning. I just want to say I'm so glad that Essos has finally found someone. He's been so lonely these past few years, unless, of course, you were one of the lucky ones to warm his bed."

I furrow my brow, unsure what she's getting at. The way she delivers her words makes me think they're intended to convey that she was one of those lucky ones.

"Oh, I'm sorry." I pause. "And you are?"

"I'm Ellie. I'm sure you don't really know who I am. I'm just a lowly wood nymph." She giggles and flips her long dark hair over her shoulder. I'm trying to make myself focus on her, but I'm fighting a tide of rage. Only looking away soothes my anger. I catch sight of Essos dancing with Zara, but his blue eyes are glued to us, and he looks even more pale than usual.

Before I can say more to her, Helene swoops in. "Oh, no, no, we don't waste our time on nymphs." She shakes her head at the girl, practically hissing. "Go see if some lesser god is interested in what you're selling, honey."

Helene pulls me away. I try to turn back to Ellie but am dragged across the floor. The storm of anger I felt when I met her makes me wonder what is happening to me. I want to talk to Finn and see if he can help calm me, but Helene doesn't let me go.

She has her hair pulled back in a tight, high bun and is wearing a stunning royal blue satin dress complemented by simple diamond earrings and a large statement necklace with one sapphire and two large diamonds on either side. I'm surprised she doesn't topple over with the weight of the gems. The man she is leading me to is perfectly matched to her with a royal blue vest and a wide, welcoming smile.

"My dear Daphne, I want to introduce you to my hunk of a husband. This is Kai. Kai, *this* is Daphne."

When I say the man is tremendous, I mean that he is tall and wide, and a truck of a human being. Kai looks like he is about to burst out of his suit with one wrong move, but it's cut perfectly for his figure. This is certainly not a man I would want to meet in a dark alley. His head is bald and polished to a shine. He gives me this big, broad smile with perfect white teeth, and I feel like all my worries have melted away.

He holds out a large hand, and I take it, my own hand disappearing in his. "Daphne, I've heard great things about you and can't wait to welcome you into the family." He shakes my hand enthusiastically. His deep voice sounds like I could go swimming in it. I feel mesmerized and almost miss when Helene stomps on his foot. Kai picks up on the cue, not from any sort of pain, but because of how dramatic Helene was when she did it.

"What he means to say is he can't wait to see *if* you join the family, since nothing has been decided yet and she still has to impress Posey."

"Did I hear my name?"

Helene grimaces. Her eyes meet mine with a dramatic roll. "Speak of the devil."

She turns to greet a tiny woman wearing a gold gown, and I can only assume this is Posey. She's tiny, maxing out at 4'11", but the Marie Antoinette-style beehive on her head adds an extra six inches. It's elaborate, with flowers and birds sticking out of it.

"No, dear, that would be your prick of a brother." Her voice is high-pitched and squeaky. Posey pushes herself between Helene and Kai to offer me her hand. I see Xavier in the background, hiding a smirk behind his drink. When he catches that I've seen him, he raises his glass in my direction before turning to the buxom woman in front of him.

Posey waits for me to greet her the way she demands to be greeted. It's as if she expects me to fail, so I fall into the deepest curtsey of my life, my nose almost touching the ground.

"Your majesty, Lady Posey, Queen of the Gods, Goddess of Mothers, it is a true honor and a privilege to be graced by your presence and be given the chance to make your acquaintance." I stay low, waiting for her to allow me to rise.

"Sister, please let the poor girl stand up while you scrutinize her. At least then you can view her best assets." I hear Galen behind me, and my heart skips a beat. I expect to feel better now that I'm in his presence, but the memory of Essos plunging a knife into my chest flashes again, and I feel sick.

"Fine, fine, rise." She waves her hand at me. I straighten, towering over her slightly. I feel Galen put his hand on the small of my back, and I glance at him, unsure why he's being so bold.

"So, you're the one that has everyone in a tizzy." I can feel eyes on us as Posey draws attention to her.

"I suppose so," I say, trying to keep my voice calm.

"Your Royal Majesty," Posey finishes for me. At my vacant look, her eyes darken. "You cannot address me the way my sister here does. You will address me with the rights due a queen. So, you are to end any sentence with 'Your Royal Majesty.'" Her tone is unforgiving. I remember Helene covering this, and the look she's giving me tells me that I should have remembered.

"My apologies, Your Royal Majesty," I say, unsure if I need to do something else to show that I am contrite. When awkward silence settles, I opt to compliment her. "I do love your hair, it's quite beautiful." Posy smiles, touching at a few carefully arranged curls. "Your Royal Majesty," I rush to add when Kai clears his throat with a pointed look. I love this giant of a man already.

"Yes, well, it was all the rage when I was in the mortal realm. I had a necklace made for Marie Antoinette and, well, let's just say she was not a fan."

I nod along with her, thinking back to a story I learned in history class about a necklace that started the downfall of Marie Antoinette and wonder if it is the same one.

Posey whips out a fan and starts to flap air toward her face while sipping champagne.

Helene intervenes. "Daphne here still has to prove herself to the rest of us, so we should let her go back to mingling," she says, trying to release me. She waves to an older woman, but one glance at Posey, and the woman feverishly shakes her head before disappearing into the crowd.

"Does she? I thought this was a done deal," Posey says passively. She snaps at a waiter and demands a drink. The poor waiter looks like he wishes he could turn to stone because he doesn't have what she wants immediately. Posey seems to think she has more important things to do than be here for this ball.

"Sister, while Essos can make his decision, it's ultimately up to the girl to decide if she will have him," Galen says, admonishing his older sister. Helene's eyes flash to Galen, and Kai stands up taller, ready to get involved. "In fact, why don't we get this show on the road? Everyone knows the real party is going to start once that happens, so let's just do it. Where is Essos?" Galen shouts, causing the music to halt.

Helene grips my upper arms, pulling me toward her and Kai, shifting her body between us.

Cat grabs my hand and pulls me to one side while Galen walks to the musicians to make them stop. He's shouting, looking for Essos relentlessly. Zara and Finn are off to the side as well, both looking worried. I glance at the floor to see that Galen has found Essos, and I don't even get a chance to ask them why they're so worried.

"We need to talk," Cat whispers desperately. "You can't do this. Don't listen to Galen." My eyebrows crease. Cat is trying to take me to Finn and Zara as covertly as possible, but Galen has us in his crosshairs. Cat stops moving once she realizes he's looking at us. She's utterly pale and still, her fingers digging into my arm.

"King Essos believes that he has found himself a new bride, but I want to tell you that I have been fortunate enough to have found *myself* a bride!" Galen shouts to the room, raising a glass. "So, while I know this is big brother's night, I think he'll do the right thing and let me have one teeny moment first, won't you, big brother?" He doesn't wait for Essos to respond before barreling forward.

The Galen that I'm seeing right now is the same Galen that I saw the night before, and I'm not a fan. Essos is seething. He doesn't want to look away from Galen, but his gaze travels to Xavier and Posey, whose faces are blank. Only Posey gives him a response, a subtle shake of her head, so small I'm not sure I actually saw it.

"Thanks for your silence. I'll take that as acceptance, because accept you must!" Galen is frenetic, the crowd stepping away from him to give him space. "I have fallen in love with one of the beautiful creatures that you have brought to your home, and I happen to know that she feels the same way. Daphne, dear, please step forward. Daphne!" he shouts.

I hesitate, not liking how this is going down. I wanted it to happen quietly. My body moves of its own accord, compelled toward the two brothers. I feel Cat grab my arm, not wanting to let me go, and I don't want to go. She squeezes my arm, holding tight to me. Galen's eyes flick to where she holds me, and my skin burns, prompting her to release me. A muscle in Essos's jaw flexes when he sees Cat, and I wince. It's not a dangerous burn, more like when you accidentally touch a hot pan that's been out of the oven for only a few minutes, still hot enough to cause an instant reaction.

I am no longer sure of this decision, and, frankly, want to tell them both to fuck off. Cosmically, though, I am stuck. My fate has led me here, to this room. I have already lived among these gods once, and I will do it again. I know that my options are limited at this moment. I have seen what my life with Galen was and can be. I am sure that his actions now and of late are due to finding his love murdered by his brother. I can't imagine the anxiety he must feel, knowing we're both in the same room. The threat that Essos could hurt me again is all too possible.

"Daphne, darling, do you have feelings toward me too? Do you want to stay here with Essos, or do you want to come away with me and find freedom? You know how I feel about you—we need to let everyone know." Galen reaches a hand toward me, beckoning me to him. "The time is now, my love. Now. So, do you want me, too? You have to say it." I nod my head, unable to find my voice. "I need to hear you use your words. You need to verbalize it, otherwise, no one will believe you."

The words are stuck in my throat, but he waves his hand at me, urging me forward.

"Yes." My voice cracks on the word. I can't tear my eyes away from Galen. The room is silent, not even a murmur from the crowd to interrupt what's happening. I think everyone around me can hear my heart beating in my chest.

"Good girl. Now come over here. We have to seal it with a kiss," Galen says, all eyes on us. My eyes flick to Essos, who has gone utterly still. Something terrifying burns in his eyes as he looks at me, and it's overwhelming. He doesn't say anything but looks at Xavier and Posey again for something before meeting my eye. The muscles in his neck are straining like he's trying to move but *can't*.

I swallow nervously, crossing slowly to Galen. When I reach him, he grins and whispers to me. "I've never been happier than I am at this moment." His tone is not that of a man who has just found his long-lost love. His tone is angry and bitter, and it hits me a moment too late that I have made a terrible, terrible mistake. I start to pull back, gaze flicking around the room for an escape.

He slides his hand in my hair and pulls me closer to him. I meet his eyes a moment before his lips crash into mine, hard. I have a small modicum of hope, expecting there to be fire and love behind it the way there was in the memories. Instead, there is just pressure. Never have I been kissed like this. When we break apart, my lips feel swollen and bruised, and not in a good way. I shove him back as I risk his ire, dragging the back of my hand across my mouth, smearing my lipstick. I don't get a rush of memories like I hoped, or even a spark of anything. If my memories are inaccessible, that may just be something I have to live with, because I've decided that even if I chose Galen right now, I'm not *choosing* Galen.

No one in the room dares to breathe, standing still and silent as I face the crowd. I catch sight of Finn, who looks furious, and Cat, who looks heartbroken. But it's Essos's eyes that tell me what I'm afraid to know. I see grief on his face, weighing him down so much that he falls to his knees. Zara rushes forward and grabs him, the confusion on her face mirroring mine.

"How does that feel, big brother?" Galen shouts belligerently. He nudges me forward. "Go give him a farewell kiss. A first and last. A parting gift."

I frown at him, pulling back from his grip. "Don't be cruel, Galen," I scold, but this only makes him smile more.

"You don't even know how cruel it will be. Go give him a kiss."

I cross my arms, shaking my head, unwilling to move.

When I don't budge, his entire demeanor changes. "*Now*, Daphne." His tone is flat, devoid of emotion. He grabs my upper arm and yanks me forward. I stumble, and Essos moves as if to catch me, but it's a halfhearted attempt; he doesn't manage to even get on both feet.

Startled by this change, I walk to Essos, my shoes on the ground the only sound to be heard. Zara helps him stand, still looking confused. She's hoping I can provide an explanation, but I can't. Essos can barely look at me. Behind me, someone smashes a glass to the ground, causing me to jump.

"I SAID KISS," Galen screeches, and another glass breaks.

Essos has started to gather his wits. The mask he wore comes down, and to see the full might of his fury is terrifying. His jaw is clenched as he twists to look at Xavier with a murderous glare in his eyes. He looks ancient, pained, as he reaches for me, giving his brother a withering look over my shoulder. None of that anger bleeds through when he touches me. Essos's hand is gentle, his fingers barely grazing my skin as he brushes a stray tendril of hair out of my eyes.

"I am more sorry for this than you will ever know," he whispers. I think there might be tears in his eyes, but I never get a chance to really look before he closes them. He leans down and presses his lips to mine. I'm not even sure he truly kisses me, as his touch is featherlight, but then it feels as if a door inside my mind slams open, and the memories pour in.

I SEE my first time meeting Essos, him pulling me from the streets of Solarem before I'm trampled by a chariot. I see us dancing under the stars on the beach, pressed cheek to cheek with only the moon to guide us. Gone is the Essos dressed in black all the time; in his place is a man always smiling with a brightness to rival the sun.

I see us adopting Spot and Shadow, and I hear his laughter as I name Dave. I see him get down on one knee in the park where he first saw me, before we even met. I see our wedding day, before the citizens of Solarem, both of us beaming, him looking sharp in a black tux with a stargazer lily pinned to his lapel, and beside him, I glow in a white dress with gold detailing around it, a tiara with sun rays on my head. I see him open a gift from me—a sun pendant. It's the same sun pendant that I saw him wearing when this all started. My name was engraved on it before it was worn away by centuries of rubbing.

I see us working together as partners and equals to rule our domain together. Neither one of us is more important than the other. Mixed with all this joy, I see the heartbreak we shared, awful decisions we had to make, and the loss of a pregnancy. I see the fights we had, some small, some large, but we always found our way back to one another.

I see familiar memories—ones that previously had Galen in them are replaced with Essos, the truth in them shining through. All these memories are brighter, the colors perfectly right. They're not oversaturated or greyed out or in black and white. Galen wasn't lying when he told me that he had the ability to pull forth memories, but he could also twist them as he needed. All the signs were there, and I missed them.

I see our last months together, something dark and ominous hanging over the house as we struggled with the pressure of Galen always being around. The future uncertain as we sought seers to help guide us, going as far as seeking the ever-elusive Fates, who never deigned to surface.

I see Essos stepping into our bedroom to find Galen standing over me on our bed only half dressed, laughing. Blood stains the sheets around me, and the skirt of my white dress is hiked up around my waist, a dagger jutting out of my chest. Galen laughs and laughs as I stretch out my hand to Essos, feeling my heart pump the life out of me. Galen didn't rape me, but letting his brother believe it was punishment enough. Essos will spend eternity wondering if he failed me in every way possible by underestimating his brother.

In my last memory, Essos rushes to me. His hands shake, and he doesn't know what to do. He tugs on my dress, pulling it down, and then he touches my chest on either side of the dagger, pressing around it, trying to stop the bleeding. We both know that it's already too late. I'm dying, and no amount of wishing otherwise will change that. He cups my face with his hand, hesitating when he realizes that he's leaving bloody handprints behind. He kisses me, tasting of salt as the tears flow freely down his face.

"I will find you across time. There is no force in the universe that will keep me from you. You are my sun," he vows to me as my heart slows and the last of the air leaves my lungs all while Galen stands over me, laughing and laughing and laughing.

WHEN IT ENDS, I'm left speechless and lost. My eyes are out of focus, and when they do focus on something, it's the pain on Essos's face. I have chosen his brother over him. I have thrown away everything that we shared. Now that the door is wide open, I can access all my memories. A strangled noise works its way out of my throat as I collapse, Essos catching me before I hit the ground.

"You know not what you have done, brother. When she erupts, she will destroy you, and I won't stop her," Essos says, the words barely more than a whisper. He holds me to him, looking at Galen, who is smug with triumph.

There will never be enough words to express the regret that burns deep in my soul. I look up at Essos, tears streaming down my face. I feel as though I've been punched in the gut over and over again. I open my mouth to apologize to him, but I can't make a sound.

Essos closes his eyes and kisses my brow. "I know, my love. I know." The same sound that carried me out of the world is what I hear now. I find my strength and stand up, turning to face Galen as he laughs, standing on a chair and towering over us all. I thrust my hand toward him, and the chair collapses, falling apart under him, but it doesn't stop his laughter. Cat and Zara gasp, and I find I'm also surprised I was capable of that. The movement was natural, stemming from a well within me that is part of a nature I'm just remembering. What has been dormant within me has awoken...and it is *pissed*.

"There is nothing you can do about it now, princess. Signed, sealed, and delivered. You chose me." Galen looks around and addresses the room. "Do you see that? The almighty King of the Underworld can't even keep his own wife—how do you expect him to continue to keep souls? I demand a vote! Not only does his own wife choose someone else, but his focus on the Underworld is slipping.

"He's so focused on a tight little pussy that he not only let a mortal slip into the Underworld, but he actually let a soul return to the mortal realm. Clearly, he's not the ruler we need. He is no longer fit to rule the Underworld. We deserve better. The souls deserve better. Our economy deserves better. What else has been slipping under his watch that we've missed? I nominate myself as his successor—after all, his queen chose me."

There are murmurs around the room as everyone considers what Galen is asking. I look at Essos, alarmed. He's not looking at me now, just watching every move that his brother makes. His features are back to the bored ambivalence I saw so much during the past three months, which I now recognize, too late, as his unwillingness to tip his hand to his brother. I recognize my husband for who he is. If he's worried about the vote of no confidence, he won't show it.

Regardless of whether anyone else recognizes Essos and I as still married, he is my husband, and I won't wed again. We've never had to face the question of the reincarnation of a god. We're supposed to be immortal, invulnerable. What happened to me shouldn't have happened at all.

I want to scream and shout and take it all back, but I know there's nothing I can do. I made my bed, and now I have to lie in it. Around the room, minor gods and goddesses are taking Galen's side, and there is little that can be done to stop the vote now that it's in progress. My brain is trying to play catch-up, and I can't identify those who are voting Essos out. I stare hard at each one. I may not remember their names now, but I *will* remember their faces.

Helene won't even look at me, her disgust so strong I can almost taste it. I remember being close with her once. But it is the look on Posey's face that sharpens my anger into a blade. Posey, who normally looks like she's smelled something rotten, looks triumphant. She's hated Essos for the power he wields in Solarem, and she's hated her husband for always willingly giving it up to Essos. I wouldn't be surprised to find out the bitch danced on my grave. Her glee at this chaos, at Essos being removed from power, is one step too far. Galen is so focused on rallying his people to his side that he finally loses sight of me. While the debate rages, Essos pulls me away and sneaks me into a room just down the hall from the ballroom.

He shuts the door before turning to face me.

I rush him and wrap my arms around him. "Oh Es, what did I do?" I start to cry, and he holds me tight against him.

He gives me only a moment before pushing me away slightly and looking me in the eye.

"I know, my love. I know."

I lean up and kiss him hard on the mouth, a real kiss, our first kiss with all of my memories, and I am filled with love and joy. I try hard to hold on to this feeling. Love, real true love.

"I have so many questions. Why couldn't you tell me? Did you know it was me the whole time? Have I reincarnated before?" I demand, pounding a fist on his chest. Essos wraps his hands around my wrists, holding them there against his chest. He chuckles darkly, leaning to press a kiss to each of my fists.

"I would know your soul across a thousand lifetimes. Of course, I knew it was you. You've never been reincarnated before, but the Council insisted that I *try* to find a new mortal bride, so I did have other Callings. I ended them all for one reason or another.

"After Galen—" Essos swallows thickly, looking away from me for a moment before continuing "—killed you, the Council demanded that, should your soul ever return to us, you should be allowed no memories so that you could make the decision to become queen of your own accord. Galen insisted that he loved you, and he loved you first, and it was only fair that he have his shot. He cited that he was getting to know you before you and I ever met, and that *I* am the one who interfered with the woman who should have been his. I don't know why Posey intervened, but there was nothing that could be done. Without you on the Council, I was outvoted, like this bloody bullshit now. Not that it mattered—strings were being pulled behind the scene. Helene admitted to me later that she was told she was voting on something else, otherwise, she never would have voted for this." I'm nearly burned by the vitriol in his voice. "It was a fucking farce, and I had to swallow that pill on the heels of...I was in no emotional shape to put the pieces together until it was too late."

I touch his arm gently. "Essos, he never...Galen never raped me. He just wanted you to think that."

Essos tugs me into his arms, kissing the crown of my head, "I know. Helene took care of everything after. I told her how I found you, and she found out, because I..." He's beyond words, and I can feel the drop of something on the top of my head. I burrow deeper into his arms.

"I'm here," I promise, though we both know it's only temporary. What comes next, neither of us knows. "Why aren't you out there defending yourself, defending our realm?" My words are desperate.

"I can't. He's been building support for this moment for centuries, positioning the God of War as the natural successor and rightful heir to the Underworld. God of the Dead apparently isn't a good enough qualification. The only thing that could have stopped this mutiny is having the ace in the hole, the trump card."

"The Queen of the Underworld. But why? I'm the Goddess of Spring, what can I do?"

"Goddess of Spring and Chaos. You've always underestimated yourself. When we were wed, do you remember how we sliced our palms and joined them for the remainder?"

I try to recall it, but my head swims and I stagger into Essos's chest. "Let's go with not quite."

"You were squeamish about it then too. As my queen, my consort, and my wife, you got some of my powers. Just a small kernel, but it linked you forever to the Underworld. It's how I was able to keep your gardens in bloom all these centuries."

"You have a brown thumb...everything used to die when you tended it," I remember, fighting to not get lost in the surge of memories.

"Yes, and by the time we were wed, you wouldn't let me near

your babies. Regardless of our marital status, you are the rightful Queen of the Underworld. You may have gotten only a kernel of the power through our marriage, but it lives in you. It's why Xavier and Posey never mixed their blood during their wedding—she wanted to keep her powers to herself."

"You are my husband. You are my heart. I will *not* go with Galen—I won't marry him. What about *his* wife?"

Essos's gaze looks toward the door then back to me. "Callie is still gone. I don't want to talk about my brother. I have my wife back for the first time in centuries." He kisses me again, pulling me against him. This kiss is different; it's hungry and all-consuming.

I reach up and run my hands through his hair, remembering how that drives him wild. One of his hands slides down my waist and the other cups the back of my head as he walks me back into a wall. I stretch up on my toes, trying to close the gap between us as much as I can.

My heart aches with how much I missed my husband. He lifts me up, and I wrap my legs around his hips, thankful that the high slit in my dress allows me the maneuverability. He holds me against the wall as I fumble with his pants, undoing his belt and buttons and sliding my hand inside. He groans as my hand finds his hardness. He starts to place kisses down my neck, working toward my breasts. This is not the time nor the place, but it has been *centuries* since we were together, since I've been able to feel the love that we share. We should have spent the night entwined like this, but we can't—because of me.

There is no foreplay, only urgent need. I run my hand over the length of him, relearning the feel of him. It's muscle memory, knowing what to do to make him hunger for me. Bracing my back against the wall, he uses one hand to slide between my legs and push aside my underwear. He groans again as he finds me wet and ready, and I bite my lip as he slides his fingers over the exact right cluster of nerves. My body aches for the feel of him inside me. I tilt my head and nip his ear, causing him to pause.

"Play nice, kitten," he says. "Or I will have to punish you."

"Punish me another time. The clock is ticking before we're found."

He kisses me hard on the mouth, his tongue darting against mine. He lets me down for a moment so I can take off my underwear. He watches me, unable to tear his blue eyes away from me. I don't want to take my eyes off him either; I'm afraid to blink and lose this moment like I lost all my memories.

Once we're ready, he lifts me again, not wasting a moment. I rest my head against the wall and don't break eye contact as he enters me.

I bite down hard on my lip to keep from crying out as he thrusts himself deep inside me. A small whimper escapes my throat, as he pulls back and thrusts again, to the hilt this time. I hold on to him, my fingers digging into his tuxedo. I don't want to let him go. I'm so happy to have found him again, even if I'm going to lose him once more. We hold tight to one another, our hips moving together, desperately seeking release. I don't want this to end, but I can feel the rising tide in me. I press my mouth to his, trying to muffle my moans as both of us find that moment of bliss that we have needed.

Afterwards, I can't look at him, knowing that I've thrown us away. I keep my back to him as I look around for my underwear, confused as to how they got so far away. Finally, I give up. Essos fixes his pants, watching me from the corner of his eye. I feel his hand on my shoulder, and I turn to look at him, and he sees the tears sliding down my face.

"I know I'm out of practice, love, but I didn't think I was that bad." He brushes at a tear.

"Nonsense. I've ruined everything," I say, looking up at him.

He shakes his head. "No, you didn't. I'll fix this. I promise I will. He won't get away with it, but I have to go. I swear to you, nothing in this world can keep me from you," he says softly. My husband has always been so generous and kind; I cannot imagine how this is eating at him. Under his calm demeanor, he must be furious. Furious at Galen for intervening, furious for having his hands tied, furious as me for not trusting him as he asked.

"But what am I supposed to do? I love you. I'm your wife. I can't stay with him; that's out of the question. He murdered me. I can't stay *here*." I feel the rage rising in me, the lights flickering in response. Essos looks around the room as he rubs my arms gently to soothe me.

Maybe I can go into hiding while my memories return. Maybe we can run away to the mortal realm and spend our days eating pasta in Positano while Galen tries to take power and hopefully forgets about us.

"You have to stay here, at least for now. He won't harm you again now that he thinks he won."

A fresh wave of tears streams down my face, and I sniff, holding back a wave of sadness. "Even though he tricked me and lied to me outright?" Essos cups my face, brushing a tear with his thumb. "That hardly seems fair."

He gives me a grim smile. "Especially because he tricked you. This is a game of gods, my love. There is nothing fair about it. Just keep your head down. I'll figure something out as your memories return."

I know my time with him is growing short and, rather than waste any more of it, I lurch forward and press my lips to his, hungry for more of him. His answering kiss is just as eager before he breaks away from me.

"I have waited a thousand years for you. I will wait a thousand more if I have to." He presses a final kiss to my brow, and I savor the feel of his lips on my skin before a noise interrupts my reverie.

We both snap our heads towards it, fearing the worst. As

badly as I know Essos needs to leave, I squeeze his hand tighter, not wanting to let it go. He returns it with another comforting squeeze before pulling me into a tight embrace. His hands thread through my hair, and I can hear the wild beating of his heart. He is real. *We* are real.

"I love you. Never doubt that." Essos ducks his head so he tells me this eye to eye.

I press my forehead to his, fighting the furious tears building in my eyes. "Forever. I love you forever, and I always will. Don't doubt me, either."

There is a knock at the door, and I turn to look at it. Quickly, Essos's lips crush to my forehead before he dematerializes, leaving me cold and alone all over again.

34

I straighten my hair and dress before opening the door.

Finn is standing on the other side of it, and I exhale. He checks behind him before pushing his way into the room and closing the door behind him.

"Shit, Daphne." He shakes his head. "You really made a mess of things."

"What's happening out there?"

"Well, your new beau is the King of the Underworld in waiting, thanks to your endorsement, and Essos is out. Galen is calling for his head. Where is he?"

"Gone," I say simply. I can't tell him what I don't know.

Finn spies my underwear and picks them up. "Not without a parting gift, it would seem," he says harshly. I snatch them from his hand and gesture for him to turn around while I put them on. Finn obliges like the gentleman he is.

"I'm not really sure what you're expecting, Phineas," I say sharply. "I'm sure you were aware of the rules Posey set out, which is why *you* didn't tell me what was happening, either.

Otherwise, this entire situation could have been avoided. What do you have to be mad about?"

"What do I have to be *mad* about? I don't know—Essos is a king, and he disappeared to get his rocks off instead of fighting for his realm. Besides, you know I couldn't risk the Calling being stopped," he counters.

"Then stop blaming me. You could have done more. You *knew* Galen was playing me. You've known it since he got here, and all you did was be cryptic. Don't lay this mess at my feet. We all had our parts to play." I grab hold of the anger that is becoming my new companion, and I let it fester and grow. It taps into my power, into the darkness in my heart that Helene admired when she got here. I let it mold me into something else. Something strong. Over my heart, a black stain appears on my dress, growing outward and morphing it from purple to black. Layers appear, adding tiers to the dress, while the neckline creeps up my throat in black lace and extends down my arms as well. I watch the transformation happening with interest until the last of the purple is blotted out.

If Galen wants the Queen of the Underworld, he'll get her.

"I see your powers are returning, my queen." When I look at Finn, he has dropped to one knee, head bent. I glance at him with a frown. I've never demanded such shows of deference, never asked anyone to get on their knees for me—not like Posey does.

"Slowly, a little too slowly for my liking. I'm going to need everything I have to fight Galen. Enough of that."

Finn rises, not taking his eyes off me. I wave a hand over my face, changing my makeup from a natural look to heavy dark eyes and red, red lips. The curls in my hair lift, twisting themselves together in a complicated updo. It may not have birds and flowers in it, but it does the trick.

Finn gives me an approving look. "You'll be needing this." He summons my old crown—not my favorite, but the one of death and spikes.

I rest it on my head. "How do I look?" I ask, twisting the top layer of my tulle skirt. I peek at him through my dark lashes.

"Like the queen of death and ruination. Like someone who is going to make Galen very sorry that he picked this fight." His tone is somber.

"Good." I walk out of the room with my head held high, mouth firm. Finn follows behind me, arms behind his back. I can feel the change in the air, a sudden static tension. People have fallen in line behind Galen, the next presumptive King of the Underworld, and I see Posey standing by his side.

I never liked that bitch.

As I sweep through the room, people fall to their knees in the same pose as Finn.

"The queen is back," is whispered among them. Posey looks pissed that people are doing this without my demanding it. This is the difference in our reigns. I may rule what is dead and beneath the earth, but she forces respect. I command it.

My gaze scans the room for Cat and Zara, and I'm pleased to find them standing beside Kai. There is still so much I need to relearn, alliances and loyalties, especially after Galen's coup. But now that I remember, my trust in Helene is solid, and Kai is the god equivalent of a teddy bear, albeit a very deadly teddy bear. They're safe right where they are, and it's one less concern. Essos would never take them from me, and I won't send them away.

After finding my friends, I look for the cause of my strife. The beat of my heart snags for an entirely different reason now.

"My love," Galen says, abandoning Posey's side to come to me.

My lips twist into a small smile. I hold out my hand to him. "Shall we dance?" I ask him, trying to keep my emotions in check. One look at Posey and the flowers in her hair wilt. I may be the goddess of spring and flowers and brightness, but rebirth comes from the dead decaying flowers before it. I can take just as much as I can give.

"Of course." Galen laughs and wraps an arm around my waist, pulling me against his body. He drags his nose along the column of my neck, inhaling deeply. To outside observers, it probably looks like a gentle, loving gesture, but I know it for what it is. "You stink of him," he hisses in my ear, squeezing my side.

"Music!" I call out. The musicians and the workers don't know what to do. They were here for Essos, for the King of the Underworld. I have to do what I've always done in his absence—step in and take control.

The music starts, the musicians playing at a faster tempo than what we practiced. I'm grateful that I can keep up. I was graceful once, dancing until all hours of the morning with my friends before Essos, before dying. Galen and I are both too distracted by the urgency to keep up to match wits.

"I had hoped to be the one to break you in now that you have your memories back," Galen whispers in my ear.

I'm not subtle in my response, sending my stiletto into his foot.

"I'm afraid you're just going to have to keep waiting until we're husband and wife." It's a false promise; I'll never wed him, but it at least buys me time. He sends me into a back-breaking dip before whipping me up against his chest.

"You're damaged goods now. There is nothing quite like the way a god fucks." He runs his nose along the curve of my neck the same way Essos did. I clench my teeth so hard I think I crack a molar. "Perhaps I should just tie you to a bed and let the rest of the guests have their chance to put a queen in her place."

I can't show on my face how his words send a trill of terror down my spine. "I never thought you were one to share."

His hand squeezes mine, crushing it. I can feel the tiny bones grate against each other.

"You're right. Once I have what I want from you, then I'll throw you to the wolves. Once you've given me an heir, I won't have the need for an uppity bitch like you. You always thought you were too good for me. Always had your sights set higher."

"What of your son and daughter, are they not good enough?" I will die again before I take Galen to bed.

"They're part nymph, practically useless to me, but you...I thought we had something once."

At the change in his tone, I glance at him. I have no idea what he's talking about, but I refuse to tip my hand that I don't have all my memories back. "Maybe once. But any hope you may have had at rekindling such fondness flew out the door when you stabbed me in the chest. It wasn't enough for you to leave me lying there for your brother to find, you had to let him think..." I can't voice it.

"I let him think that I tasted from the Goddess of Spring, and I watched it eat him alive. It was almost as satisfying as when I twisted the knife and watched the life leave your eyes. It's going to be even better when I am crowned King of the Underworld and I kill my brother for taking what was mine. When I do, I'll make sure he knows the babe that quickens in your womb is mine."

Even thinking that he has won, he's unhinged. I cannot *believe* I didn't see through him earlier. The signs were there, and I ignored them all like an asshole because he showed me what Essos couldn't. Galen is so unbalanced, I can't believe that Xavier would allow his brother to act with impunity. He of all people preached about the importance of not setting that precedent, and yet... I need to gather allies, people to help me put an end to Galen, but I don't know who I can trust.

Essos said that Galen felt I belonged to him because he met me first, but trying to remember how that happened makes my head pound.

"Promises, promises." I say, before twirling across the floor.

"Be careful what you wish for." I twist away from him as the song ends.

He's the God of War, God of Pain, God of Suffering. Raping and pillaging are his expertise—why should his brother and this realm be any different? Xavier was right to be worried—killing gods is a slippery slope. It's a shame Xavier is too much of a pushover to do anything about this. Posey has been calling the plays for centuries; it's why when Xavier tires of a task, he hands it off to Essos, accomplishing two things at once—pissing off Posey and getting work off his desk.

I focus on playing the consummate host. Without my husband, it is my job to greet and welcome people—this is my home, after all. The lower gods and goddesses come out of the woodwork to welcome me back. Everyone congratulates me on my return, some more tentatively than others, mostly those loyal to Essos. The faces of people start to click as I remember those around me—the snakes and the true friends. I know that I need to be careful with my next move.

Xavier whisks me onto the dance floor and away from a dull conversation. He holds me at an appropriate distance. I remember not hating him as much as I hated Galen, but we were hardly the picture of functional in-laws. He did almost marry his sister.

"Your Highness," he says with a dip of his head. I keep my focus on the room around me, not looking at Xavier. "Where is my brother? He needs to relinquish control to Galen." I force my eyes to meet his cold blue ones. This entire family has blue eyes of varying degrees. I used to love being able to look at my husband's siblings and be reminded that they have a little bit of him in them, but this betrayal runs too deep, and I get no comfort.

"You won't find my husband unless he wants to be found. Galen will not be king until we are wed; the crown on my head assures that. My blood assures that," I say icily. It was a gamble, walking out in my crown, but having the citizens of Solarem still recognize me as queen, even a long-lost one, helps to bolster my precarious position. The annoyed look on Xavier's face confirms we're all playing fast and loose with the rules as we figure out this uncharted territory. Knowing Xavier, there was no plan in place if I didn't choose Essos, and why would there be? I should have known him regardless. And maybe I did. I was so drawn to him, but Galen's voice, Galen's meddling, ruined it.

"You forget your place, sister." He twists my wrist. "You married into the regency, not the other way around. That little drop of blood shared during your wedding ceremony may grant you some protection, but Galen is a blood-born prince. If you want to keep that crown, you will need to marry Galen, and you will need to convince Essos to hand over his powers. There is a bloodless way of doing this, and being an obstinate bitch for the sake of it is only putting your 'beloved' at more risk."

I retaliate the only way I know how; I stomp on his foot, and he does his best not to visibly groan.

"You seem to forget that I am the Queen of the Underworld. I may not be one of the *beloved* original gods, but I will not be disrespected again. My *murder* was disrespectful and set the precedent that you are so afraid of. When Galen and I wed, he can assume his desired role as king, but I am the queen, and this is *my* dominion."

"That is correct—you will wed Galen. Your marriage to Essos ended when your heart stopped beating."

"There is nothing you can say or do that will change that Essos is my husband. He is my king. What of Callie, Galen's wife? Has so much changed that we're polygamists now?"

"No one has heard from Callie in over a thousand years," Xavier tells me stiffly, but he doesn't answer my question.

"So glad to learn your wife still has you by the balls, that you will bend every which way to appease her. You may be content ruling on the sidelines, but I'm not. I will set my own course and rule my realm until you pull your head out of your ass and end this coup."

The song ends, and Xavier steps away from me. "Long live the queen," he says with a flourish before walking away.

Helene grabs my arm and drags me outside and away from the party.

"I would greatly appreciate it if your family would stop manhandling me," I snap before she pulls me into a hug.

"I've missed you." She releases me only to slap me across the face. I hold my cheek for a beat before turning to face her. "You ruined everything, Daphne. What the actual fuck happened?" Cat and Zara step outside, closing the door behind them. I wave my hand, and the door locks, preventing anyone from following them out.

"I'm going to let that one go, but don't ever strike me again." I hold her gaze, refusing to blink first. Helene might sit on the Council with a crown of her own, but I've been walked over enough tonight to last a lifetime. Helene looks at Cat and Zara, whom I turn to embrace.

"Holy *shit*," Zara says, taking in the whole look of me. The crown, the dark eye makeup, and the dress. She drops into a curtsey.

I force a laugh, holding Cat's hand. "Don't be silly," I say, shaking my head, grabbing Zara's arm and pulling her upright.

"What the hell just happened?" Cat asks.

Helene huffs, crossing her arms.

"A lot happened. I don't even know where to begin." I haven't started to process everything that happened tonight. How can I lead my friends through it?

Helene takes a step toward me. "Start with how you let Galen play you like a goddamn fiddle," she says disparagingly.

"Have some respect." Zara snaps at her, and murder flashes in Helene's eyes.

"Quick to jump to her defense now that she's queen, you little ass-kisser. You wanted to fuck her husband yesterday. So quick to change your tune," Helene snarls.

"Galen knew which insecurities to play on. Every single touch was a carefully planned ruse with a memory. What I saw as Galen and me were really memories that belonged to Essos and me. Seems a real hole in the rules that he was able to do that." In desperate need of some quiet, I walk away from the party. I kick off my shoes as I go, those heels digging into the sand only slowing me down. I don't bother to see if the others follow.

"You're right, it was. Why do you think I showed up once I found out he was here? But you wouldn't talk to me—you didn't tell me he was interfering. Finn was the only one who wised up, so he made the complaint that got the Calling Ball pushed up. He hoped it would be enough to get you away from Galen. I'm sure Posey was telling Galen how to circumvent the rules. She's always had it out for you after your wedding got all that press and her wedding was overshadowed by a bump watch for you."

"I don't remember everything yet. I have bits and pieces, and most of that is what Galen tainted." I keep my thoughts to myself about Finn making the complaint. I can't keep lashing out at my allies. I need to have them on my side, and that means keeping my temper in check.

Once I'm far enough away from the party, I sit in the sand and put my head in my hands. "I royally fucked this one up," I say, trying to tamp down a fresh wave of grief. I cannot let it wash over me, because I need to stay sharp. I need to hone my anger instead.

"Oh, stop." Helene plops down on the sand beside me. "You can't let my shithead brother win. I know Essos won't rest until this is fixed. That means that you can't, either. Galen can't win."

"I hate to say it, but it's looking pretty bleak," Cat says, joining us on the sand.

"Can I be the first to apologize for making out with your husband? Is he even still your husband?" Zara says, interrupting the moment.

I can only chuckle at her boldness. "Of course, he is. Something as trivial as death isn't going to keep us apart. I don't care if we're still considered married or not. He *is* my husband, and I'll keep saying it louder for the people in the back." I raise my voice at no one in particular. "You are forgiven. Just don't let it happen again. Besides, Essos knew who I was and was kissing you back," I say.

I can see now that every move that Essos made was strategic, but I can still be mad that he was swapping spit with Zara. Before Galen arrived, he tried to keep Zara at arm's length. He was affectionate, but it was the night of the ball after the sea monster attack that I saw Essos with his hands all over Zara. Was that a clever ruse meant to distract Galen from me? To make Galen think that Essos was more interested in Zara?

"Do you look the same?" Cat asks biting on her thumb. There are tearstains on her cheeks, and I want to smooth them away.

"Yes, actually. I'm not sure how that was managed, but I'm also guessing it wasn't just my looks that clued everyone in to who I was?" I look at Helene for confirmation.

"No, the imprint of your soul is the same. It's like looking at a photo that features the backs of people's heads. We all knew you well enough to know. That's why this whole charade was tedious. Essos had to go through the motions during his other Callings and pretend he might pick someone else. I think Posey was hoping that he *would* find someone else, or decide to—" Helene coughs "—decide to marry someone else so she could wrap you up in a bow for Galen. It's why Essos let people like Cat and your friend Tiffany stay—it at least looked like he was taking it seriously, and it's why I dismissed everyone else."

"How did he do it?" Zara prods.

"Galen?" This I actually do know. "As the God of War, he manipulates memories. He can peer in your head, pick out a memory, and make it something so much bigger than it was. He's banned from doing it to any of the Council, which I was a member of once upon a time, but I guess because I didn't have my full powers and memories, that didn't apply to me. Then again, Posey seems to be running roughshod over everyone. I can't believe I fell for his shit." I mutter that last part half to myself as I start to muse over these new power structures. Essos and I were always the first to push back against Posey regarding Council affairs, to her eternal frustration. The kingdoms were divided fairly with power, but Posey always insisted that as Queen and King of the Gods, she and Xavier should have more. Maybe that changed with my death—maybe she finally got her way.

"Galen knows how to manipulate people. He's a master at it—you can't blame yourself. He's the God of War—he has centuries of experience picking at the exact right thread that causes the entire tapestry to unravel," Helene admits begrudgingly.

"Who should I blame?" I challenge Helene. She's picking up the dry sand and letting it slide through her fingers back onto the beach.

"Let's start with Galen. He timed this perfectly. Your soul was trapped in a gem on the dagger. As part of the agreement for Galen to have a chance to win your heart, the Council had to release your soul from it. No one was told it was released, though I'm sure Essos felt it." Helene's information still has holes in it, but at this point, it wouldn't surprise me to find out that the only person who really knows what happened is Galen.

I think about the moment I felt sick during the flag football game, how I felt like I was being stabbed. Galen must have been in the Underworld then. Essos had to have been shielding my presence in the Underworld somehow—that's why he was able to get away with hiding me as long as he did.

"Can I ask what might be an obvious question?" Zara asks. I lean forward to look at her, raising an eyebrow, waiting for her to continue. "If you were a goddess, and gods can't be killed, how did you die?"

Helene clears her throat. "The weapon used has gone missing. No one knows how or why it exists. No one knows where it is."

The world drops out from under me. I'm sure Galen knows exactly where it is. It wouldn't surprise me to learn that he's had it for ages, waiting for the right moment. As God of War, he maintains our armory.

I want to let my internal strife show. I want to pull my hair and scream and cry, but the women sitting beside me are relying on me. I can't fall apart, not in front of them.

"I bet the sea monster that tried to drown you was orchestrated by Galen to earn your trust," Cat points out, bringing us back to Galen and away from the unknown.

I clench my hands around fistfuls of sand, then release them, diamonds sliding between my fingers. "I can't trust anyone," I say, staring at the horizon.

Zara picks up one of the diamonds and shows it to Cat. I can feel her shock and awe as she picks up a handful of them, glancing at my hands and then the diamonds.

"You can trust me," Cat says, taking one hand.

Zara grabs my other hand with a nod. "Me too," she confirms.

We glance at Helene at the same time. "There was once a time you called me 'sister,' and that's how it felt to me too," Helene says. "I was closer to you than to my brothers. When you died…" She pauses. "It was one of the worst days I have lived through, and I couldn't even grieve properly, because I had to be there for Essos."

I am grateful she was there for him when I couldn't be. "I remember," I say. She was the only sister I had in my life. She was my friend first, and originally was annoyed when I started to see her brother. Though I was rubbing elbows with Helene, the princes, Essos, Xavier and Galen were all notoriously playboys. I never wanted anything to do with them, but then Essos saved my life and told me I could repay him with dinner. I was a minor goddess—I shouldn't have been on his radar as a potential match —but our chemistry was undeniable. It took Helene some time to warm up to us, but even she could see that Essos was different with me. And to me, Helene was more than a sister—she helped Essos and I reconcile after a fight that almost ended everything before we really began. She was there every step of the way for us. It was Helene who held the knife on our wedding day, slicing our palms and tying them together.

"Well, then I forgive you for being a bonehead." She says it easily.

Finn comes running down the beach toward us. I regret being an asshole to him earlier; he truly tried his best to prevent this from happening, and I shouldn't punish him for that.

"Daph!" he shouts before coming to a stop in front of us. "Your betrothed is looking for you for the last dance."

"Wait," Cat nearly cries, grabbing my arm. I pause and look to her. "Are Zara and I..."

"Safe," I reassure her. "As safe as I can make you. The only people who can force a soul into their afterlife are Essos and myself. It's why Helene's dismissals meant you were able to still have your goodbyes—she just sent those girls to their rooms. If you want to move on, that's entirely up to you, but let's get through tonight, and whatever you want, I'll do." It's the only way I can thank my friends for their support. Their presence is important to me, but their safety and comfort matter more. I'll talk to them tomorrow, see how they're really feeling about everything. It's one thing to make bold proclamations now, in the heat of the moment, but once this all settles in, I want them to make their decisions with all the information.

"Of course, tomorrow," Cat murmurs. I can already see the wheels turning in her head.

"Shall we, ladies?" I rise and help my friends get up. I'm going to need all the allies I can get in the coming days. My circle, the people I trust, are all here. I change Cat's and Zara's dresses to black versions. If they're going to be in my court, they have to represent accordingly.

I dust off my dress, lift my head high, and stroll into the lion's den.

35

Galen stands in the middle of the dance floor, awaiting my arrival. I sweep into the room, changing my gown again to a deep red color and shedding off layers to reveal a red satin dress. The slit up the leg ends indecently high near my hip; the dress, if it can even be called that, is little more than a few strips of material sewn together. The neckline hangs loosely over my breasts, thin straps just barely holding it up. It's completely backless, leaving me on display. It's the way I feel, right now—bare and exposed. I stride across the floor with Helene, Cat and Zara flanking me. When I reach Galen, I give him the smallest dip of my head as I slip into a curtsey.

He responds in kind with a bow before taking my hand and leading me into a dance. I smile along with him, as if this is where I want to be. I am a much better dancer now than I was before getting my memories back.

"In time, you will come to see that this is the right thing. That we are the ones truly meant to be together."

I try to suppress a shudder, knowing that it will only anger him. His tune has changed—he's leveled out, no longer talking about whoring me out when he's done with me. We're *meant* to be together now.

These mercurial moods only make him more dangerous.

"Unfortunately, Grandfather Time isn't here to confirm that." It slips out before I can help it.

He tugs me closer to him, digging his fingertips into my back, crushing my hand in his other. I don't know why I have to needle him, but I do.

"Let me rephrase, Daphne. You will either bend to my will, or I will slaughter your friends here and now, including my daft clown of a sister. She knows better than to take sides." He presses a kiss to my neck, right where my pulse thunders. It's an empty threat, at least to Helene. Kai's muscles are more than just for show— unless Galen still has that weapon. Gods aren't meant to die.

My heart wilts in my chest at the thought of being responsible for their deaths. It was already my fault that Cat and Zara are dead. If not for me, I doubt the bus would have crashed, though I can't say for certain without Essos's confirmation. The thought of Galen killing them where he might soon have complete control over them, is not a thought I am willing to entertain. I have to remind myself that he can't do that, not yet. There hasn't been an official transfer of power, and some of what Essos can do won't be achievable without the blood of my husband.

Galen spins me out, and as my body twirls, I let my mind spiral and try to find a solution. Some way to get out of this, get away from him.

Then it dawns on me.

There *is* a potential way out. It's old, something that we haven't had cause to invoke in millennia, certainly not for a god. I can see a bright shining light, and I just have to step into it.

I stop moving, breaking free from Galen's grasp. I stomp my foot, and vines unfurl from the ground and wind their way around Galen's ankles, holding him in place. The musicians miss several notes, stopping to watch what is happening. I hear the whispers around me, people wondering why everything has stopped.

"My darling betrothed," I start, keeping my voice even. "I think, given the circumstances, it is only fair that we have a *proper* celebration of our impending nuptials. A celebration fit for the gods!"

The crowd begins to murmur, wondering what I could mean by that.

"I propose we host the Trials." This time, there is outright chatter about what I have said. I see Galen's eyes flash red—blood red, with rage. "Show them all just how much I mean to you."

I might have missed much since my first death, but I remember how things work for this crowd. They love the blood and gore of the Trials, which mortals in ancient times would undergo to prove themselves to the gods. The Trials haven't been held in recent memory. At the very least, not in my recent memory.

Just the thought of this sets the crowd buzzing at the dangers that would come.

"That sounds absolutely sporting," Xavier says, stepping forward, his wife on his arm for once. Her lips are pressed into a thin line as Xavier squeezes her hand, holding her in place. Behind them, someone—I assume Finn—begins a chant.

"Tri-als! Tri-als! Tri-als!" More and more people are joining in, and they're getting louder and louder with each round. The crowd is being whipped into feverish excitement. When *was* the last time that they held the Trials? Has there ever been one for the gods?

"SILENCE," Galen booms. He's unable to move from the spot where I am holding him. I watch his feeble attempt to pull a foot free. If he wants out, he's going to have to flex his own power. The result instead knocks him off balance, almost causing him to fall.

"It would appear I have been left without a choice," he says.

I feel the same way.

I raise one shoulder, turning my head away from him. "It's best to give the people what they want. At the end of the tournament, we will have the largest and most glorious wedding that anyone has ever seen. Of course, not to outdo Xavier and Posey and their lovely wedding. I believe one year shall give us enough time to plan out and execute the Trials properly." I try to buy as much time as I can. There is a groan from the crowd—they want a bloodbath *now*.

"Three months," Galen counters without missing a beat.

"Twelve months," I say defiantly. The vines on his legs creep up to his knees. I pull my shoulders back and square them, ready to fight this one out. They say love is all about picking your battles, and this is one of those battles. I get more booing from the crowd.

"Six months," he says. I can almost feel the desperation rising off his skin. "And in that time, you and I will continue to rule this realm as partners."

"*I* will continue to rule this realm as its queen," I say through gritted teeth. "You will be permitted only to advise on matters."

"As your betrothed and rightful king, I will rule and take your opinion under advisement." His words are cutting and set my teeth on edge.

"Ah! Lovers, perhaps this discussion is meant for another time. Behind closed doors, and with some hanky-panky." Xavier steps forward.

I turn to him quickly. He feels a tickle in the back of his throat, and I know it. He tries to cover it up, but he starts coughing into his free hand, finding dirt. His eyes flick from the dirt in his hand, which he casts aside, to me. His retaliation is instant, my lungs filling with water. I try to cover my need to cough, but it splits my focus. Galen finds his way free from my vines. I ease up, Xavier clearing his throat, and the water vanishes. It would seem the weather boy has learned a few tricks in my absence.

"For six months, you shall both have a say in the running of your realm, but given that my brother is of royal birth, he will have the stronger vote. You two are to live in separate wings of the house until you are wed. It is only proper. Then you shall have the wedding bash of the millennium." He pauses, and when neither of us objects, he claps. "Wonderful, glad to know that all parties are agreed. Now that we have our next party planned, everyone—get out."

A few in the crowd look offended and start talking to their neighbors about what the next six months will bring. Many don't make the move to leave. They don't recognize the authority behind the King of Gods.

"I'm sorry," Xavier says, placing his hand over his heart. "Was that rude? Please, *get out.*" Finn starts to usher people out the front door. Helene is taking cups from people's hands and pushing them toward the door as well. Even without my vines binding him, Galen is rooted to his spot, watching people leave. I don't move an inch either, stuck in this odd standoff with him and Xavier.

Some people I don't recognize approach Galen and give them their congratulations while eyeing me up and down. Others are just mad that the party is over. More than a few people approach me to welcome me back.

After all the guests have departed, only Xavier, Posey, Helene, Kai, Galen and I remain. Finn ushered Zara and Cat to their rooms, knowing that this is out of their depth.

As the last group leaves, Galen advances on me quickly, grabbing my throat and pushing me against a wall, squeezing. I panic, unsure what my mortality looks like now. My powers aren't fully back, but I have righteous anger on my side. He is out of control, and it's my fault. My falling into his trap emboldened him and gave him the opening to make his play for the throne. The well of my powers was never as deep as those of the royal children; it's why they're rulers of their own realms—all except Galen. For now, I can handle small rebellions, but nothing I do will let me outlast him.

"Where is Essos!" Galen shouts in my face, spit flying. He squeezes harder, and my hands claw at his, desperate to put some space between his grip and my windpipe. I dig my nails into his skin, trying to get him to let up. When I get no traction, I drag them down his face. I'm elated by the blood I draw. His hands only tighten in response.

Xavier and Helene spring toward him, but I hold up a hand to stop them. Galen's grip relaxes, as he has to heave. He stops to look at me before throwing up actual flowers, releasing me fully as he throws up a second time.

I cough and clear my throat, gingerly touching the bruises already forming around my neck. Healing them will take too much out of me right now, and I need to be able to fight back before anything else. I am shaking inside about what he has just done, but I cannot let him see how he has affected me. My anger is the only thing keeping me going right now.

"Let us make one thing clear, *betrothed*. This is my home. My realm. Xavier can pander to you all he wants, but you're in my house now."

Xavier crosses his arms, a smug smile on his face. I want to hit him for his alleged neutrality that is anything but neutral. He chose to protect a murderer over me, and I will *never* forget that.

"Even if I knew where Essos was, the last thing I would do is tell *you*, you pathetic, murderous cockroach."

Galen takes another step toward me. With all my power, I push him clear across the room. My power is draining fast, but I cannot show him this. I'm sure he knows that my well goes only so deep, but how many other goddesses have been reincarnated? My upper lip feels wet, but I ignore it. I will push through another nosebleed to show him that I am not to be trifled with.

Essos was wrong to think that I was safe around his brother at all.

"Lay hands on me again. I dare you." My voice is gravely and low, danger in every word.

Xavier steps between us before things can escalate further. I am grateful for this at the moment, as a headache starts to build, the adrenaline rush from tonight wearing off. I wipe my nose with the back of my hand, and a quick glance at my wrist confirms that I indeed have another nosebleed.

Xavier rubs his chin, as if reaching for a beard that is no longer there. "Enough. Both of you are acting like children. I laid out the rules very simply. There will be Trials, to be determined by myself and the Council, and you will both rule over this realm. We cannot leave death unregulated." He pointedly ignores my blood.

"I need access to Essos's gold," Galen says quickly, and two men I've never seen before appear beside him. Glaring, I wave my hand and turn them into trees. Galen starts toward me, and Xavier steps between us.

"For the love of—well, me, can't you two play nice?" Xavier pleads.

My eyebrows shoot up, and I gape at him. "Excuse me? He killed me! Literally stabbed a knife in my chest *six times*," I shout, while Galen starts to yell about me turning his people into trees.

Helene steps in then. "Please, okay, clearly this is not going to work well, and you need some babysitters if you're both going to survive." Helene summons chairs and pushes them into the backs of our knees, forcing us into them. "You wanted this, Galen. Now you need to make it work."

I cross my arms and look away from this mess, wondering how I got here. How did I let myself be so manipulated by Galen? Fury rises off my skin as I think about all that he has done and all that he has taken from me. His actions tonight have shown who he truly is—who I have always known him to be. The Galen that smashed the marble countertop was the real one, not the Galen who feigned concern when I almost passed out in the shower.

"Now, that sounds like a great idea. How about some pre-marital counseling to ensure that you both go into this with open hearts, eh?" Xavier waves a hand, clearing the ballroom of any mess from tonight. "That should save you some effort. Now, please, go to your separate wings, and in one month, we will reconvene and determine how to host the Trials. Seems more sporting to have them staggered, but that will be up to the Council to determine. In that time, you'll have some counseling to ensure that yours is a happy union and that the Underworld will continue to run the way it must. There is a reason someone has to be in charge of it, and that's because I do not want more work. Am I clear?" Without waiting for us to respond, Xavier makes his way toward the door with Posey in tow. She follows him like the good little wife she is supposed to be, but her eyes are narrowed on me. "Helene," Xavier says as they're about to depart, "do you think you can manage these two until we can set up the Trials?"

Helene, for her part, covers up her anger rather well. Kai, knowing his wife, places a hand on her shoulder, supporting her in suppressing the urge to murder us all. "Of course. I have nothing better to do, brother. No weddings to bless, or my own job. I would much rather play babysitter for my brother and my other brother's wife."

"Good! Such a good sport. Now, if you will excuse us." Xavier holds his hand out for Posey, and she takes it, but not before giving Galen a meaningful look. "And don't forget to turn those trees back into his men," he shouts before vanishing with Posey.

Helene rolls her eyes. She watches me, waiting for me to comply, and when I don't, she gives me a scolding look, motioning at the two trees still flanking Galen.

"Fine." I look away, reverting them to their normal form. They look confused by all the changes that took place while they were trees.

Galen stands and straightens his tux jacket. "I'll go to the master bedroom and stay there," he says.

I jump out of my seat. "You will not!" My strength is draining, but I'm ready to square off with him again. Apparently, when I thought about having to pick my battles with Galen, I decided they were all my battles. I can't give him an inch anywhere.

Helene leans her head back and stomps her feet. "Literally, is this going to be babysitting the entire *fucking* time? Is everything going to be a fight? No, Galen, you will not sleep in our brother's room. It is bad enough that you stole his wife and his domain. You can wait six fucking months before taking his bedroom as well. The room you've been staying in this whole fucking time was good enough for you before and will still be good enough now. Daphne can stay in the room she's been in for months, I will stay in my room, as before, and until you two are married, no one will stay in the master. On that note, go the fuck to bed. I'm sick of you both." Helene kicks off her heels and leans over to pick them up before striding away. Kai sheepishly dips his head toward me, then follows Helene.

"You *will* learn to love me," Galen says as I walk away, leaving him there to plot and plot and plot. I don't bother to grace him with a look. The only one with a lesson to learn is him. There is nothing he can do that will ever change how I feel about him.

36

I walk into my room and close the door behind me. The last fifteen minutes took more out of me than the entire Calling. I lean against it, then sink to the floor. Resting my head in my hands, I think of all the ways that I fucked up. I can feel my mind reaching for sleep or some way to process the events of tonight, but I'm terrified of what will happen when I close my eyes.

I don't even know how to process this. My head is still pounding, and I think my nose might still be bleeding, but these are the least of my concerns.

I think of Essos, and where he might be, as Dave walks over and nudges my hand with his snout. I start to pet him, and he nudges closer to my face to lick the tears as they start to fall. True to his nature, Waffles has not moved from my pillow, where he lies and watches me curiously, not even lifting his head. It's all side-eye, and I deserve it.

I have profoundly fucked up, and I don't know how to fix what I've done, but I know that I have to.

There is a gentle knock at the door, and a small voice on the other side as Cat calls my name. I contemplate opening the door and letting her in. But I can't stand the thought of having to talk to anyone at this point, so I silently wait for her to cross back to her room and go to sleep. That is the second night in a row I have blown off my best friend, but there is not enough left in me to care.

Tomorrow is another day. Tonight, I need to find a way to pull the broken pieces of myself back together. I cross the room, kicking my shoes off as I walk to the window. I stare out at the beach and think about where my husband could possibly be now.

On the beach, men are patrolling, and I wonder if this will be my new normal—men circling my home to keep Essos away and me in. It's a fleeting thought, because I know Galen. I know that he will do everything that he can to control me. Cat and Zara are weapons that can be used against me. My love for Helene will cause him to doubt her, and there is no way that he's going to allow me to have an ally that close, even if it is what Xavier wants.

I strip off the dress and stand completely naked for a moment, looking at myself in the mirror. I know that this is not the same body I had when Galen murdered me, but I touch my chest in the spots where he stabbed me. This violation is not something that I will let go, but if I want to survive—if I want there to be some-thing left for Essos to return to—I'm going to have to play his game his way. I was brash and foolish tonight in how I acted, letting him get under my skin.

I fill the tub and start to pull the pins from my hair. I try to remember all the different faces that I have seen tonight, and while some come easily to me, others leave me clawing for an association. I'm at a disadvantage until my memory comes back completely. I'll have to see if Finn can help me get more back faster, but there are centuries upon centuries upon millennia of memories to recall. Am I still at risk of nosebleeds if I get them back too fast?

I open the blinds beside the tub. I can see the sun starting to peek out along the horizon as I slide into the water before it's fully warmed. A chill runs up my spine as I sink in and try to call on memories of my husband that Galen hasn't tainted.

I close my eyes and find a memory of Essos. He enters the bathroom to see me sitting in the tub in our room after a longer day than usual at work. In the memory, he sits at my vanity and removes his shoes. I smile, recalling the coyness of this memory. How I looked at him, what he accused me of...

"Are you undressing me with your eyes?" he asks, feigning shock and outrage. He takes off one shoe and then the other.

"Only seems fair," I say, swishing water around, attempting to gather bubbles to cover my obvious state of undress.

He stands, loosening his tie. "You're right, we should both be soaking wet right now." He strides to me and places his hands on either side of the tub. He kisses me hard on the mouth, keeping just far enough away that I have to stretch to him. I sit up a little more, rising to meet him before becoming distracted by a splash and a sudden displacement of water. I laugh, realizing that my power-conserving husband used his power to strip his clothes away and climb into the tub with me. His crystal-blue eyes twinkle with mischief as he pulls me closer to him.

I sink deeper into the tub before submerging myself entirely. I have to find a way to fix this and banish Galen from my home. I linger under the water, my whole body hot from using too much power. I hold my breath and stay under as long as I can, until my lungs burn and I have to come up. My hesitations around water are gone, the negative association washed away in the confusion of finding myself again. I sit back up, pulling in a large gasp of air, and open my eyes to find Essos sitting in the bathroom. I startle, but he brings a finger to his lips.

"Please, just listen to me, my love," he whispers. The dogs are lounging at his feet, never having given warning that he was there. "Trust you to be a force of nature and not listen to a damn word I said. I asked you to lie low, and you challenged him instead."

I open my mouth to contradict him, but he silences me with a look.

"I was wrong—I thought that having you would mean he wouldn't hurt you, but he will do anything to hurt me, even if that means hurting you." Before I can object, he continues. "Not that you're saying or doing anything he doesn't deserve, but holy hells, Daphne." He runs his hands over his face, and he looks so much more tired than I have ever seen him.

"He doesn't need a reason—he's going to do it anyway. I might as well get some digs in there myself." I draw my knees to my chest.

"But if you play the part, maybe you can beat him at his own game. Every battle can't be *the* battle. Let him sleep in our room, let him use my office. I don't care. None of this mattered without you, and I need you to survive."

"I won't provoke him...as much. But I'm not going to share a bed with that monster." I hedge.

The corner of one lip tugs up in a smirk. "I know you can say that you are not going to poke the bear, but I know you—we were married for centuries. Your favorite pastime is kicking the bear in the face. Especially after what he did to you. You died, and the sky wept for you." He doesn't sound heartbroken, just matter-of-fact.

"How did you just let him live after what happened to me?" I ask, and my voice catches, giving away the betrayal I feel.

He goes perfectly still before meeting my eyes. "You think I had a choice?" he whispers, and I can barely hear him. I look away from him and out the window, where the sun is starting to rise. The sky is a violent red color. I remember the old rhyme, *Red sky at morning, sailors take warning*. There's a storm brewing somewhere.

Essos stands and crosses the room, barely making a sound as he kneels beside the tub. I turn to look at him, and he pushes the wet hair away from my face.

"Not killing him was the hardest thing I have ever had to do. Getting up every day after you died was the next hardest thing. I woke up in an empty bed. I spent my days knowing that Galen was alive and breathing and you weren't. Xavier felt that, while it would have been justified, he didn't want to open the floodgates. Their explanation for your death was neat and clean, and muddying it with Galen's death would have been a 'complication.'" He doesn't look away from me; his eyes stare through me and into the betrayal I am feeling. Essos doesn't care that talking to me is pulling back the scab on this old, old wound, one he thought he had finally healed with my return. He does it anyway. He does it because he knows that I need to hear the words. I need him to tell me why he didn't scorch the earth and punish Galen for what he did.

"I had to spend my days overseeing the ushering of new souls into the Underworld. More loss and sadness. And then I had to go to bed alone, knowing that the woman I love was dead while my asshole brother walked around like he was hot shit." He looks down at the water and then back up at me. I lean forward and press my forehead to his. His eyes close, and I tilt my head, my lips meeting his.

There is no heat behind the kiss; it's just sweet. We've done this a hundred thousand times, and it feels like home.

Essos pulls away and cradles my face in his hands, then sits there a beat, just looking at me, as if trying to memorize every detail of my face. "I love you, a thousand times. I love you. I will rip the sun from the sky and tear the moon in half to get back to you, and nothing and no one will stop me." He leans forward and kisses my forehead.

"I love you," I whisper back. I've missed hundreds of years of these words, years of declarations that he loved me. You don't realize how much you miss hearing *I love you* until you don't have it. A tear slips from my eye, and he uses his thumb to wipe it away.

"I have to leave now. I will be back for you. Do not ever doubt it. I will kill my brother if I have to," he vows to me. Essos kisses my lips one last time before standing up. I grab his arm like he's the life preserver I need him to be. He takes my hand and threads his fingers through mine before bringing it up and kissing my knuckles.

"Come back to me," I say, and let go of his hand.

In a blink, he is gone, and I am alone in the bathroom, blinded by the rising sun.

ACKNOWLEDGMENTS

I have so many people to thank for their support in my journey to bring you *The King's Game*.

Lexie, Danielle, Katie and Tracy, your enthusiastic early support for this story made it so I could keep going. Your need to learn more about what happens next made it crucial that I keep writing.

My sister, Jennifer, for pimping out my books and this story. I'm glad I hope I made you proud.

Michael, my love, my heart, the king to my queen. That you took the time to read this book and repeatedly tell me how much you love it means *every* and more to me.

To my INCREDIBLE editorial team - Tashya and Amanda - your comments and feedback helped me to make this the strongest story it could be. Your deep love of Helene is noted, and just MIGHT get you a story for her.

To Hannah for pushing me on this journey.

My mom and dad, who convinced me that I can do anything and everything, and for giving me the BEST advice in the world. *Don't wait for your ship to come in, row out and meet it.* I think I'm doing a damn good job of meeting my ship.

Lastly, but never ever least, my readers, for picking up this book and seeing the journey through. Thank you, thank you, thank you.

COMING SOON

Daphne and Essos's story continues in...

THE
QUEEN'S
GAMBLE

Pre-order here now!

COMING SOON

Interested in contemporary romance? Check out the next book in my Love in the Big Apple series book.

Madison Avenue Mediator

Available for pre-order now!

ABOUT THE AUTHOR

Nicole Sanchez has been writing stories on any scrap of paper she could get her hands since before middle school. She lives in New Jersey with her high school sweetheart and love of her life along with their two quirky cats. When she isn't writing or wielding the Force, she can be found traveling the world with her husband or training for her next RunDisney Event.

For more books and updates:
    Newsletter
    Website
    Facebook Reader Group

Also by Nicole Sanchez

Love in the Big Apple Series:

Central Park Collision

Las Vegas Luck

Madison Avenue Mediator

Game of Gods Series:

The Queen's Gamble

Anthology Work:

Wicked Games

Made in the USA
Monee, IL
16 May 2024

58352998R00252

ESSENTIAL
ALGARVE

Original text by Christopher Catling

Updated by Emma Rowley Ruas

© Automobile Association Developments Limited 2009
First published 2007
Reprinted 2009. Information verified and updated

ISBN: 978-0-7495-6001-0

Published by AA Publishing, a trading name of Automobile Association Developments Limited, whose registered office is Fanum House, Basing View, Basingstoke, Hampshire RG21 4EA. Registered number 1878835.

Automobile Association Developments Limited retains the copyright in the original edition © 1999 and in all subsequent editions, reprints and amendments

Colour separation: MRM Graphics Ltd
Printed and bound in Italy by Printer Trento S.r.l.

A03616
Maps in this title produced from mapping © MAIRDUMONT / Falk Verlag 2008

About this book

Symbols are used to denote the following categories:

- map reference to maps on cover
- address or location
- telephone number
- opening times
- admission charge
- restaurant or café on premises or nearby
- nearest underground train station

- nearest bus/tram route
- nearest overground train station
- nearest ferry stop
- nearest airport
- other practical information
- tourist information office
- indicates the page where you will find a fuller description

This book is divided into five sections.

The essence of the Algarve
pages 6–19
Introduction; Features; Food and drink; Short break including the 10 Essentials

Planning pages 20–33
Before you go; Getting there; Getting around; Being there

Best places to see pages 34–55
The unmissable highlights of any visit to the Algarve

Best things to do pages 56–79
Good places to have lunch; top souvenir ideas; activities; good viewpoints and views; places to take the children and more

Exploring pages 80–187
The best places to visit in the Algarve, organized by area

Maps
All map references are to the maps on the covers. For example, Faro has the reference 17G – indicating the grid square in which it is to be found.

Admission prices
Inexpensive (under €3)
Moderate (€3–€6),
Expensive (over €6)

Hotel prices
Prices are per room per night: € budget (under €90); €€ moderate (€90–€150); €€€ expensive to luxury (over €150)
Note: Some listings have a range to reflect low- to high-season prices.

Restaurant prices
Price for a three-course meal per person without drinks: € budget (under €15); €€ moderate (€15–€25); €€€ expensive (over €25)

Contents

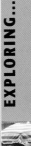

BEST THINGS TO DO

EXPLORING...

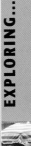

56 – 79   80 – 186

The essence of...

Landscape and climate combine in the Algarve to create a region of year-round appeal. In winter the Algarve basks in balmy sunshine. In summer it remains green and equable due to the cooling effect of Atlantic breezes. Travelling around you will encounter breathtaking views: sheer cliffs battered by Atlantic waves at Cabo de São Vicente (Cape St Vincent); sheltered valleys with their patchwork of orange groves; vineyards and olive trees or castle-topped peaks, with Moorish-style houses tumbling down the hillside; and brightly painted sardine boats in the harbours.

THE ESSENCE OF THE ALGARVE

features

When tourists first visited the Algarve in the 1970s, Portugal was just opening its doors to the world, having finally shrugged off a dictatorship that had clung on to power since 1932. Keen to catch up with the rest of Europe, Portugal leapt in a decade from a basic agricultural economy to the post-industrial age, and the freedoms that came in the wake of the revolution resulted in the Algarve's rapid development.

More than a quarter of a century on, the Algarve is firmly on the map as a rewarding and inexpensive holiday destination. Fortunately, it has managed to achieve this without overwhelming the features that make it so special. Swathes of the Algarve remain delightfully wild and unexploited, with scores of little bays and coves where you can laze the day away if you choose, while the endless expanses of golden sand farther east allow everyone to stake out their own private beach territory.

Perhaps the most attractive feature of the Algarve is simply that it combines so many different attractions – beaches, luxurious hotels and manicured golf courses, nightlife and sunshine. It is ideal for exploring churches, slipping into centuries-old hilltowns to observe the way of life, or rambling gently along cliff paths and through orange-scented groves, enjoying the wild flowers and butterflies.

GEOGRAPHY

● The Algarve, Portugal's southernmost province, is separated from the Alentejo, the next province north, by a range of low mountains known as the Serra de Monchique to the west and the Serra do Caldeirão to the east.

● To the west and south the region is bounded by the Atlantic Ocean, and to the east the River Guadiana forms the frontier between Portugal and Andalucia (Spain).

LANDSCAPE

● The Algarve divides into three main regions: the coast *(litoral)*, where most of the intensive tourist development is located; the foothills *(barrocal)*, where most of the agriculture is concentrated; and the almost uninhabited mountains *(serra)*, which support extensive cork oak forests.

● The Algarve includes mainland Europe's southwesternmost point, the legendary Cabo de São Vicente (Cape St Vincent). The western end of the coast is composed of eroded sandstone cliffs of many colours, with numerous marine grottoes and wind-eroded rock stacks, while to the east the coast is flat and sandy, with long beaches and barrier islands forming shallow lagoons.

CLIMATE

● The mountains separating the Algarve from the Alentejo also shelter it from cold continental air in winter, so that the region's winter climate is markedly milder than the rest of Portugal, though it does have high rainfall, due to Atlantic fronts.

● The coast is traditionally divided into the *barlavento* (windward) region (from Cape St Vincent to Albufeira), which bears the brunt of the southwesterly winds, and the more sheltered *sotavento* (leeward).

food & drink

Algarvian cooking has absorbed Spanish, Moorish and African influences, but nothing epitomizes the region better than the simple charcoal-grilled sardine, savoured out of doors at a seafront café on a balmy summer's evening.

ALGARVIAN DISHES

The region's cuisine reflects the ready availability of all kinds of fresh fish, from eels, lampreys and swordfish to lobsters, whelks, limpets and barnacles. Lobster, sea bass, mullet and bream are costed according to their weight and seasonal price (preço variavel) – check before you order to prevent an unexpectedly expensive meal. Most fish are simply grilled over a charcoal brazier, to seal in the fresh flavours, but tuna is more often baked with a sauce of peppers and tomatoes, and stuffed with a mixture of sausage, bacon, tomatoes and rice.

Shellfish features in two of the region's most typical specialities: amêijoas na cataplana and arroz de marisco. The latter is the Algarvian version of paella, a rich, slightly liquid mixture of clams, prawns and fish, cooked with rice, onions,

tomatoes and peppers. *Cataplana*, named after the copper vessel in which it is cooked, is a delicious stew of clams, sausage, ham, onions, garlic, chilli and herbs. The tightly clamped *cataplana* seals all the flavour in, to be released in a cloud of fragrant steam when the dish is ceremonially opened at your table. Some restaurants offer up to a dozen different *cataplana* variations, using combinations of pork, chicken, lobster, monkfish, shellfish and prawns.

PORTUGUESE DISHES

You will also find dishes from other parts of Portugal on the menu, including *caldeirada* (fish soup), based on stock made from the heads and bones of locally caught fish, enriched with paprika, onions, tomatoes and potatoes. *Bacalhau à brás* is fried salted cod with potatoes, onions, garlic, olives and eggs. The ubiquitous *caldo verde* (green soup) is a popular starter, made from potatoes, onions and finely shredded cabbage, with spicy *chouriço* sausage for added piquancy.

INLAND CUISINE

Though fish is also popular inland, you will find dishes on rural restaurant menus that rarely feature on the coast. Pigs' trotters with beans and black pudding, or liver and rice, may not be everyone's choice, but few can resist the spicy taste of chicken *piri-piri* (flavoured with chilli oil), a speciality of the Monchique region, or *caldeirada de cabrito*, a casserole of lamb or kid with onions, tomatoes and potatoes. Game (wild boar, quail, partridge and pheasant) features in season, and if nothing else appeals, try delicious *bife à Portuguesa* – grilled sirloin steak.

WINE

Although the Algarve has its own wines, they lack the finesse of nobler ones from the north of Portugal. Try white port *(porto branco)* served chilled as an aperitif, rather than post-prandial red. *Dão* and the similar *Barraida* are good all-purpose wines: both red and white versions are aged in barrels to acquire an oaky flavour, but the best remain soft and fruity. In hot weather, try something lighter – such as semi-sparkling *vinho verde* (green wine – so called due to its youthfulness rather than its colour), with a palate-cleansing lemon tang.

short break

If you have only a short time to visit the Algarve and would like to take home some unforgettable memories you can do something local and capture the real flavour of the region. The following suggestions will give you a wide range of sights and experiences that won't take very long, won't cost very much and will make your visit very special.

● **Step back in time** and visit Silves (➤ 106–109), which under Moorish rule boasted marble-clad palaces and bazaars full of eastern splendour.

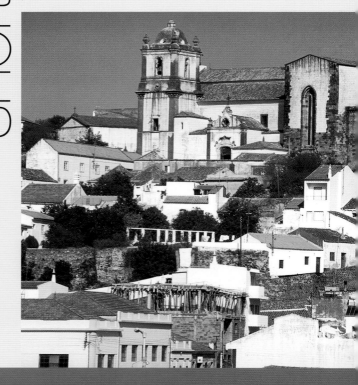

● **Eat sardines for lunch.** Unloaded fresh each
morning they are charcoal-grilled at restaurants all
along the coast, advertising their presence with a
delicious aroma. Simply add lemon juice and
accompany with at least a couple of glasses of
vinho verde.

● **Blow the cobwebs away** on top of the cliffs at
Fim do Mundo (World's End), as Cabo de São
Vicente (Cape St Vincent, ➤ 40–41) is known,
gazing out over the waves to the distant horizon.

- **Go for dinner** in a traditional restaurant and listen to the plaintive sound of Portuguese *fado* music.

- **Walk to the Fonte de Benémola** near Querença for a taste of the Algarvian countryside, as a contrast to the more developed coast.

- **Visit Praia da Rocha** (➤ 124–125) at sunset to enjoy the changing colours of the sandstone rocks and cliffs as the sun goes down.

- **Play a round of golf** at one of the region's 30 or so golf courses (➤ 76–77). The Algarve is one of Europe's top golfing destinations.

- **Join in a village festivity** (➤ 24–25) for the fun of fireworks and to sample local wines and kebabs or fish cooked over an open fire.

- **Spend a lazy day** on the beach, but rather than joining the hordes at Albufeira or Monte Gordo, head for one of the barrier islands, such as the Ilha de Tavira (➤ 169), and find your own private area of sand dunes and sea.

● **Visit the capital,**
Faro (➤ 138–142), for
its sophistication, its
timeless Old Town
(Cidade Velha), the
regional museum
illustrating a way of life
that only just survives,
and to enjoy the
frisson of the
fascinating skull-lined
Capela dos Ossos in
the Carmo church
(➤ 44–45).

Planning

Before you go

WHEN TO GO

JAN	FEB	MAR	APR	MAY	JUN	JUL	AUG	SEP	OCT	NOV	DEC
15°C	16°C	18°C	21°C	24°C	30°C	35°C	37°C	33°C	28°C	19°C	17°C
59°F	61°F	64°F	70°F	75°F	86°F	95°F	99°F	91°F	82°F	66°F	63°F

High season   Low season

Temperatures are the average daily maximum. Average daily minimum temperatures can be 8 to 10°C (14 to 18°F) lower. The best time to visit is May to June and September to October when it is warm and dry without being uncomfortably hot. Temperatures in July and August are very high, often pushing into the mid-30s °C (mid-90s °F), and at other times of year there may be rainfall. April and November can still be very pleasant in terms of temperature. If you want to miss the crowds, avoid the school holidays, particularly July and August, when half of Lisbon, as well as many north European holidaymakers, clog up the roads and beaches. If you are looking for sport rather than sunbathing, the Algarve is an all-year destination.

WHAT YOU NEED

● Required
○ Suggested
▲ Not required

Some countries require a passport to remain valid for a minimum period (usually at least six months) beyond the date of entry – contact their consulate or embassy or your travel agent for details.

	UK	Germany	USA	Netherlands	Spain
Passport (or National Identity Card where applicable)	●	●	●	●	●
Visa (regulations can change – check before you travel)	▲	▲	▲	▲	▲
Onward or Return Ticket	○	○	○	○	○
Health Inoculations (tetanus and polio)	▲	▲	▲	▲	▲
Health Documentation (► 23, Health Insurance)	○	○	○	○	○
Travel Insurance	○	○	○	○	○
Driving Licence (national)	●	●	●	●	●
Car Insurance Certificate	●	●	●	●	●
Car Registration Document	●	●	●	●	●

ADVANCE PLANNING WEBSITES

www.algarvenet.com
www.thealgarve.net

www.visitalgarve.pt
www.algarve-information.com

TOURIST OFFICES AT HOME

In the UK
Portuguese National Tourist Office
✉ 11 Belgrave Square,
London SW1X 8PP
☎ 0845 3551212

In Ireland
Portuguese National Tourist Office
✉ 54 Dawson Street,
Dublin 2
☎ 01 670 9133

In the USA
Portuguese National Tourist Office
✉ 590 Fifth Avenue, 4th Floor,
New York, NY 10036-4702
☎ 646/723-0200

In Canada
Portuguese National Tourist Office
✉ 60 Bloor Street West,
Suite 1005, Toronto,
Ontario, M4W 3B8
☎ 416/921-7376

HEALTH INSURANCE

Nationals of other EU countries can get medical treatment in state hospitals on production of a European Health Insurance Card (EHIC), although private medical insurance is still advised and is essential for all other visitors. Most private clinics and doctors in the Algarve will treat you in your hotel, provided you have insurance cover.

Dental services are excellent in the Algarve. Dentists advertise their services in the free English- and German-language magazines available.

TIME DIFFERENCES

GMT	Portugal	Germany	USA (NY)	Netherlands	Spain
12 noon	12 noon	1PM	7AM	1PM	1PM

The Algarve observes Greenwich Mean Time during the winter months; during the summer, from late March to late October, the time is Greenwich Mean Time plus one hour (GMT+1).

NATIONAL HOLIDAYS

1 Jan *New Year's Day*

Feb (dates vary)
Shrove Tuesday and Ash Wednesday

Mar/Apr *Good Friday and Easter Monday*

25 Apr *Day of the Revolution*

1 May *Labour Day*

Jun (date varies)
Corpus Christi

10 Jun *National Day*

15 Aug *Feast of the Assumption*

5 Oct *Republic Day*

1 Nov *All Saints' Day*

1 Dec *Restoration of Independence Day*

8 Dec *Feast of the Immaculate Conception*

25–26 Dec *Christmas Day and St Stephen's Day*

Most shops, offices and museums close on these days.

Note that Shrove Tuesday, Ash Wednesday and St Stephen's Day (Boxing Day) are not strictly national holidays, but many places close.

WHAT'S ON WHEN

February *Carnival* (weekend preceding Shrove Tuesday): steel barriers go up all over the Algarve on the Saturday before Shrove Tuesday, sealing off town centres from traffic so that the weekend's carnival can proceed without interruption. Typically, Saturday sees local children take part in a costume parade through the streets, while the irreverent 'satirical parade' takes place the following day. Loulé Carnival has the biggest and best procession, with colourful floats, bands and scantily clad dancers. Be warned, though, that water bombs, eggs, flour and other substances can be hurled at spectators during this and other carnival parades, so don't wear your best clothes.

April *Holy Week* (especially Palm Sunday, Good Friday and Easter Saturday): religious processions in the streets of many towns, when actors re-enact scenes from the Passion and Crucifixion of Christ.

May *May Day Folk Festival* (1 May): traditional singing and folk dancing, with food and drink on sale in Alcoutim, Albufeira, Alte and Monchique. *International Film Festival* (FiCA): Portugal's longest-running film festival takes the form of a short-film competition. Most screened in Portimâo.

May–June *International Music Festival:* sponsored by the Gulbenkian Foundation, this is the biggest arts festival in the Algarve, with top international artists performing in a number of centres, including Faro, Lagoa, Loulé, Portimâo and more.

June *Alcoutim Handicraft Festival* (2nd or 3rd week): see the best of the region's crafts as stalls line the streets of Alcoutim.

July *Algarve Jazz Festival* (all month): local and international musicians come together for this celebration, held mainly in Loulé.
International Motorbike Rally: (3rd weekend) attracts more than 30,000 bikers to Faro over four days.

August *Fatacil* (3rd week): Lagoa's big country fair is a showcase for local agriculture, industry and commerce, with live bands, handicrafts and food and wine tastings.
Summer in Tavira: fado, folk and classical music, plus folk dancing in the open air in the city's parks and gardens.
Seafood Festival (11 Aug): Olhâo celebrates the fruits of the sea with a market, folk music, dancing and *fado* music.
Banho de 29 (29 Aug): fireworks and live music to celebrate the end of the holiday season in Lagos.

September *Powerboat Championships* (end Sep): held at Praia da Rocha, with boats reaching speeds of 360kph (220mph) on open water.

October *Feira de Faro*: Faro's handicraft festival.

Information Pick up a copy of *Algarve Guide* from the airport as you arrive or from one of the tourist information centres. It contains useful visitor information; www.bguide.pt

Getting there

BY AIR

Faro airport

4km (2.4 miles) to city centre

🚌 N/A

🚐 20 minutes

🚗 10 minutes

Most visitors arrive by air, although you can drive to the Algarve from all parts of continental Europe. Faro airport (tel: 289 800 800; www.ana.pt) is served by scheduled and charter flights from most European airports. Because of the region's popularity as a winter destination, seats on direct flights get booked up well in advance so reserve ahead. TAP Air Portugal is the national airline (tel: 707 205 700 – national enquiry line; www.flytap.com).

Transfers

Buses Transol (tel: 282 402 241; www.low-cost-transfer.com) runs transfers from the airport to towns across the Algarve (departures every 45 mins daily from 7am–11:30pm). You can pre-book tickets on the web. Otherwise Eva Bus routes 14 and 16 run from the centre of the capital to the airport (www.eva-bus.com).

Taxis Agree taxi fares before you set off from the airport, although fares to the various resorts should be posted on a board in the Arrivals Hall. All fares include baggage, but there may be a supplement to pay if you travel between 10pm and 6am and at weekends or holidays.

BY TRAIN

International trains arrive at Lisbon from St Pancras via Paris, Irún, Salamanca and Guarda (25–28 hours). Connections from Lisbon to Faro run four or five times daily (3–4 hours). It is a rather expensive and time-consuming option, but may work as part of a rail tour (www.eurostar.com, www.raileurope.co.uk or www.cp.pt).

BY BUS

Check out www.eurolines.com

Getting around

PUBLIC TRANSPORT

Trains The Algarve railway line follows the south coast from Lagos in the west to Vila Real de Santo António in the east. Ugrades to the track all along the 130km (80-mile) line ensure a smoother service, but being single-track, journey times can be longer than distances suggest. Stations can be 6km (4 miles) or more from the towns that they serve, so check the map before deciding to use the train. It is cheap and provides views of fine coastal scenery. Tourist offices have timetables, and tickets should be bought before you board the train, or else you risk a fine. For further information on CPT trains, tel: 808 208 208; www.cp.pt.

Buses Modern express bus services link most towns in the Algarve. Services are provided by a number of companies. The biggest is EVA (www.eva-bus.com), which sells a useful *Passe Turístico* (Tourist Pass), which allows unlimited use of the network for three days. Bus routes principally follow the main roads, and so are not a reliable way of exploring the more remote countryside. Timetables and route maps are available from tourist offices and main bus stations *(terminal rodoviário)*. Have plenty of small change ready when boarding.

Ferries Although most people now travel from Portugal to Spain along the motorway bridge that links the two countries across the Guadiana, ferries do still operate. The car and passenger ferry from Vila Real to Ayamonte departs at 40-minute intervals throughout the day, and fishermen ferry passengers from Alcoutim to San Lúcar on demand. Ferry services also take visitors to the barrier islands in the Ria Formosa Nature Park during the summer months, departing from Tavira and Olhão at regular intervals during the day.

TAXIS

In towns, it is usual to hire taxis from a rank. They may stop if flagged down, especially in the countryside. Rates for some journeys are fixed. Short journeys across town should be metered. For longer journeys, you can negotiate an hourly rate. Try to find a driver who speaks your language and who has a modern, well-maintained car.

DRIVING

- Drive on the right.
- Speed limit on motorways: 120kph (74mph); on main roads: 90 or 100kph (56 or 62mph); on urban roads: 50kph (31mph).
- Seat belts must be worn in front seats at all times and rear seats where fitted.
- Random breath-testing takes place. Never drive under the influence of alcohol.
- Petrol *(gasolina)* comes in two lead-free grades: 95 (octane) and 98 (octane). Diesel *(gasóleo)* is also available. Most villages and towns have a petrol station, and they are generally open from 8am to 8pm.
- If you have booked a rental car you will be met by a representative of the rental company and taken to the depot, which is a short drive away on the approach road to the airport. All the car rental companies in the Algarve run their own breakdown and rescue services, details of which will be given to you when you rent your car.
- Main highways have orange SOS telephones for use in an emergency.
- Members of motoring organizations such as the AA and RAC can use the services of the ACP (Automóvel Clube de Portugal), tel: 808 502 502; www.acp.pt.
- Random roadside police checks can impose heavy fines on motorists who are not carrying proof of insurance, rental documents, driving licence and passport.

CAR RENTAL

The major car rental firms are represented in the Algarve, as well as several local companies who offer slightly cheaper rates. All rental firms send a courtesy bus to meet you at the airport on arrival, transporting you to their depot on the Faro airport road; alternatively, they will deliver the car to your hotel or villa.

FARES AND CONCESSIONS

Buses offer a *passe turistico,* which currently costs €23.30 for 3 days of travel. Some museums and attractions have lower admission prices for students or young people on production of a valid student/youth card, and for senior citizens on production of a passport. For children under 12, admission to many museums is free.

Being there

TOURIST OFFICES

Algarve and local tourist board
Avenida 5 de Outubro 18, 8000-076
Faro ☎ 289 800 400

Albufeira Rua 5 de Outubro 18,
8200-109 Albufeira ☎ 289 585 279

Faro Rua da Misericórdia 8–12,
8000-269 Faro ☎ 289 803 604

Lagos Rua Vasco da Gama, São
João, 8600-722 Lagos
☎ 282 763 031

Loulé Avenida 25 Abril 9, 8100-506
Loulé ☎ 289 463 900

Monchique Largo São Sebastião,
8550 Monchique ☎ 282 911 189

Monte Gordo Avenida Marginal,
8900 Monte Gordo
☎ 281 544 495

Olhão Largo Sebastião Martins
Mestre 8-A, 8700-349 Olhão
☎ 289 713 936

Portimão Avenida Zeca Afonso,
8500-516 Portimão
☎ 282 470 732

Silves Rua 25 de Abril, 8300-184
Silves ☎ 282 442 255

Tavira Rua da Galeria 9, 8800-329
Tavira ☎ 281 322 511

MONEY
Currency The euro (€) is the official currency of Portugal. Banknotes are in denominations of 5, 10, 20, 50, 100, 200 and 500 euros; coins are in denominations of 1, 2, 5, 10, 20 and 50 cents, and 1 and 2 euros.

TIPS/GRATUITIES

Yes ✓ No ✗		
Restaurants (service included)	✓	10%
Bar service	✓	small change
Taxis	✓	10%
Porters	✓	€1
Chambermaids	✗	
Cloakroom attendants	✓	small change
Tour guides	✗	

Exchange Euro traveller's cheques are widely accepted and some places accept dollar or sterling travellers' cheques also, although cash can be more useful in the countryside. Exchange bureaux generally have better rates on offer than the banks, but it is best to shop around when you get there.

Credit cards Credit and debit cards are accepted in most hotels and restaurants, but not all shops. They can also be used for withdrawing euro notes from automatic teller machines (ATMs). Banks can be found in most towns, although they do not necessarily offer the best deal for changing money.

POSTAL AND INTERNET SERVICES

Post offices *(correios)* are found in main towns. In Faro, the most central post office is on Largo do Carmo, and *posta restante* services are available here, and at all main post offices. Stamps can be bought from newsagents and hotel kiosks. Open: main office Mon–Fri 8:30–6, Sat 9–12:30. Smaller offices close 12:30–2:30.

Internet access Some post offices offer either a fixed or wireless service and almost all hotels now provide a connection of some kind. Many upmarket hotels have wireless connections in all the rooms, while others will have wireless or fixed access in public spaces. Internet cafés are common in all middle- to large-sized towns. In all of these, the state of equipment, speed of connection and prices can vary greatly (€1–€4 for 30 minutes). In general, internet cafés are the cheapest option, with some offering great value packages, ideal if you are staying in the same area for a few days.

TELEPHONES

Telephone booths can be found in every town. On rare occasions where a booth cannot be found, the local bar usually has a public phone. Most phones only take phone cards or credit cards. Phone cards (for 50, 120 or more units) can be bought at newsagents and cafés. A 50-unit card should give around 5 minutes of international calling time.

To call the Algarve from the UK, dial 00 351 (the international country code for Portugal) then the 9-digit number, which starts with a 3-digit area code (282, 289 or 281).

Emergency telephone numbers
Police, Fire or
Ambulance ☎ 112
National Forest
Protection ☎ 117

International dialling codes

From the Algarve to:
UK: 00 44
Germany: 00 49

USA and Canada: 00 1
Netherlands: 00 31
Spain: 00 34

EMBASSIES AND CONSULATES

UK ☎ 282 490 750
Germany ☎ 289 803 148
USA ☎ 217 273 300 (Lisbon)

Netherlands ☎ 289 820 903
Spain ☎ 281 544 888

HEALTH AND SAFETY

Sun advice The sun can be intense in the Algarve at any time of the year, and it is possible to burn with less than an hour's exposure. If you are out walking on clifftops or bare hills, it is best to cover vulnerable parts of your body, including your neck, legs and arms.

Drugs Pharmacies *(farmâcia)* open Mon–Fri 9–1, 3–7, and Sat 9–1. Some open through lunch, and there is a late-night duty rota, posted in pharmacy windows. Bring supplies of any drugs you take regularly, as there is no guarantee they will be available locally. Many drugs are available from chemists in Portugal that require prescriptions in other countries. This is partly because pharmacists are skilled paramedics, trained to diagnose a range of problems and sell appropriate medicines.

Safe water Tap water is safe to drink, but can be unpleasant to taste because of the minerals it contains. Bottled water is widely available; ask for sparkling water *(água com gás)* or still water *(água sem gás)*.

PLANNING

Personal saftey Theft from cars and other petty crime is a problem. If you are the victim of theft, get help from a hotel or holiday representative because they know the correct procedures and can deal with the bureaucracy. To make an insurance claim you must report thefts to the local police station and get a copy of the written statement.
- Leave valuables in the hotel safe.
- Don't leave valuables in cars.
- Beware of pickpockets.

ELECTRICITY
The power supply in Portugal is 220 volts AC. Sockets take two-pronged continental plugs, so an adaptor is needed for non-continental appliances, and a transformer for devices operating on 100–120 volts.

OPENING HOURS

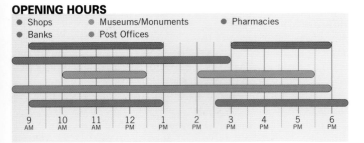

- Shops
- Banks
- Museums/Monuments
- Post Offices
- Pharmacies

9 AM | 10 AM | 11 AM | 12 PM | 1 PM | 2 PM | 3 PM | 4 PM | 5 PM | 6 PM

Shops catering for tourists open all day in the high season, until 9 or 10 in the evening, including Sundays and public holidays. Larger stores and supermarkets may ignore the lunch break and are open continuously from 9 to 7, with some supermarkets staying open until 10pm (until 5pm on Sundays). Shops in malls often stay open until midnight.

Times of museums and churches vary and are prone to change, especially in smaller places and after lunch – see individual places for details. Pharmacies open late on a duty rota (posted on the door).

LANGUAGE

A knowledge of Spanish and/or French makes Portuguese easy to read, but speaking it is somewhat trickier. Portuguese sounds very different from Spanish. Even so, most Portuguese understand Spanish and in tourist areas English is widely spoken. Knowing a few Portuguese words will make your trip more rewarding. Below is a list of some words that might be useful. The AA's *Essential Portuguese Phrase Book* lists over 2,000 phrases and 2,000 words.

yes/no	*sim/não*	help!	*ajuda!*
please	*se faz favor*	today/tomorrow	*hoje/amanhã*
thank you	*obrigado*	yesterday	*ontem*
hello/goodbye	*olá/adeus*	how much?	*quanto?*
excuse me!	*desculpe!*	open/closed	*aberto/fechadohotel*
hotel	*hotel*	rate	*preço*
room single/	*quarto simples/*	breakfast	*pequeno almoço*
double	*de casal*	toilet	*sanita*
one/two nights	*um/duas noite(s)*	bath/shower	*banheira/duche*
reservation	*reserva*	balcony	*varanda*
bank	*banco*	pound sterling	*libra esterlina*
exchange office	*casa de câmbio*	American dollar	*dólar americano*
post office	*correio*	exchange rate	*câmbio*
money	*dinheiro*	bank card	*cartão do banco*
foreign currency	*moeda estrangeira*	credit card	*cartão de crédito*
restaurant	*restaurante*	daily fixed menu	*ementa turística*
bar/café	*café*	wine list	*lista de vinhos*
table	*mesa*	lunch	*almoço*
menu	*ementa*	dinner	*jantar*
aeroplane/airport	*avião/aeroporto*	single/return	*ida/ida e volta*
flight	*vôo*	first/second class	*primeira/segunda*
train/train station	*comboio/estação*		*classe*
	de comboios	bus/bus station	*autocarro/estação*
ticket	*bilhete*		*de camionetas*

Best places to see

1 Algar Seco, Carvoeiro

If you just want to laze around on a beach, Algar Seco is an excellent choice, with its colourful cliffs and rock stacks.

There is a marked difference between the beaches of the sandy eastern *sotavento* (leeward) section of the Algarve and the rocky western, or *barlavento* (windward) section. Armação de Pêra, to the west of Albufeira, is the axis on which the Algarve is tilted and the point at which this decisive change takes place. West of here the land rises gradually until it reaches the high cliffs and boiling seas of Cape St Vincent; to the east, flatter coastal terrain gives way to endless strands of golden sand, gently dipping into a warm and shallow sea.

The cause of the tilt is the collision zone between the Eurasian and African continental plates, which lies only a short way south of the

Algarvian coast. The African plate is moving northwestwards, pushing the European land mass slowly upwards. This explains why the junction between land and sea is more dramatic in the west, marked

by steep sandstone cliffs, and why the coast is broken up into a number of rock-strewn coves.

The result is a series of wind- and sea-eroded rocks whose evocative shapes make this part of the coast unique, and nowhere else has these rock formations in such quantity or variety as Algar Seco.

Here, children will love exploring the rock platforms and pillars, arches, chambers and caves, the miniature gorges, clefts and pools that litter the shore. Snorkellers will find weed-encrusted rocks like miniature coral reefs below the waves. There is not much sand, but the other features compensate, including the colourful show of light and shade that begins as the sun sinks at dusk.

✚ 6B ✉ About 1km (0.5 miles) east of Carvoeiro, signposted to the left from the centre of town 👋 Free 🍴 Several restaurants (➤ 131–132) and cafés in Carvoeiro

2 Alte

Discover the many charms of this pretty hill village, built around a series of gushing springs *(fontes)*.

Alte sits on top of a hill in the limestone foothills known as the Barrocal (► 146–147). Winding roads climb to the village through a region dubbed the 'Garden of the Algarve', where fig trees and citrus groves surrounded by drystone walls alternate with almond orchards and stands of gnarled and ancient olive trees.

The focal point of the village is the parish church, one of the most interesting in the Algarve because of its wealth of 18th-century woodwork and its baroque *azulejos*. Rope mouldings (in the Manueline style) decorate the west door, the vaulting of the chancel and the arch of the so-called 'Chapel of the Landowner', with its coat of arms of the counts of Alte. Painted and gilded woodwork surrounds the altar, while angelic musicians and cherubs scamper among the vine and acanthus leaves.

From the church, cobbled lanes lead eastwards for a five-minute stroll to a series of springs *(fontes)*, where the water gushes out of pipes set in niches decorated with *azulejos* and plaques inscribed with verses by the local poet, Cândido Guerreiro (1871–1953), in praise of water. The water here betrays its

volcanic origins with a sulphur smell, but it tastes fresh enough and many local people come here to fill huge containers, believing that the water prolongs their life and keeps them healthy.

About 200m (220yds) upstream is another set of springs, Fonte Grande. From here, keen walkers can follow the footpath upstream for 3km (2 miles) to the source of the River Alte at the foot of the Serra do Caldeirão mountain range. Less keen hikers can rest at one of the two restaurants, or picnic at tables under the shade of the trees, before browsing through the crafts on sale in the shops around the church square.

✚ 9D ✉ 20km (12.5 miles) north of Albufeira ⓧ Church: daily 8–1, 3–7 (opening times may vary) ✋ Free 🍴 Fonte Pequena restaurant/bar (€; ➤ 162)

3 Cabo de São Vicente

Come at sunset on a clear day to get the most from a visit to the cliffs that were once believed to mark the end of the world.

Cabo de São Vicente is the most southwesterly point of the European mainland (not counting Madeira, the Canary Islands and the Azores). It really looks and feels like the end of the earth (which is why the Portuguese dubbed it 'Fim do Mundo' centuries ago). With its towering cliffs plunging 70m (230ft) to the pounding surf, and its stiff westerly breezes, this is a place that stirs the

imagination and works a strong magic over the many visitors who flock here.

The Romans named it the Promontorium Sacrum (Sacred Promontory). Recognizing the spiritual pull of the spot, they built a temple to the presiding *numen* (deity). Nothing now remains of this, but there is a lighthouse whose beam can be seen up to 100km (62 miles) out to sea. The lighthouse is open to visitors if the keeper is not otherwise engaged. If you do get a chance to look inside, you will see Europe's biggest and most powerful lighthouse lantern, lit by a massive 3,000-watt bulb.

Your own memories and impressions will be dictated by the weather: stallholders selling chunky handknitted sweaters in the car park are a reminder that it can be chilly here no matter how hot it is a few kilometres inland, and there can be fog, rain or howling gales. On the other hand, nothing enhances the pristine beauty of Cabo de São Vicente more than watching sea birds playing in the air above the crashing waves, or the sight of the rose-tinted sun sinking slowly into the ocean at dusk.

➕ 1B ✉ 6km (4 miles) west of Sagres 🖐 Free 🍴 Snack bars on site and in Sagres; O Telheiro do Infante (€€–€€€; ➤ 101), overlooking the beach at Sagres

4 Caldas de Monchique

www.monchiquetermas.com

Visit this centuries-old spa town in the Monchique hills and sample the sulphurous waters once enjoyed by the Romans.

Caldas de Monchique is a charming little spa struggling to maintain its position long after it has ceased to be the fashionable resort of bourgeois Portuguese looking for an instant cure-all. These days people come as much to enjoy the typically Algarvian food in many of the local restaurants as to put themselves through the strict dietary regime normally involved in a spa cure.

As with many spas built at the crux of the 19th and 20th centuries, the buildings reflect the belief that good company and relaxation are just as important for the cure as water consumption – hence a casino was regarded as *de rigueur* and the hotels were built with grand public rooms for dancing and conversation. The spa complex has benefited greatly from a renovation project and was

reopened with great aplomb by the Portuguese Minister of Tourism in the summer of 2001.

The Romans got here first. More than 2,000 years ago they built a spa on the site of the present sanatorium, calling it Mons Cicus, from which the spa, and the nearby

market town of Monchique, derive their name. Today it is the picturesque appearance of the little spa that appeals, set among dense woodland on the edge of a mini ravine, with its pastel-painted houses in fanciful styles.

Footpaths thread through woods and along the river, taking you to springs where you can sample the water – pleasant enough to taste even if it is warm and smells sulphurous. For something stronger, there are cafés where you can sip coffee, or try the local speciality *medronho*, a fiery liqueur distilled from fermented arbutus berries.

✚ 6E ✉ 18km (11 miles) north of Portimão 🖐 Free 🍴 1692 (€€€, ➤ 58) 🚌 Bus service links Caldas de Monchique to Portimão

5 Capela dos Ossos, Faro

Intimations of mortality may occupy your mind as you contemplate the skull-encrusted Chapel of the Bones.

The Chapel of the Bones is a must for unsqueamish children, who will find this ghoulish site enormous fun.

Unfortunately, the Carmelite monks who created the chapel from the bones of their pre-deceased brothers would be horrified at such disrespect: the Chapel of the Bones belongs to a southern European tradition of reminding onlookers of their mortality and shocking them into a more sober and upright life. Perhaps the intended *memento mori* effect (the inscription over the entrance translates as 'Stop here and think of the fate that will befall you') would have been better achieved by a less decorous arrangement of skeletal remains. As it is, the chapel is too neat and tidy to be macabre, with leg and arm bones used to create a classical architectural arrangement of arches, capitals and pilasters.

It is worth taking some time to look at the church to which the chapel is attached. The Igreja do Carmo was built in 1719 and has an imposing baroque facade, flanked by twin bell-towers – its ancient grandeur now somewhat compromised by its setting among modern tower blocks. Both the main altar and the side altars are decorated in the typical Portuguese baroque style known as *talha dourada*, with intricately carved and gilded woodwork, featuring scores of cherubs playing among acanthus leaf and vine foliage.

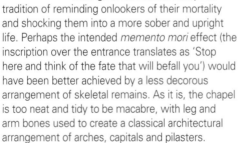

Historically, the church has played an important role, for in 1808 it was here that the people of Faro met, under the pretence of holding a normal religious service, to plot their ultimately successful resistance to the Napoleonic occupation of the town.

✚ *Faro 2d* ✉ Largo do Carmo, Faro
🕔 Nov–Apr Mon–Fri 10–1, 3–5:30, Sat 10–1; May–Oct Mon–Fri 10–1, 3–6, Sat 10–1 ✋ Inexpensive 🍴 Cafés in pedestrianized centre of Faro

6 Castelo de Silves

The Algarve's best-preserved castle symbolizes the splendour of Silves in its Moorish heyday.

The streets of Silves were once packed with traders, bazaars overflowed with exotic goods, and the gilded domes of many minarets gleamed in the sun. The bustling capital of 12th-century Moorish Algarve, known as Xelb, is today a sleepy place with 12,000 inhabitants. Only the castle indicates the town's former wealth and importance.

The castle was built to last and, despite bearing the brunt of fighting during the Christian Reconquest of Portugal in the 12th and 13th centuries, it remains substantially intact.

Following the rampart walk, you can take in views over the rooftops of the town to the River Arade, once the site of a bustling harbour, and across countryside planted with the orange, almond and carob trees introduced by the Moors.

Excavations continue to uncover the castle's secrets: exposed walls show the remains of earlier Phoenician and Roman fortifications and vestiges of the Moorish palace. The domed cistern is still used as a reservoir for the town's water supply. This same cistern kept the castle's Moorish inhabitants alive for six weeks during the 1189 Siege of Silves. When the Moors finally surrendered, the Crusaders went on an orgy of looting, confident that the Moors would soon be driven from the Iberian Peninsula. Their joy was short-lived: Moorish forces from Seville returned to exact revenge, and it was another 60 years before Afonso III brought the Algarve back to Christianity.

➕ 7D ✉ Largo do Castelo, Silves ☎ 282 445 624
🕐 Mid-Jul to mid-Sep daily 9–6:30; mid-Sep to mid-Jul daily 9–5:30. Last entry half-hour before closing. Closed public hols ✋ Inexpensive 🍴 Cafés (€) near castle entrance and alongside the cathedral, including Café Inglês (€–€€; ➤ 133)

7 Estói

Due to open in early 2009, the palace and gardens at Estói will be returned to their former glory.

Behind high walls, in the small village of Estói, lies this lavish rococo palace, built in the 18th century for the Conde de Carvalhal. The family wealth declined, and the palace was acquired first by the Viscount of Estói and then by Faro city council. In 2006 restoration started on the building and gardens, and the Pousada chain was given responsibility for managing the new hotel to be housed in the palace and a new wing.

The main entrance from the church square leads down a cobbled road to the heart of the complex for wonderful views of the outer facade and formal French-style gardens. Designed to

please the senses, the walls of the garden are decorated with *azulejos* depicting bucolic scenes of shepherds and shepherdesses, while naked youths frolic with dolphins in the fountains. Elsewhere buxom goddesses drape themselves languorously around water-filled shells against a tiled background of cranes and bulrushes. On the lower terrace, the stone-lined nymphaeum shelters a copy of Canova's famous statue *The Three Graces*, flanked by fine mosaics.

The palace itself combines elements of the neo-baroque and neo-rococo with innumerable decorative details to admire, and is one of the finest examples of Romantic architecture in the country. Step inside to get a full idea of the grandeur of this palace where the former dining room has been transformed into a Renaissance-style lounge and the great hall into a spectacular Louis XV mirrored and gilded dining room, also open to non-residents. Don't miss the 19th-century baroque-style tiles in the former kitchen, now home to the hotel bar.

✚ 18G ✉ Rua da Barroca, Estói, 8005-458 Faro ☎ 218 442 000; www.pousadas.pt ❸ Due to reopen early 2009; check website for details 🖐 Free 🍴 Inside Pousada

8 Milreu

Exploring the extensive remains of the Roman villa at Milreu demonstrates how little life in the Algarve has changed.

The villa at Milreu was probably built by a 1st-century AD fish magnate. This theory is based on the fact that the wonderful mosaics that decorate many of the rooms show fish leaping in and out of the frothy waves. These images adorn the walls and rooms on both sides of the villa – the bathhouse to the left (west), with its hot and cold pools and its hypocaust system for providing underfloor heating, and the living quarters, to the right (east). Separating the two is a large courtyard garden. Another plausible theory is that this was not a private villa at all, but a spa and temple complex. The huge building that survives to roof height to the east of the site is interpreted as a nymphaeum, a shrine to the local water nymphs, which was converted for use as a church in the early Christian period, reusing the pools and piscinas as baptismal fonts. Visitors coming to worship at this shrine would have used the bath facilities, which are somewhat grand just for a private villa. The sheer number of stone cubicles in the apodyterium (changing room) alongside the bath complex would seem to support the theory that this was a public facility – unless the owner was in the habit of throwing lavish poolside parties!

➕ 18H ✉ West of Estói ☎ 289 997 823 🕐 Tue–Sun 9:30–12:30, 2–6 (until 5 Oct–Apr). Closed Mon and public hols 🖐 Inexpensive 🍴 Cafés (€) in front of parish church ℹ Junta de Freguesia ☎ 289 991 620

Parque Natural da Ria Formosa

Learn all about the wildlife of the Algarve's lagoons, and meet an unusual breed of poodle.

The Parque Formosa Nature Reserve stretches for some 30km (18 miles) along the coast, from Ancão, west of Faro, to Manta Rota, near the Spanish border. It consists of scores of sandy islands, linked by shallow lagoons, salt marshes and water channels, which are home to birds, plants and insects. While the outer islands facing the Atlantic bear the brunt of oceanic wind and waves, these shallow lagoons are warm and sheltered, providing perfect spawning conditions for many fish, and an ideal feeding ground for birds.

The best place for getting acquainted with the complex ecology of the reserve is at the visitor centre at Quinta do Marim, 1km (0.5 miles) east of Olhão. Displays provide information on conservation activities and wildlife, and maps can be obtained showing recommended walking routes. You can also enquire about visiting the kennels where the rare Portuguese water dog, the Cão de Água, is bred to save it from extinction. These endearing 'poodles', with big limbs and curly black hair, have web-like membranes between their paws which enable them to swim very effectively.

Algarvian fishermen once trained the dogs to help them by diving and shepherding fish into their nets. Two areas of the reserve are readily accessible by boat: ferries depart from the harbour in Olhão to the Ilha da Armona, and to Farol on the Ilha da Culatra. From these sand spits you can watch the birdlife of the lagoons, or find your own private strip of unspoiled beach and sand dune for sunbathing.

✚ 12A ✉ Visitor centre: 1km (0.5 miles) east of Olhão, signposted to the Parque Natural, and *campismo* (campsite) ☎ 289 700 210 🕐 Visitor centre: Mon–Fri 9–12:30, 2–5:30. Closed Sat, Sun and public hols. Park visits: Mon–Fri 8–8, Sat, Sun and pub hols 10:30–6:30 🍴 Plenty of choice in Olhão (€–€€)

10 Ponta da Piedade

Consider taking a trip by boat to explore the spectacular free-standing pillars, rock stacks and grottoes of this cove near Lagos.

For coastal scenery, the coves around Ponta da Piedade are hard to beat. The same geological processes and erosive forces that carved out the rock sculptures at Algar Seco (► 36–37) have been at work here too, creating a coastline of ochre and

rust-red cliffs, stacks and arches, which resemble the ruins of some fantasy castle.

From the cliff-tops at Ponta da Piedade you can walk along a path to the various sea grottoes (➤ 89), but the going can be precarious. From the lighthouse there are paths along the coastline with views to the foaming waters below. There are also steps descending the cliff face from the lighthouse down to a rock platform where local fishermen wait to take passengers on trips to see the cliffs between here and Praia da Luz. This is worth doing, especially during the nesting season, when you may get a good close-up of cliff-nesting birds, such as cattle egrets and little egrets.

Or join one of the boat trips that depart from Lagos, such as those operated by Bom Dia. Trips last either 2 or 5 hours; the longer trip includes lunch. Full-day trips are available as well, allowing time for swimming and snorkelling in addition to lunch.

✚ 4B ✉ 2km (1.2 miles) south of Lagos
🍴 Bar Sol Nascente (€), opposite lighthouse
🚤 Bom Dia Actividades Marítimas
✉ Marina de Lagos loja (shop) 10, 8600 Lagos ☎ 282 087 587; www.bomdia.info
🕐 Office: 9–6 in winter; 9–9 in summer. Closed Dec–Feb. Cruises: daily, including grotto trips, BBQ cruises and family fishing (➤ 103)

Best things to do

Great places to have lunch

1692 (€€€)
Upmarket restaurant with a beautiful formal dining room and large sunny terrace. International menu, with fine wine and cigars.
✉ Caldas de Monchique, 8550-232 Monchique ☎ 282 910 910; www.monchiquetermas.com 🕔 Lunch, dinner

Beach Bar (€–€€)
Book ahead in high season at this well-positioned beachside restaurant, with its seafront terrace, specializing in grilled fish.
✉ Praia de Burgau, 8650 Burgau ☎ 282 697 553 🕔 Lunch, dinner; closed Mon and Dec

Café Aliança (€)
The service may be slow, but people come for the atmosphere and decor in the dimly lit interior of one of Portugal's oldest cafés.
✉ Praça Francisco Gomes 6, 8000-168 Faro ☎ 289 801 621 🕔 Daily 8am–midnight

Fortaleza da Luz (€€)
The town's 16th-century fortress have been turned into a popular restaurant. Fresh fish, Portuguese cuisine and flambé dishes.
✉ Rua da Igreja 1, 8600-149 Praia da Luz ☎ 282 789 926; www.fortalezadaluz.com 🕔 Lunch, dinner

Imperial (€€)
Grand restaurant renowned for its chicken and rice dishes, and its *serrabulho de marisco* (mixed seafood with pork).
✉ Rua José Pires Padinha 22, 8800-354 Tavira ☎ 281 322 306 🕔 Lunch, dinner; closed Jan

Mesa dos Mouros (€€)
Pretty converted house in the cathedral square.
✉ Largo da Sé 10, 8000-138 Faro ☎ 289 878 873 🕔 Lunch, dinner; closed Sun

O Soeiro (€)

In a shady corner and with river views, O Soeiro is frequented by ferrymen waiting for passengers wanting to cross to Spain. You can watch your chicken or pork being grilled over a charcoal brazier.

✉ Rua do Município 4, 8970-066 Alcoutim ☎ 281 546 241 🕙 Lunch; closed Sat, Sun and last 2 weeks in Sep

Paraíso da Montanha (€)

Visitors flock to this restaurant for its excellent chicken *piri-piri*, roast kid and the mountain views.

✉ Estrada da Fóia, 8550-375 Monchique ☎ 282 912 150 🕙 Lunch, dinner; closed Thu and 15 Nov–15 Dec

Santola Restaurant (€€€)

Pretty restaurant next to the castle chapel, with a terrace overlooking the beach. Fresh seafood is the speciality.

✉ Largo da Fortaleza, 8365-108 Armação de Pêra ☎ 282 312 332 🕙 Lunch, dinner

Sítio do Forno (€€)

Panoramic views of Amado beach from the terrace of this cliffside restaurant, which specializes in fish caught in the family boat.

✉ Praia do Amado, Carrapateira, 8670-230 Bordeira ☎ 963 558 404 🕙 Lunch, dinner; closed Mon

Spas, baths and wellness centres

Spas are very much in vogue in the Algarve and many hotels now offer wellness centres and spa facilities. All except Moinhos Velhos are open to non-residents.

The Lake Resort
The Blue Spa offers a comprehensive range of hydrotherapy treatments such as Dead Sea mud wraps, Vichy showers and desert heat thermotherapy, while the Green Spa offers all types of massage, reflexology, hot stone massage, shiatsu and more.
✉ Praia da Falésia – Apartado 811, 8126-910 Vilamoura
☎ 289 320 733; www.thelakeresort.com 🕐 Daily 9–8

Moinhos Velhos
This health retreat promotes fruit and vegetable juice fasting, detoxification, yoga, meditation and complementary health remedies.
✉ Cotifo – Barragem da Bravura, 8600-077 Lagos ☎ 282 687 147; www.moinhos-velhos.com

Quinta da Calma
Provides a variety of natural healing treatments such as yoga, tai-chi, massage and oi-gong.
✉ Quinta da Calma, Apartado 3053, 8135-901 Almancil
☎ 289 393 741; www.quintadacalma.com

Real Spa Thalasso at Grande Real Santa Eulália
In addition to massage and beauty treatments Real Spa offers a range of thalassotherapy treatments using sea water (► background picture).
✉ Praia de Santa Eulália, PO Box 2445, 8200-916 Albufeira ☎ 289 598 030; www.granderealsantaeulaliahotel.com 🕐 Daily 8–8

Termas de Monchique

These baths, created around natural mountain springs which have been renowned for their therapeutic properties since Roman times, offer a variety of water-themed treatments as well as massages and wraps.

✉ Caldas de Monchique, 8550-232 Monchique ☎ 282 910 910; www.monchiquetermas.com 🕒 Wed–Mon 9–7, Tue 10:30–7

Vila Sol Spa and Golf Resort

This spa has a long list of options ranging from facial and body treatments to hydrotherapy and massage, including hot stones and aromatherapy.

✉ Alto dos Morgadinhos, 8125-307 Vilamoura ☎ 289 300 550; www.vilasol.pt 🕒 Daily 9–7:30

Vilalara Thalassa Resort

Vilalara provides arguably the best thalassotherapy treatment in Europe. Osteopaths, doctors, hydrotherapists and physiotherapists use the latest therapy techniques. The centre also provides countless beauty treatments.

✉ Praia das Gaivotas, Alporchinhos, 8400-450 Porches, Lagoa ☎ 282 320 000; www.vilalararesort.com 🕒 Daily 9–6

Vila Vita Parc

The Arab-inspired architecture and sumptuous interiors create the ideal ambience in which to experience relaxation, revitalization, regeneration, prevention diagnosis and therapies. There are also cosmetic, beauty, physiotherapy and medical treatments available.

✉ Alporchinhos, 8400-450 Porches, Lagoa ☎ 282 320 351; www.vilavitahotels.com 🕒 Daily 9–6:30

Top souvenir ideas

- Almond fruits – delicious almond paste sculpted to look like apples, pears or strawberries.

- A *cataplana* cooking pot so that you can re-create typical Portuguese stews at home.

- A large decorative bowl painted with flowers or fruits from the village of Porches (➤ 119).

- Excellent quality leather sandals, shoes or bags at bargain prices.

- A lace tablecloth or shawl bought in a street market.

- A folding X-shaped 'scissor' chair from Monchique (➤ 118–119) – thought to be of Roman origin.

- A panel of *azulejos* (decorated tiles) from one of the shops in Porches (➤ 119) or Silves (➤ 106–109).

- A religious statue from one of the many antiques shops in Faro Old Town (➤ 138–142) or Lagos (➤ 84–87).

- One of the heavy-knit woollen jumpers on sale in Sagres (➤ 94–95).

- A bottle of *aguardente* (local brandy), white port or *medronho* (the Algarve's best-known spirit), made from the fruit of the strawberry tree *(Arbutus unedo)*.

Places to buy ceramics and pottery

ALBUFEIRA
Vista Alegre Atlantis

For quality porcelain, rather than the more rustic Algarve pottery, try this place in the shopping mall north of Albufeira. Vista Alegre is recognized as the finest producer of Portuguese porcelain.

✉ Algarve Shopping – Loja 0.130, Guia, Estrada Nacional 125, 8200-417 Albufeira ☎ 289 562 204; www.vistaalegre.pt ⏱ Daily 10am–11pm

ALTE
Ceramica d'Alte

On the main road below the village centre, producing ceramics on site. Watch the potter and painter as you browse.

✉ Estrada National 125, 8100-012 Alte ☎ 289 478 530 ⏱ Daily 10–1, 3–6

LAGOS
O Poticho

Traditional pottery from all over Portugal.

✉ Rua 25 de Abril 24, 8600-763 Lagos ☎ 282 760 729 ⏱ Daily 9–7; closed Sun in winter

LOULÉ
Alegret 2

Terracotta jars, garden ornaments and wood-fired cooking pots with an attractive patina.

✉ Rua Miguel Bombarda 66–68, 8100-746 Loulé ☎ 289 412 893 ⏱ Mon–Sat 9–7

Casa Louart

Some of the prettiest hand-painted pottery in town; bold designs of fruit and flowers.

✉ Rua 5 de Outubro 69, 8100-683 Loulé ☎ 289 413 794 ⏱ Mon–Fri 9:30–1, 3–7; Sat 9:30–1

MONTE GORDO
Artesanato Anajo
A good selection of traditional and well-priced arts and crafts.
✉ Rua Gonçalo Velho 32, 8900-461 Monte Gorde ☎ 281 544 878 ☻ Daily
10–7; closed Sun in winter

PORCHES
Olaria Algarve Pottery
In a shady Algarve mansion, Olaria produces patterned ceramics,
and you can watch the artists at work.
✉ Estrada Nacional 125, Alqueres, Porches, 8400-451 Lagoa ☎ 282 352
858; www.porchespottery.com ☻ Daily 10–6

Olaria Pequena
This converted farmhouse has been home to Scottish ceramicist
Ian Fitzpatrick since the 1980s. He produces tableware and tiles
using traditional methods but gives them a modern twist with
locally inspired motifs such as fish, lemons and olives.
✉ Estrada Nacional 125, Porches, 8400-489 Lagoa ☎ 282 381 213;
www.olariapequena.com ☻ Mon–Sat 10–1, 3–6

TAVIRA
**Artesanato
Regional Casa
Matias**
Traditional pottery,
based in the
market.
✉ Mercado Ribeira,
Rua do Cais, 8800-000
Tavira ☎ 281 326 734
☻ Mon–Sat
10–1, 3–7

Activities

Birdwatching: the lagoons and wetland marshes attract wading birds big and small, from shy flamingos and stilts to storks, herons and egrets.

Fishing: join a deep-sea fishing expedition and pit your wits against such game fish as swordfish, marlin and shark.

Golf: the Algarve is renowned for its scenic courses; why not sign up for a session with the resident pro?

Horse-back riding: beginners and children are welcome at any of the Algarve's growing number of stables, for a scenic forest or coastal ride.

Hunting for wild flowers: you cannot visit the Algarve in spring or early summer without being impressed by nature's profusion (but remember not to pick them).

Keeping fit: make the most of the sports facilities to tone up your muscles, improve your golf handicap or perfect your tennis.

Sailing: with its many private coves and marine grottoes, the western Algarve is an ideal place to enjoy a short coastal voyage.

Shopping for souvenirs: head for Loulé (➤ 64, 148–149) for a good selection of crafts, or browse the pottery workshops of Porches (➤ 65, 119) for a colourful, hand-painted plate.

Walking: from forests to cliff-tops, from mountains to riverbanks, the Algarve is ideal walking country – buy the Sunflower walking guide *Landscapes of Portugal*, by Brian and Eileen Anderson, for ideas.

Water sports: learn to dive or windsurf with one of the several licensed diving and water-sports schools.

Best beaches

Algar Seco, Carvoeiro
The clear waters off this
sheltered cove are perfect for
snorkelling and the tides and
wind have worked away at
the cliffs to form impressive
grottoes and pinnacles
(➤ 36–37).

**Amado, south of
Carrapateira**
A long sandy beach that lies
at the foot of rugged cliffs
(➤ 91).

Arrifana, Aljezur
A wonderful beach that has
the added attraction of a
coastal fort ruin to forage
in (➤ 90).

Benagil, near Carvoiero
Fishermen are more than
happy to transfer visitors from
the crowded beach at
Carvoiero to the more
secluded Benagil (➤ 113).

**Bordeira, north of
Carrapateira**
Backed by dunes and a little
river valley, this broad
expanse of sand is a relaxing
place to head for (➤ 91).

Cabanas Velhas, Salema
If you want an attractive, unspoiled beach then head for Cabanas Velhas (➤ 97).

Praia do Camilo, Lagos
Worth trying when Praia de Dona Ana gets busy. Not so many rock features, but still very attractive (➤ 73, 88).

Praia do Castelejo, 5km (3 miles) west of Vila do Bispo
This is a vast sandy beach backed by dramatic cliffs (➤ 97).

Praia de Dona Ana, Lagos
This is a lovely beach where the rocks look like fossilized sponge (➤ 88), but it can get crowded.

Praia da Rocha, Portimão
This is the widest cliff-backed stretch of beach in Europe. Dramatic rock formations highlight the golden sands in Algarve's oldest resort (➤ 124–125).

Good viewpoints and views

VIEWPOINTS
- Alcoutim castle (➤ 170)

- Aljezur castle (➤ 90)

- Cabo de São Vicente (➤ 40–41)

- The peak of Fóia mountain (➤ 127)

- Silves castle (➤ 46–47)

VIEWS

- Beautiful seascape views from the cliffs of Arrifana (➤ 72)

- From the lookout at Cordoama towards the cliffs (➤ 97)

- Cape St Vincent: the best place to watch the sunset (➤ 40–41)

- Looking west from the Ponta da Piedade (➤ 54–55)

- The ramparts walk at Castro Marim (➤ 172–173)

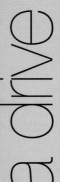

around the western highlights

The scenery on this drive varies from fishing ports and wave-battered cliffs to river valleys and sandy beaches.

Head northwest on the N120, over the Serra de Espinhaço de Cão foothills, to Aljezur.

Climb to Aljezur castle (▶ 90), then cool off on the wonderful beach at Arrifana, where you can explore the ruins of an old coastal fort and look out to the Pedra da Agulha (Needle Rock) at the end of the cliffs.

Head south on the N268 towards Vila do Bispo (▶ 97). Just north of Carrapateira, take the right turn at the signs for the O Sítio do Rio restaurant (▶ 100) and follow the coast road for a dramatic tour past Bordeira and Amado beaches and the rugged cliffs that separate them.

Stay for a swim or stroll if time allows. This is one of the most dramatic routes in the Costa Vicentina Nature Park

and it leads back to the main road
south of town; continue your journey.

*Continue on the N268 southwards
to Sagres.*

From here you can visit Cabo de São
Vicente (➤ 40–41), or Ponta de
Sagres (➤ 94–95), to see the site
of Henry the Navigator's school of
seamanship.

*Return to Vila do Bispo and take the
N125 east towards Lagos.*

Stop at Vila do Bispo for its church and
the Nossa Senhora de Guadalupe
chapel, beyond Raposeira (➤ 97).

*About 3km (2 miles) beyond
Raposeira, turn right to follow roads
(some of them unmetalled but well
maintained) through Figueira,
Salema, Burgau and Luz.*

Look out for birds as you go, and pick
any of the beaches en route for a dip –
or walk on the cliff paths above Luz.
Alternatively, end the day at Praia do
Camilo (➤ 69, 88), watching the
sunset from the clifftops.

Distance 120km (75 miles)
Time 6 hours
Start/end point Lagos ✚ 4C
Lunch Sítio do Forno (€€; ➤ 59)

Places to take the children

EXCURSIONS
Santa Bernarda Pirate Ship Cruises
This two-mast, mock-pirate caravel offers various tours of the coast, including swimming stops, exploring caves and grottoes in small boats and beach barbeques. The boat is equipped for passengers with disabilities.

✉ Santa Bernarda Cruzeiros Ltd, Rua Júdice Fialho 4, 8500-702 Portimão
☎ 282 422 791; www.santa-bernarda.com ③ Mon–Fri 9:45 and 2:30
✋ Expensive

KARTING
Almancil Karting
Karting circuit designed as a small replica of the Brazilian Grand Prix track and inaugurated by the late Ayrton Senna. Separate children's track.

✉ Sítio de Pereiras, 8125-022 Almancil ☎ 289 399 899;
www.kartingalgarve.com ③ Jun–Sep daily 9–8; Oct–May daily 9–4
✋ Expensive

THEME PARKS AND WATER PARKS
Aqualand Algarve
Exciting attractions, with names like 'Raging Rapids', 'Flying Carpets' and 'Crazy Leap', make this a must for the daring. The park has the longest speed slide in the Algarve.

✉ Estrada Nacional 125, Sitio das Areias, 8365-908 Alcantrilha ☎ 282 320 230; www.aqualand.pt ③ Daily 10–6; closed last week in May–end of 2nd week in Sep ✋ Expensive

AquaShow
Combined waterpark and bird garden with a wax museum.

✉ Semino Estrada Nacional 396, 8125-303 Quarteira ☎ 289 389 396;
www.aquashowpark.com ③ Jun–Jul 10–6:30, Aug 10–7; 1 Sep–15 Sep
10–6, 16 Sep–30 Sep 10–5:30 ✋ Expensive

Krazy World

A real mixture of things to do, from swimming pools to petting zoo to exotic animal shows to a fairground.

✉ Signposted from the Estrada Nacional 125, 8200 Guia ☎ 282 574 134; www.krazyworld.com 🕐 Jan–Jun, Sep–Oct Wed–Sat 10–6; Jul–Aug 10–7:30 ✋ Expensive

Slide and Splash

Experience the exciting 'Black Hole' whirlpool at this popular park. Facilities include shops, bars and a restaurant. Slide and Splash runs buses during the summer, collecting customers from pick-up points in the main coastal resorts.

✉ Estrada Nacional 125, Vale de Deus, Estômbar, 8401-901 Lagoa ☎ 282 340 800; www.slidesplash.com 🕐 Jul–Aug daily 10–6; Apr–May, mid-Sep to Oct 10–5; Jun to mid-Sep 10–5:30; closed Nov–Mar ✋ Expensive

Zoomarine

One ticket provides entry to the marine zoo and water park. Shows featuring dolphins, seals and parrots are staged throughout the day, and other attractions include an aquarium, cinema, sea museum, funfair and swimming pools with slides and whirlpools.

✉ Estrada Nacional 125 Km65, Guia, 8200-864 Albufeira ☎ 289 560 300; www.zoomarine.com 🕐 Nov to mid-Mar Tue–Sun 10–5; mid-Mar to mid-Jun daily 10–6; mid-Jun to mid-Sep daily 10–7:30; mid-Sep to Oct daily 10–6 ✋ Expensive

ZOOS
Lagos Zoological Park

Three hectares (7.5 acres) of land have been transformed into various habitats, home to exotic birds, monkeys, emus and wallabies, to name but a few. There are refreshment facilities, as well as an area where children can interact with the animals.

✉ Sítio do Medronhal, Barão de São João, 8600-013 Lagos ☎ 282 680 100; www.zoolagos.com 🕐 Apr–Sep daily 10–7; Oct–Mar daily 10–5 ✋ Expensive

Golf courses

Almost all golf courses in the Algarve require a handicap certificate and most have a dress code. Remember to check your tee-off time when booking. For more information on golfing in Portugal, see www.portugalgolf.pt

Alto Golf

This clifftop course enjoys superb views of the sea and the Serra de Monchique mountains. Designed by Sir Henry Cotton, the challenging course is famous for its 16th hole, one of the longest in Europe. There is also a golf school with practice bunker and putting green. 18 holes, par 72.

✉ Quinta do Alto do Poço, 8501-906 Alvor ☎ 282 460 870; www.altoclub.com

Pestana Golf Resort

The base for the David Leadbetter Golf Academy, with three scenic 18-hole courses: Gramacho. Vale da Pinta and Silves, 10km (6 miles) away.

✉ Carvoeiro, 8400 Lagoa ☎ 282 340 900; www.pestanagolf.com

Pinheiros Altos

This par-72, 18-hole course begins in attractive pine woods, while the back nine holes run alongside the Ria Formosa Nature Reserve.

✉ Quinta do Lago, 8135-863 Almancil ☎ 289 359 910; www.pinheirosaltos.com

Quinta do Lago

Designed by Sir Henry Cotton, the two 18-hole, par-72 courses feature lakes and challenging bunkers. Rated one of the best golf complexes in Europe, the Portuguese Open and other international tournaments are regularly hosted here.

✉ Quinta do Lago, 8135-024 Almancil ☎ 289 390 705; www.quintadolagogolf.com

San Lorenzo

To play this 18-hole course (par 72) it helps to be a guest at Le Meridien Dona Filipa (➤ 161) or Penina hotels: non-residents can only reserve 24 hours in advance and priority is given to residents. Keen golfers consider the expense worthwhile for the chance to play a course that is rated number two in Europe.

✉ Quinta do Lago, 8135 Almancil ☎ 289 396 522

Vale de Milho

Nine-hole, par-27 course, with challenging water hazards.

✉ Apartado 1273, Praia do Carvoeiro, 8401-911 Carvoeiro ☎ 282 358 502

Vilamoura

The Vilamoura Oceânico estate, west of Faro, has five courses designed for a range of abilities, from the testing old course to the 18-hole Victoria course, set among lakes.

✉ Vilamoura ☎ Oceânico Old Course 289 310 341; Oceânico Pinhal 289 310 390; Oceânico Laguna 289 310 180; Oceânico Millennuim 289 310 188; Oceânico Victoria 289 320 1000; www.oceanicogolf.com

Places to stay

Le Meridien Penina Golf and Resort (€€–€€€)

This is one of the most luxurious hotels in the Algarve. Facilities include an Olympic-size swimming pool and a championship golf course. There is a choice of three restaurants and in the summer a shuttle bus carries guests to the beach at Alvor.

✉ PO Box 146 Penina, 8501-952 Portimão ☎ 282 420 200; www.starwoodhotels.com/lemeridien

Monte do Casal (€€–€€€)

This is a picturesque hotel hidden in the hills to the north of Faro, with views over the pool to the sea. Rooms and suites all have access to the pool and garden, and breakfast is served on private terraces. The restaurant is known for its fine cuisine.

✉ Cerro do Lobo, Estói, 8005-436 Faro ☎ 289 991 503; www.montedocasal.pt

Oriental (€€)

A beautifully designed, luxury hotel with distinctive oriental touches. All 86 rooms overlook the beach at Praia da Rocha and have views of the Atlantic.

✉ Avenida Tomás Cabreira, Apartado 160, Praia da Rocha, 8500-802 Portimão ☎ 282 480 800; www.tdhotels.pt

Pousada do Infante (€–€€)

This splendid *pousada* is built in traditional Algarvian style, with red-tiled roofs and a cloister-like loggia providing shaded terraces

to its rooms. There are good facilities for guests including a swimming pool and tennis courts.

✉ 8650-385 Sagres ☎ 282 620 240; www.pousadas.pt

Quinta da Cebola Vermelha (€€)

Outside Boliqueime this six-bedroomed *quinta* has stylish accommodation surrounded by fruit and olive trees. Breakfast is served on the terrace, lunch is available beside the salt-water pool, and a three-course dinner is served three times a week on request.

✉ PO Box 141, 8100-908 Boliqueime ☎ 289 363 680;
www.quintadacebolavermelha.com

Quinta do Lago (€€€)

In a magnificent setting on the Ria Formosa estuary. Each room has its own garden terrace and there are tennis courts, outdoor and indoor pools, and two golf courses alongside. Other activities include horseback-riding, clay-pigeon shooting, windsurfing and deep-sea fishing.

✉ 8135-024 Almancil ☎ 289 350 350; www.quintadolagohotel.com

Sheraton Algarve (€€–€€€)

This is not just a hotel – it's a complete resort, with a nine-hole golf course and golf academy, a large outdoor pool and tennis courts. There is a good choice of both casual and more formal restaurants.

✉ Praia da Falesia, 8200 Albufeira ☎ 289 500 100; www.sheraton-algarve.com or www.starwoodhotels.com/sheraton

Vila Galé Albacora (€–€€€)

Beautiful low-level hacienda-style hotel on the river 3km (2 miles) outside Tavira. A great place to relax, with its pools, spa and gym.

✉ Quatro Águas, 8800-901 Tavira ☎ 281 380 800; www.vilagale.pt

Vila Vita Parc (€€€)

Facilities at this Moorish-inspired hotel include six pools, tennis and squash courts, children's playground, pitch-and-putt golf course, health club, five restaurants and a nightclub.

✉ Alporchinhos, 8400-450 Porches ☎ 282 310 100; www.vilavita.com

Exploring

To many the Algarve is known as Portugal's holiday playground, with its long sandy beaches and offshore islands. Its main towns are Faro, Portimão and Lagos, but most tourists head for the resorts of Albufeira, Carvoeira, Praia da Rocha and Vilamoura, while sports enthusiasts make for Vale do Lobo and Quinta do Lago.

For a much quieter stay the town of Sagres and the western coast around Cabo de São Vicente or the much quieter Tavira in the east can't be beaten.

Although many are drawn to the beautiful, busy coastline, more and more people are travelling into the unspoiled rural hinterland where country life still follows the pace of a bygone age and the land is dominated by the hills of the Serra de Monchique.

Western Algarve

To the people of 15th-century Portugal, the western shores of the Algarve represented the end of the civilized world – beyond lay only uncertainty. Today, and even in the finest weather, the wave-battered cliffs of Cabo de São Vicente (Cape St Vincent) can appear suitably apocalyptic, and the Costa Vicentina, that part of the Algarvian coast that faces west on to the full force of the Atlantic, has some of the finest surfing beaches in Europe.

Lagos

The west, being furthest from Faro airport, and lacking the long sandy beaches of the east, remains the least developed part of coastal Algarve, and is the part that appeals most to visitors in search of tranquillity, wildlife and the opportunity to experience Portuguese culture relatively untouched by the trappings of mass tourism.

LAGOS

Lagos is an atmospheric town encircled by massive 16th-century walls that effectively shut out the 21st century, including the western Algarve's biggest concentration of hotel developments to the west of the town. Holidaymakers tire of the beach and drift into Lagos to discover a maze of cobbled streets too narrow for cars to penetrate. Café owners have set up tables and chairs, tempting visitors to stop and sample their delicious coffee and cakes, in between exploring the town's churches, museums, art galleries, antiques shops and bustling market.

Parking spaces are available along the Avenida dos Descobrimentos, the palm-lined road that runs beside the River Bensafrim. Sheltered from the open sea, the river was adapted for use as a canal to provide access to the town's harbour. Sleek white yachts and battered fishing boats sit side by side in the modern harbour, and signs point the way to the offices of companies offering fishing trips and voyages to the caves and coves of Ponta da Piedade (▶ 54–55).

The social hub of Lagos lies at Praça Gil Eanes, with a huge statue of Dom Sebastião at the centre of the square. This modern statue (1973), the work of sculptor João Cutileiro, portrays Prince Sebastian, who believed it was his mission to conquer North Africa and convert the Moors to Christianity. He gathered an army of 18,000 men and set sail from Lagos in 1578. When his ill-equipped army met a vastly superior force at Alcacer-Quibir, in Morocco, only 100 Portuguese survived.

🚑 4C 🚉 Lagos railway station (☎ 808 208 208, national enquiries), 1km (0.5 miles) north of the town centre 🚌 Bus terminus: Rossio de São João (☎ 282 762 944; www.eva-bus.com), with services to and from Aljezur, Burgau, Odeceixe, Portimão, Sagres, Salema and Vila do Bispo
🛈 Rua Vasco da Gama, São João, 8600-722 Lagos ☎ 282 763 031

Forte da Ponta da Bandeira

This 17th-century moated fortress was built to defend the town and port. Reached by a bridge and impressive gatehouse, it contains a small maritime museum documenting the place of Lagos in the Age of Discovery.

✉ Cais de Solaria ⏰ Tue–Sat 9:30–12:30, 2–5, Sun 10–1, 2–5. Closed Mon and public hols ✋ Inexpensive

Mercado dos Escravos (Slave Market)

Though not much to look at, this covered arcade, below the Customs House on the eastern side of Praça da República, is of great historical importance, for it was here, in 1444, that modern Europe's first slave market was established.

Despite this, Portugal was the first nation to abolish slavery, as part of the humanistic reforms of the Marquês de Pombal in the 1750s.

✉ Praça do Infante Dom Henrique, 8600-525 Lagos 🎫 Free

Museu Municipal Dr José Formosinhó

The Igreja de Santo António is one of the most lavishly decorated churches in the Algarve. Early 18th-century carved and gilded woodwork covers the entire east wall and frames wall paintings depicting scenes from the life of St Anthony, a Franciscan friar and native of Portugal, who devoted his life to care of the poor.

The adjoining museum is packed with curiosities. Religious artefacts such as vestments and baroque paintings form an important part of the collection, but the timeline runs from prehistoric pottery to Roman statuary found at Milreu (➤ 50–51) and pre-World War II German banknotes. There is also an interesting display of Portuguese chimney pots, which demonstrate the regional differences.

✉ Rua General Alberto da Silveira, 8600-594 Lagos ☎ 282 762 301
🕐 Tue–Sun 9:30–12:30, 2–5. Closed Mon and public hols
🎫 Inexpensive

Ponta da Piedade

Best places to see, ➤ 54–55.

a walk from Lagos to Luz

Early evening is a good time for this walk, when you can enjoy the setting sun. Ambitious walkers can take the whole route from Lagos to Luz and back; alternatively you can take the bus one way and walk back – check the times of buses between Lagos and Luz at the tourist information centre in Lagos. A third option, which is ideal for walkers with children, is to take the much shorter route to Ponta da Piedade and back.

Start from the centre of Lagos heading west along Avenida dos Descobrimentos, past the Forte da Ponta da Bandeira. Follow the main road uphill and out of town and turn left at the first set of traffic lights to Praia de Dona Ana.

Explore the beach at Praia de Dona Ana where the rocks are like fossilized sponge, then climb back up retracing your steps to the main road (300m/330yds), taking a left and continuing up the hill. After 500m (545yds) you'll see a sign pointing left for Praia do Camilo. Leave the road and walk to the café at the clifftop where you can pick up the route (keep the sea on your left) for Ponte da Piedade. If you have a car leave it here by the café.

Goats and walkers have eroded the tracks here but they all lead in one direction. Don't go close to the cliff edge as rock falls and subsidence are not uncommon.

At Ponta da Piedade, you will find fishermen waiting to take visitors on short trips to the nearby grottoes.

From Ponta da Piedade, the path turns westwards along the clifftops. Porto de Mós, with its beach and café, is reached after about 20 minutes. From here, a track heads westwards, continuing for some 50 minutes to Luz.

The most prominent feature in the landscape is the *atalaia* (obelisk) above Luz, marking the highest point (109m/358ft) reached by the cliffs on this stretch of coast.

Distance 6km/4 miles (1km/0.5 miles from Praia do Camilo to Ponta da Piedade)
Time 3 hours (long walk); 30 mins (short walk)
Start point Municipal tourist information centre in Lagos, or the Praia do Camilo car park
End point Luz
Lunch Paraíso (€–€€; ➤ 101)

More to see in Western Algarve

ALJEZUR

Aljezur is the largest town on the scenic N120 road to Lisbon. High on the hill above Aljezur are the ruins of the massive 10th-century Moorish castle, captured by Dom Paio Peres Correia in 1246. He is said to have charmed a beautiful Moorish maiden who opened the castle doors to him one moonlit night. Good beaches nearby include Arrifana (10km/6 miles southwest), and Amoreira/Monte Clérigo (8km/5 miles northwest). To the north is the pretty, pottery-producing village of Odeceixe, beside the river that marks the boundary between the Algarve and the Alentejo.

✚ 3E ✉ 32km (20 miles) northwest of Lagos 🍽 Café (€) in Largo 5 de Outubro 🚌 Bus service from Lagos, for times see www.eva-bus.com

ℹ Largo do Mercado, Estrada Nacional, 8670-054 Aljezur ☎ 282 998 229

BURGAU

Burgau stands on the southeastern edge of the Costa Vicentina Nature Park, which extends in a broad sweep north from here to Odeceixe. The park encompasses 80km (50 miles) of coastline, whose poor soils and windswept salt-laden air have prevented farming and left an untamed landscape in which wildlife thrives – especially birds of prey and wading birds. Burgau is a good base for exploring this region, with a choice of accommodation in the village.

✚ 3B ✉ 12km (7.5 miles) west of Lagos ✋ Nature Park: inexpensive 🍽 Beach Bar (€–€€; ➤ 58); several more on the seafront at Burgau (€) 🚌 Bus from Lagos

CABO DE SÃO VICENTE

Best places to see, ➤ 40–41.

CARRAPATEIRA

Sleepy Carrapateira owes its popularity to its proximity to some of the west coast's best beaches (➤ 68–69). West of the town is Bordeira, guarded by the ruins of a 17th-century fortress and backed by huge dunes and a lagoon. Amado, further south, has the so-called Pedra do Cavaleiro (Knight's Rock) to protect it. The thundering surf all along the coast here appeals to water-sports enthusiasts, but the landscape of towering cliffs and vast beaches is just as attractive for walkers and photographers.

🕂 2D ✉ 38km (24 miles) northwest of Lagos 🍴 Small café (€); in main square 🚍 Bus from Lagos

LUZ

Luz – also known as Praia da Luz – marks the westernmost point of mass tourist development in the Algarve. The original holiday village here won praise and awards for sensitive development, its white-washed low-rise accommodation echoing the traditional houses and blending in harmoniously with the topography. Unfortunately, recent developments have been handled with less care, but Luz is still an excellent base for family holidays.

The beach at Praia da Luz has rock pools to explore, as well as sandy stretches, and at the height of the season there is a well-organized watersports school and sea-sport centre offering tuition for sailing, diving and windsurfing. A number of artificial scoops from the beach rocks have been identified as ancient tanks for salting and curing fish.

For those who want to get away from the beach, a gateway on the seafront promenade leads to the scant remains of a Roman villa. At the other end of the village is a 17th-century *fortaleza* (fortress), which has been turned into a popular restaurant. Nearby, the village church has a pre-1755 earthquake Gothic chancel decorated with elaborate 18th-century gilded carving.

✚ 4B ✉ 8km (5 miles) west of Lagos 🍴 Numerous cafés, including the Kiwi (€) on Avenida do Pescadores; Fortaleza da Luz (€€; ➤ 58) 🚍 Bus from Lagos

SAGRES

Sagres is Europe's most southwesterly community. Just 6km (4 miles) east of Cabo de São Vicente (➤ 40–41), it sits atop a rocky plateau, scoured by the same winds that send the sea crashing against the rocks of the nearby beaches. Even more bleak is the promontory south of the town, the site of the **Fortaleza (Fortress) de Sagres,** where Prince Henry the Navigator established his school of seamanship in 1443.

The sailors who came to study here lived an almost monastic life as they prepared to sail to new worlds, having mastered astronomy, navigation and cartography. The walls of the small town that Henry had built on the clifftops still survive, offering superb views across the rocky promontory, as does the simple chapel, with its altarpiece depicting St Vincent holding a ship. Nearby is a 15th-century Rosa dos Ventos (wind rose) inscribed into the rock, 43m (141ft) in diameter, which may once have been fitted with a weathervane to indicate the wind direction. The Vila do Infante, where Prince Henry lived, along with many other original buildings, was destroyed by the English buccaneer Sir Francis Drake in 1587, when Portugal was under Spanish rule.

Although the modern town has little to hold the attention, there are compensations to staying in Sagres, including pristine coves to explore. Local fishermen keep the restaurants well supplied with fresh fish and seafood, and also offer boat trips to view the magnificent Costa Vicentina from the sea. There are many clifftop walks, and in spring and autumn you can watch migrating birds flying over the headland or wheeling past the cliffs.

✚ 1B ✉ 32km (20 miles) west of Lagos 🍴 Numerous cafés (€) around main square; O Telheiro do Infante (€€–€€€; ➤ 101) overlooking the beach 🚌 Bus from Lagos

ℹ Rua Comandante Matoso, 8650-357 Sagres (☎ 282 624 873)

Fortaleza de Sagres

✉ Ponta de Sagres, 8650-360 Sagres
☎ www.ippar.pt/monuments/castelo_sagres 🕐 May–Sep 9:30–7:45, Oct–Apr 9:30–5:15. Closed 1 May, 25 Dec 💷 Moderate

SALEMA

Despite the shops, bars and restaurants catering for visitors, Salema still has the air of an unspoiled coastal village, where the fishermen haul in their catch by the first light of dawn. Several offer fishing excursions to visitors, supplying tackle, tuition for beginners and lunch. Equally popular are birdwatching excursions into the marshes west of the village. For sun-worshippers, there is a sheltered beach at Ponta de Almadena and another at

neighbouring Boca do Rio; the two are linked by a 2km (1.2-mile) clifftop walk. Also between Salema and Burgau is the beach at Cabanas Velhas.

➕ 3B ✉ 17km (11 miles) west of Lagos 🍴 Several cafés and bars (€) in Rua dos Pescadores 🚌 Bus from Lagos

VILA DO BISPO

Vila do Bispo (Bishop's Town) was renamed after this former royal town was given to the Bishop of Algarve by King Manuel I in 1515. It was a rich prize, for the bishop enjoyed the revenues from the town's many windmills. Today only a couple of old mills remain, minus their sails, but the skyline is dominated by a dozen or so white modern turbines turning the prevailing winds to good use. The highlight of the town is the 18th-century parish church, Nossa Senhora da Conceição, decorated with *azulejos* depicting dolphins and dating from 1726. It has a fine painted roof and the sacristy houses a museum displaying 16th-century painted panels and statues of saints.

Nearby Raposeira, 1km (0.5 miles) to the east, has a house that claims to be a former residence of Henry the Navigator. From the same period are the Manueline doorways of the parish church, its pyramid-roofed bell-tower and the chancel arch. Even older is the Chapel of Nossa Senhora de Guadalupe (private property), to the north of the N125, east of Figueira, which dates from the 13th century and may have been built for the crusading Knights Templar.

The beaches of Praia da Cordoama, with its dramatic lookout, and Praia do Castelejo are close to town and clearly signposted.

➕ 2B ✉ 24km (15 miles) west of Lagos 🍴 Cafés (€) around Praça da República 🚌 Bus from Lagos

HOTELS

CARRAPATEIRA
Monte Velho (€€–€€€)

Sitting on Portugal's wild Atlantic coast within the natural park, this rural retreat makes a good base for outdoor activities such as surfing, walking and bike riding. Rooms are bright and rustic, and each has its own porch area looking out over the sea and rolling hills.

✉ Carrapateira, 8670-230 Bordeira ☎ 282 973 207; www.wonderfulland.com

LAGOS
Villa Mar Azul (€)

A boutique hotel on the outskirts of Lagos, with light, modern and well-furnished studios and apartments, two pools and wellness and massage facilities on site.

Rua da Misericordia, Barranco do Portomós, 8600-621 Lagos ☎ 282 760 261; www.sonelhotels.com

PRAIA DA LUZ
Hotel Luz Bay (€–€€€)

Mexican 'pueblo-style' hotel set around an atrium with a great pool area and surrounding gardens. Only a couple of minutes' walk from the beach. The tastefully decorated bedrooms are equipped with telephone, satellite TV, mini fridge and safe, and all have a balcony or terrace. Other facilities include tennis and squash courts and a sauna and Turkish bath. Excellent rates in winter.

✉ Rua du Jardim, Praia da Luz, 8600-565 Lagos ☎ 282 789 640; www.lunahoteis.com

SAGRES
Memmo Baleeira Hotel (€€–€€€)

Established in the 1960s, this hotel was given a total face-lift in 2007 and now has a minimalist white boutique interior. In addition to a fantastic sun deck and pool overlooking the Atlantic, it has spa facilities and a heated indoor pool for the cooler months.

✉ 8650-357 Vila de Sagres ☎ 282 624 212; www.memmohotels.com

SALEMA
Pensão A Maré (€)
Run by two Danes, this simple guest house sits above the beach at Salema and offers a choice of B&B or self-catering accommodation at very reasonable rates. (Minimum stay of three nights in self-catering apartments.)

✉ Edifício A Maré, Praia de Salema, 8650-194 Budens ☎ 282 695 165; www.the-mare.com

RESTAURANTS

BARÃO DE SÃO JOÃO
O Cangalho (€€)
Rustic Portuguese cuisine is the speciality of this rural restaurant, located in a traditional farmhouse. The home-baked bread comes fresh from a wood-fired clay oven, as does the roast sucking-pig, chicken *cabidela* and hunter's rabbit.

✉ Quinta Figueiras, Sítio do Medronhal, 8600-013 Barão de São João ☎ 282 687 218 ☀ Lunch, dinner; closed Mon

BURGAU
Âncora (€€)
Enjoy sea views with your food, choosing from an adventurous menu: mussels cooked in Indian spices and pork in a fig sauce are among the imaginative offerings.

✉ Largo dos Pescadores 4, 8650 Burgau ☎ 282 697 102 ☀ Dinner; closed Mon in summer, Mon and Tue in winter

Casa Grande (€€)
Set in the former winery attached to a beautifully restored manor house, this restaurant serves Portuguese and vegetarian dishes. Reservations advised.

✉ On the Burgau to Praia da Luz road, Burgau, 8650 Lagos ☎ 282 697 416 ☀ Dinner; closed Dec–Feb

Pig's Head/Cabeça de Porco (€€)

The porcine theme is reflected in the decor of this English-style pub, and in the very popular pig roasts served on Sundays. International dishes are on the menu during the rest of the week.

✉ Luz road, east of Burgau, Sítio Montinhos, Burgau, 8600-000 Luz ☎ 282 697 315 ◷ Lunch, dinner

CARRAPATEIRA

O Sítio do Rio (€€)

On the edge of Bordeira beach, this popular restaurant has a more varied menu than Sítio do Forno (➤ 59), but the view isn't as spectacular.

✉ Praia Bordeira, Carrapateira, 8670-230 Aljezur (on the coastal road) ☎ 282 973 119 ◷ Lunch, dinner; closed Tue and mid-Nov to Dec

LAGOS

Atlântico (€€)

Excellent seafood restaurant on one of the finest stretches of beach in the western Algarve.

✉ Estrada Meia Praia, 8600-315 Lagos ☎ 282 792 086 ◷ Lunch, dinner

Bar da Lota (€€)

This simple dockside eatery serves only grilled fish, straight off the boats. Sardines, bream, bass, sole and others are usually available.

✉ Porto de Pesca, 8600 Lagos ☎ 282 764 048 ◷ Lunch, dinner; closed Sun

Dom Sebastião (€€)

This popular restaurant, with its timbered ceiling, also has an open-air terrace and an extensive menu.

✉ Rua 25 de Abril 20, 8600-763 Lagos ☎ 282 780 480 ◷ Lunch, dinner

Os Arcos (€€)

Os Arcos serves the best in seafood, including live lobsters and traditional Portuguese dishes. It has tables on the square and a large indoor dining room.

✉ Rua 25 Abril 30, 8600-763 Lagos ☎ 282 763 210; www.gastronomias.com/arcos ◷ Lunch, dinner; closed Wed

PRAIA DA LUZ
Paraíso (€–€€)
This terrace beach bar sits on the delightful Praia da Luz beach and offers a choice of fresh grilled fish and seafood. As well as the more formal indoor dining room, it has an outdoor deck above the sand, where light snacks and drinks are served.

✉ Praia da Luz, 8600-156 Lagos ☎ 282 788 246 🕓 Lunch, dinner

SAGRES
A Tasca (€€)
Located at the harbour in Sagres, in a building that once served as a market, A Tasca specializes in fresh fish, including lobster and clams *amêijoas*.

✉ Sagres harbour, Praia da Baleeira, 8650 Sagres ☎ 282 624 177 🕓 Lunch, dinner; closed Wed

Bossa Nova (€)
Pasta and pizzas dominatea menu that includes vegetarian dishes and seafood, at this friendly and very moderately priced restaurant.

✉ Mareta de Beber, 8650-361 Sagres (off Avenida Comandante Matoso) ☎ 282 624 566 🕓 Lunch, dinner

O Telheiro do Infante (€€–€€€)
There are plenty of good options from the snack bar or full service restaurant – depending on your mood. The menu concentrates on seafood dishes, and the large terrace overlooks the beach.

✉ Praia de Mareta, 8650-351 Sagres ☎ 282 624 179; www.telheirodoinfante.com 🕓 Lunch, dinner; closed Tue

Pousada do Infante (€€)
Luxuriate in the comfortable atmosphere of this hotel restaurant serving locally caught fish, set on a clifftop with sweeping views around the bay.

✉ Atalaia Point, 8650-385 Sagres ☎ 282 620 240; www.pousadas.pt 🕓 Lunch, dinner

VILA DO BISPO
Café Correia (€€)
A simple, rustic, typically Portuguese restaurant that specializes in serving barnacles. Fish is predominent on the extended menu and wine is served from the cask.

✉ Rua 1 de Maio 4, 8650-425 Vila do Bispo ☎ 282 639 127 🕓 Lunch, dinner; closed Sat

SHOPPING

ANTIQUES
Casa do Papagaio
You cannot miss this shop as you walk down Rua 25 de Abril because of its live parrot, prominently positioned outside the door. Inside, the cramped store is packed with everything from junk to genuine antique statuary.

✉ Rua 25 de Abril 27, 8600-763 Lagos ☎ 282 789 666 🕓 Mon–Fri 10–1, 3–7, Sat 10–1

ARTESANATO
Artesanato São Vicente
Probably the last souvenir emporium until you reach the Americas, this large shop has a fine range of crafts.

✉ Estrada Cabo São Vicente, 8650-370 Sagres ☎ 282 624 004 🕓 Oct–Mar Mon–Fri 9–1, 3–7; Apr–Sep daily 9–7

O Baú
A good range of typical souvenirs from around the region.

✉ Waterside Village Lote 12, Praia da Luz, 8600-000 Lagos ☎ 282 789 936 🕓 Oct–Easter Mon–Sat 9–12:30, 3–7; Easter–Sep daily 9–7

O Poticho
Ceramics, basketwork and embroidery.

✉ Rua 25 de Abril 24, 8600-763 Lagos ☎ 282 760 729 🕓 Daily 9–7; closed Sun in winter

JEWELLERY
Triarte
Designer jewellery, blown glass and hand-painted silk in this small shop near the slave market. Goods made to order.

✉ Rua da Vedoria 10, 8600-252 Lagos ☎ 282 767 966 🕓 Daily 10–7; closed Jan

LEATHERWEAR
Sirocco
Sirocco is on Rua Cândido dos Reis, one of the main shopping streets in Lagos, known for leather boutiques. The shop focuses on African crafts, including leather lamps and mirrors from Morocco.

✉ Rua Cândido dos Reis 37, 8600-681 Lagos ☎ 282 762 306 🕓 Mon–Sat 10–1, 3–7

MARKETS
Lagos
Lagos's covered market has a good selection of locally produced fruit and veg, as well as breads and cheeses.

✉ Rua das Portas de Portugal, 8600-657 Lagos 🕓 Mon–Sat 8–1

There is also an open-air street market on the first Saturday of the month, selling mainly shoes and clothing.

Sagres
There is a street market on the 1st Friday of the month (opposite the post office).

ACTIVITIES

BOAT TRIPS AND FISHING
Bom Dia
Bom Dia specializes in trips to explore the marine caves of the nearby coastline. Visitors travel along the coast in a tall-masted sailing ship, using smaller boats to explore the marine grottoes.

✉ Marina de Lagos Loja 10, 8600 Lagos ☎ 282 087 587; www.bomdia.info

Lagos Kayak Centre
Take part in guided kayak trips to the grottoes and caves at Ponta da Piedade in modern kayaks.

✉ Motel Âncora, Estrada do Porto do Mós, 8600-909 Lagos ☎ 964 665 667 or 917 807 651; www.blue-ocean-divers.de

SPORTS FACILITIES
The facilities at the Luz Bay and Ocean clubs are open to non-residents and include swimming pools, saunas, a Turkish bath, gym, mini-golf, tennis and squash courts (➤ 98 for Luz Bay information).

✉ Avenida Pescadores, Praia da Luz, 8600-160 Luz ☎ 282 771 000

SURFING
Algarve Surf Shop, School and Camp
Choose from 1-, 3- or 5-day surf packages comprising transport from Lagos or Sagres, tuition and equipment rental. Real enthusiasts should opt for the full surf pack, which includes lessons, accommodation at the surf camp, breakfast and packed lunch.

✉ Rua Dr Joaquim Tello 32-B, 8600 Lagos ☎ 962 846 771 or 282 624 560; www.algarvesurfschool.com

WALKING TOURS
Portugal Walks
Guided and self-guided routes across the whole region, overseen by Dr Julie Statham, who lives in the Algarve.

✉ Quinta do Montinho 37, 8650-060 Budens ☎ 282 697 289 or 965 753 033; www.portugalwalks.com

WATER SPORTS
Blue Ocean Divers
Trips for qualified divers, training to advanced level and equipment for hire.

✉ Motel Âncora, Estrada do Porto do Mós, 8600-909 Lagos ☎ 964 665 667; www.blue-ocean-divers.de

Western Central Algarve

Between Lagos in the west and Albufeira in the east, western central Algarve takes in a stretch of coast that combines attractive resorts with port towns, where fishing vies with tourism as the major income earner. Inland lies Porches, the centre of the Algarvian pottery industry, and Silves, a majestic hilltown with enough history to satisfy any culture-seeking visitor.

□ Silves

Beyond the fertile valleys around Silves lie the foothills of the Serra de Monchique. Here two huge reservoirs trap rainfall and spring water, supplying the region's drinking water and providing recreational facilities for anglers and boating enthusiasts. Northwards again are the pretty villages of the Monchique mountains, offering cool summer retreats from the baking-hot coast, and an extensive network of tree-shaded footpaths, as well as the Algarve's highest peak, at Fóia (902m/2,960ft).

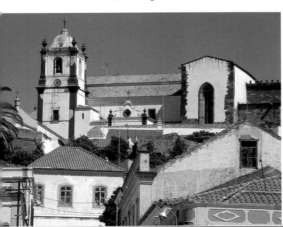

SILVES

Silves is a compact town built on a series of terraces between the River Arade and the massive castle. One way to approach the town is by sailing upriver from Portimão, following the same route taken by Phoenician traders who established their base here in the 1st millennium BC. Their riverside colony grew to become the Roman city of Silbis, and then, from the 8th century, the Moorish city of Xelb. Described by Arabic chroniclers as 10 times more impressive than Lisbon, Xelb was a city of gleaming domes and minarets, of poets, writers and musicians, traders, craftsmen and farmers.

Due to the earthquake of 1755, little now survives of the Arabic influence – at least in architectural terms. The most lasting legacy is visible in the almond and citrus groves that you see as you look down from the castle walls (➤ 46–47) across the surrounding countryside. It was the Moors who introduced these crops, along with the irrigation system.

From the castle, narrow cobbled streets descend steeply to the cathedral and the archaeological museum. From the museum it is a short stroll through the Torreão das Portas da Cidade, the medieval town gate, to the main square, the Praça do Municipio, with its town hall, ancient pillory and pavement cafés. Shop-lined

streets lead from here down to the covered market and the embankments of the River Arade, where pavement cafés offer views of the town's medieval bridge.

🚉 7D 🚂 Railway station 2km (1 mile) south of town

🚌 Bus terminus alongside Mercado Municipal ☎ 282 442 338, with services to and from Albufeira, Armação de Pêra, Lagoa, Messines and Portimão

ℹ️ Rua 25 de Abril, 8300-184 Silves ☎ 282 442 255

Castelo de Silves

Best places to see, ➤ 46–47.

Cruz de Portugal

Situated beside a busy roundabout on the northeastern entrance to the city, the Cross of Portugal is a beautiful religious sculpture dating from the early 16th century. Such crosses were erected at key points along medieval pilgrim routes and this is a rare surviving example.

✉️ 1km (0.5 miles) northeast of town, on the road to São Bartolomeu de Messines

Fábrica do Inglês and Museu da Cortiça

A cork factory near the river has been transformed into a leisure complex – Fábrica do Inglês – with gallery space, restaurants and street entertainment. The complex has a Cork Museum, celebrating one of Portugal's most important exports.

✉ Rua Gregório Mascarenhas, 8300-159 Silves ☎ 282 440 480 🕓 Museum: Jul–Sep daily 9:30–12:45, 2–6:15; Oct–Jun Mon–Sat 9:30–12:45, 2–6:15 (May–Sep until 8:45pm). Fábrica: Jul–Sep daily 9am–midnight; Oct–Jun Mon–Sat 9–midnight

Museu Municipal de Arqueologia

The archaeological museum is built around the excavated remains of a Moorish house. The complexity and beauty of the well, with its stone flagged spiral staircase lit by arched windows, descending to the watery depths, makes you realize how impressive the Moorish city must have been. The museum explains the city's evolution from prehistoric to recent times. The top floor leads out on to a restored section of the city wall, from where there is a view down over the old Moorish quarter.

✉ Rua das Porta de Loulé 14, 8300-139 Silves ☎ 282 444 832 🕓 Mon–Sat 9–5:30. Closed Sun and public hols 💷 Inexpensive

Sé (Cathedral)

Built on the site of the Moorish mosque to symbolize the expulsion of the Moors from the city, the magnificent 13th- to 15th-century cathedral is one of only a few in the Algarve to retain its medieval feel. Free from the gilded baroque woodwork of many post-earthquake churches, the rose-pink granite columns and vaults soar above the tombs of medieval knights and bishops.

✉ Rua da Sé 🕓 Daily 8:30–6:30 💷 Free

More to see in Western Central Algarve

ALGAR SECO
Best places to see, ➤ 36–37.

ALGOZ
This fast expanding village, centred around a core of modest whitewashed houses, has two churches worth visiting. The 18th-century parish church has a baptistery with *azulejos* and statues that are still paraded through the streets on feast days. On a small hill above the village is the Hermitage of Nossa Senhora do Pilar, whose interior contains 18th-century paintings of the Stations of the Cross.

✚ 8C ✉ 12km (7.5 miles) northeast of Armação de Pêra 🍴 O João (€€, ➤ 131) 🚌 Bus from Armação de Pêra or Portimão

ALVOR

Alvor lies on the eastern edge of the wide Baia de Lagos (Lagos Bay), a shallow, bird-filled lagoon formed by the estuary of four rivers. Fishing was the inspiration behind the carvings that decorate the portal of the 16th-century parish church. Local fishermen join the wading birds in the tidal estuary, searching for razor shells and clams, which are sold in the fish market on the harbour, and which form the principal ingredient of the seafood dishes served in local bars and restaurants. For a closer look at the lagoon, follow the raised footpath that winds between the salt pans close to the shore.

Land east of the town has been commandeered by several large modern hotel complexes, with development reaching all the way to Praia de Alvor and Praia dos Três Irmãos and almost filling the gap between Alvor and Praia da Rocha (➤ 124–125). The hotels are well placed for nearby Portimão and Lagos.

➕ 5C ✉ 6km (4 miles) west of Portimão 🍴 Ababuja (€€, Rua da Ribeira 11, Alvor ☎ 282 458 979; closed Wed) 🚌 Bus from Portimão

ARMAÇÃO DE PÊRA

Armação de Pêra is a growing resort full of multi-storey apartment blocks and hotels, sprawling along a stretch of sandy beach that marks the watershed between the rocky coves of the western Algarve and the sandy shores of the east. Visitors can laze on the sands within sight of the colourfully painted boats of the local fishing fleet, or engage in the many activities on offer, such as surfing at Vale de Centianes, or snorkelling at Marinha or Albandeira.

Nearby Vila Senhora da Rocha has adjacent bays sheltered by high cliffs, lined with hotel complexes. Perched high on the cliff above is the delightful Ermida de Nossa Senhora da Rocha (Hermitage of Our Lady of the Rock), with its candle-lit interior and hexagonal spire (➤ 129).

🚩 7B ✉ 14km (9 miles) west of Albufeira 🍴 Santola Restaurant, Largo da Fortaleza (€€€; ➤ 59) 🚌 Buses from Portimão and Albufeira
🛈 Avenida Beira Mar, 8365-101 Armação de Pêra ☎ 282 312 145

CALDAS DE MONCHIQUE

Best places to see, ➤ 42–43.

CARVOEIRO

Carvoeiro is a pretty fishing village which remained virtually untouched until the 1980s, when tourist development began to spread rapidly westwards. Ringed by Moorish-style buildings and the battlemented remains of former fortifications, the sheltered beach can get very crowded at the height of the season, but local fishermen will happily take visitors on trips to the other beaches, such as Benagil and Marinha, and to the nearby caves, tunnels and rock stacks of Algar Seco (➤ 36–37).

✚ 6B ✉ 14km (9 miles) east of Portimão 🍴 Cafés (€) and seafood restaurants (€€) in Estrada do Farol 🚌 Buses from Portimão
ℹ Praia do Carvoeiro, 8400-517 Carvoeiro ☎ 282 357 728

ESTÔMBAR

Estômbar is a former salt-trading town, with a pretty church, Igreja São Tiago (St James), which is worth a stop for its ornate baroque facade. Typical of the 16th-century Manueline style, its portal is carved with nautical motifs, including stylized shells and ropes in stone. Inside, the columns of the same date are carved with scenes from everyday life. The 18th-century *azulejos* depict St James in combat with the Moors, and the Battle of Lepanto (1571), a famous victory for Christian forces against the might of the Ottoman Turkish navy, as well as more conventional religious scenes. More appealing to children is the big Slide and Splash aquapark (➤ 75), east of town.

➕ 6C ✉ 4km (2.5 miles) east of Portimão 🍴 Cafés (€) around the main square 🚌 Buses from Portimão and Albufeira

FERRAGUDO

Ferragudo is a rare example of an almost untouched coastal fishing village. A timeless atmosphere prevails in the narrow cobbled streets which lead uphill to the simple village church, from whose terrace there are sweeping views across the boat-filled estuary.

To the south of the village, the remains of the Castelo de São João de Arade stand on a rocky headland. This medieval fortress, along with the Fortaleza de Santa Catarina on the opposite bank, was built to keep a watch for hostile ships and prevent them getting too far upriver. Now a private house, the fort was turned into a romantic home by the poet Coelho Carvalho at the beginning of the 20th century. From the castle, it's a short stroll to the Praia Grande. This sandy beach, protected from the open sea by a *molhe* (sea wall), is a good place to learn windsurfing. A little further south, a lighthouse guides ships up to the main estuary channel.

🕂 6C ✉ 3km (2 miles) east of Portimão 🍴 Cafés (€) along the harbourfront 🚌 Buses from Portimão and Albufeira

GUIA

Although Guia has an interesting church, richly decorated with *azulejo* tile pictures, the real attraction here is the Zoomarine Park (➤ 75) on the edge of this crossroads village. The park combines various attractions: a swimming pool, a pirate castle and a mini-fairground, with a big wheel, a bouncy castle and merry-go-rounds. There are performing dolphins, sea lions and parrots, and various animals and marine creatures, including seals, sharks and penguins, are displayed in aquariums and enclosures around the park.

✚ 8C ⊠ 7km (4 miles) northwest of Albufeira ❚❙ Cafés (€) around the main square 🚌 Buses from Albufeira

LAGOA

Lagoa is the Algarve's main wine-producing town, and the **Adega Co-operativa de Lagoa,** on the Portimão road, offers guided tours and wine tastings. As well as making both light and full-bodied red wines, the co-operative also produces *aguardente*, a sugar-cane spirit, taken as an aperitif. Another local product worth looking out for is *morgadinhos* – almond-paste sweets in the shape of animals and flowers.

Though no longer the big event it once was, Holy Week is still marked in Lagoa with processions and prayers. The parish church has an 18th-century altar noted for its statue of Nossa Senhora da Luz (Our Lady of Light). Two blocks north, the São José Convent (Convento de São José) has a pretty cloister whose garden contains a menhir (upright prehistoric stone) perhaps dating back to 4000BC.

🚣 6C ⊠ 8km (5 miles) east of Portimão 🍴 Cafés (€) around the main square 🚌 Buses from Portimão and Albufeira

Adega Cooperativa de Lagoa

⊠ Estrada Nacional 125,8400-901 Lagoa ☎ 282 342 181 (in summer only); www.adegalagoa.pt. Book in advance 🕙 Daily 9–5:30 ✋ Free

MONCHIQUE

Monchique, the main town in the Serra
da Monchique mountain range, attracts
summer visitors seeking an escape
from the roasting sun of the coastal
resorts. At 458m (1,500ft) above sea
level, the tree-shaded town usually
feels several degrees cooler.
Monchique has many natural springs,
and the nearby spa village of Caldas de
Monchique (➤ 42–43) is the source
of the commercially bottled water sold
all over the Algarve. Springs feed the
fountain that adorns Monchique's main

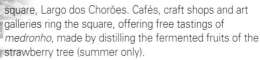

square, Largo dos Chorões. Cafés, craft shops and art galleries ring the square, offering free tastings of *medronho*, made by distilling the fermented fruits of the strawberry tree (summer only).

Ornate 16th-century carvings decorate the parish church, Nossa Senhora da Conceição, and the gilded altar has many charming details, including angels holding up the sun and the moon. In one of the side chapels, look out for the *azulejos* depicting St Michael in combat with the devil, and the suffering souls in Purgatory.

Many visitors go on to enjoy lunch in one of several restaurants lining the Fóia road that specialize in chilli-flavoured chicken *piri-piri* (➤ 14). You can work up an appetite first by walking to Fóia, the Algarve's highest peak, or following the signposted footpath above the town hall that leads to the ruins of Nossa Senhora do Desterro monastery, a short stroll with fine views.

✚ 5E ✉ 24km (15 miles) north of Portimão 🍴 Cafés in Monchique (€), restaurants on Monchique to Fóia road 🚌 Buses from Portimão and Silves

ℹ Largo de São Sebastião, 8550 Monchique ☎ 282 911 189

PORCHES

Porches is the centre of the Algarve's pottery industry. Though the village is small, there is plenty to see here, as you browse through the displays of terracotta jars and watch artists at work, painting plates and fruit bowls with sunflowers, cockerels or colourful clusters of grapes. Be sure to check whether flower pots and urns are frost proof, otherwise they will shatter if left out over the winter in northern European climes. A trip to Porches can be combined with a visit to Aqualand Algarve theme park (➤ 74), between Porches and Alcantarilha.

✚ 7C ✉ On the N125 highway, 13km (8 miles) east of Portimão 🍴 Cafés in main square or Porches Velho (€€) 🚌 Buses from Portimão and Albufeira

a walk

from Monchique to Caldas de Monchique

This gentle stroll takes you through the attractively wooded countryside surrounding Monchique to the pretty spa town of Caldas de Monchique (➤ 42–43).

Start in Monchique's main square, Largo dos Chorões. Head south on the main N266 Portimão road.

During spring, you will enjoy the almond-like scent from the mimosa trees that line the roads around Monchique.

After 10 minutes, you will reach the junction between the main Portimão road and the Alferce road, which goes off to the left (east). Take the narrow road between the BP petrol station and the restaurant.

The road now follows the right bank of one of the many small streams that spring up in the Serra da Monchique, eventually flowing down to the sea at Portimão. The road descends through olive groves and orange plantations. To the left you may catch sight of Picota, the Algarve's second highest peak (774m/2,539ft).

After 25 minutes or so you will reach the Marmelete road. Turn left and walk along the road to the intersection of the N266. From here it's a right turn down the hill to the Caldas de Monchique. As there is no pavement stay close to the side wall.

As you approach Caldas de Monchique, look out for the strawberry trees *(Arbutus unedo)* that grow abundantly in the humid environment of the spa town. The fruits of these low-growing evergreen trees vaguely resemble strawberries and are used to produce a fermented liquor which is distilled to make *medronho*, the Algarve's best-known spirit. Reward yourself with a glass on completing the walk, but beware – the deceptively smooth taste disguises an alcoholic kick that can be anything up to 90 per cent proof.

Distance 4km (2.5 miles)
Time 1.5 hours
Start point Tourist information centre, Largo de São Sebastião, 8550 Monchique ✚ 5E
End point Caldas de Monchique ✚ 6E
Lunch 1692 (€€€; ➤ 58), or take a picnic. It's also worth taking a bottle of water, especially in summer

PORTIMÃO

Portimão is one of the Algarve's main fishing ports and the settlement where tourism hasn't yet stamped its indelible mark. There is much local life as the catches are brought in at the city's harbour where a long waterfront promenade allows for easy strolling.

Fishing trips, for beginners and experienced anglers, are advertised around the quay. Other options include Arade River cruises to Silves, and trips to explore the caves and cliffs at Algar Seco (► 36–37). The tantalizing smell of grilled sardines rises above numerous atmospheric eateries just off the quayside, or housed in the humble houses where the fishermen used to live (enter through a short tunnel under Rua Sepa Pinto). This is one of the best places to enjoy typical Algarvian seafood.

With its high-quality shops, Portimão is an excellent place if you prefer real shops to those geared to tourists. Heading inland from the harbour, Rua Dr João Vitorino, Rua Direita and Largo 1 de Dezembro offer plenty of choice. The latter is laid out as a park, with fountains and flower beds, and benches decorated with *azulejo* pictures depicting events in Portuguese history. The pictures date from 1924, when Portimão was granted city status by Portuguese president, Manuel Teixeira Gomes, a native of the town. The adjacent town hall is a fine 18th-century palace, once home to the viscounts of Bívar. The largest church in the

Algarve, the Jesuit Igreja do Colegio, is on the Praça da República.

The 1920s were a prosperous time for Portimão and many of the buildings lining the city centre roads were given decorative tilework facades and wrought-iron balconies, reflecting the art nouveau designs that were in vogue. The city has benefited from massive investment, including underground parking beneath the main square and a new marina to the west.

➕ 6C ✉ 20km (13 miles) east of Lagos 🍴 Cafés and restaurants along the quayside 🚉 Railway station 1km (0.5 miles) to the northwest of the city centre, on Largo Engenheiro Serra Prado 🚌 Bus station on Largo do Dique ☎ 282 418 120. Buses to Albufeira, Alvor, Armação da Pêra, Faro, Ferragudo, Lagoa, Lagos, Loulé, Monchique, Praia da Rocha, Silves and Torralta

ℹ Avenida Zeca Afonso, 8500-516 Portimão ☎ 282 470 732

PRAIA DA ROCHA

Praia da Rocha is one of the most photographed places in the
Algarve, with its distinctive, ochre-coloured sandstone columns
rising from a broad south-facing beach. This is also one of the
Algarve's most hedonistic resorts, popular with young visitors
dedicated to making the most of the nightlife on Avenida Tomás
Cabreira, the disco- and bar-lined seafront road. At the eastern end
of the 2km (1.2-mile) beach, the Fortaleza de Santa Catarina looks
across to Ferragudo's Castelo de São João de Arade. The two

fortresses form a 17th-century defensive system designed to guard the Arade River estuary. If you are seeking an escape from the crowds, take a boat trip to the rocky coves at Praia do Vau and Praia dos Três Irmãos.

🕇 6C ✉ 2km (1.2 miles) south of Portimão 🍴 Café in the Fortaleza (€) 🚌 Buses from Portimão
🛈 Avenida Tomás Cabreira, 8500-802 Portimão
☎ 282 419 132

SÃO BARTOLOMEU DE MESSINES

São Bartolomeu is an inland town in the foothills of the Serra do Caldeirão mountains, where almonds, figs and pomegranates alternate with fields of wheat. Rua Remexido is one of several streets lined by the characteristic Algarvian houses, with whitewashed walls and window frames picked out in vibrant reds and blues. The street is named after the guerrilla leader who lived here for several years and who controlled much of the western Algarve in the 1830s, during the civil war between right-wing supporters of King Miguel I, and liberal supporters of his brother and predecessor, King Pedro IV.

The parish church, Igreja Matriz, is a fine building in a mixture of styles, with a baroque facade, an elegant stone pulpit carved from local granite, and chapels decorated with 17th-century tiles and 16th- to 18th-century statues.

Some 10km (6 miles) west of the town is the Barragem de Arade, a reservoir created by damming the River Arade, a popular resort for anglers, with water-sports facilities and several cafés.

🕇 8D ✉ 24km (15 miles) north of Albufeira 🍴 Café (€) near the church
🚌 Buses from Silves

from Portimão to Monchique

a drive

This splendid half-day drive takes in the historic town of Silves and the mountain scenery of the Serra de Monchique, but it can be extended to a whole day.

> *From Portimão, cross the River Arade using the old bridge and follow the minor road through Estômbar before joining the N125 to Lagoa.*

Church lovers will want to stop in Estômbar (► 114) for the Manueline portal and *azulejos*, and in Lagoa (► 117) for the São José Convent, with its pretty cloister.

> *From Lagoa, head north on the N124 to Silves, passing under the new motorway.*

Approaching Silves from the south gives a fine view of the walled hill town and castle. Park by the river and climb up to the castle, cathedral and archaeological museum (► 107–109).

> *Leave Silves on the road to São Bartolomeu de Messines, stopping to look at the Cruz de Portugal beside the roundabout as you leave the suburbs. After 5km (3 miles) turn left to see the Barragem de Arade reservoir. Follow the road that leads, via Amorosa, to São Bartolomeu; join the IC1 (also signposted the E01) to Lisbon. Leave at the next exit, after 15km (9 miles), signposted to São Marcos da Serra and Nave Redonda.*

Many distractions may tempt you to stop – you could take a closer look at the cork oak trees to see how the bark is stripped, or perhaps enjoy the wayside wild flowers.

At Nave Redonda, in the Alentejo, turn south to return to the Algarve along a scenic road, the N266, that climbs to Monchique (➤ 118–119).

You can extend the tour by climbing Fóia, the Algarve's highest peak, or choose a restaurant for lunch with a view.

Head south to Caldas de Monchique (➤ 42–43) and stroll around the flower-filled streets. To return to Portimão, continue south on the N266.

Distance 110km (68 miles)
Time 6 hours
Start/end point Portimão ✚ 6C
Lunch Paraíso da Montanha (€, ➤ 59)

SERRA DE MONCHIQUE

The Serra de Monchique range forms a distinctive group of hills in the western Algarve. Running from west to east, the hills act as a barrier to cold air from the land mass to the north, helping to maintain the balmy warmth of the Algarvian winter. The woodlands are a mixture of cork oak, sweet chestnut and arbutus, with the addition of pine, eucalyptus, mimosa and great plane. The hills are volcanic in origin and the igneous rocks are quarried around the village of Nave, lying between Monchique (► 118–119) and the spa town of Caldas de Monchique (► 42–43).

From Nave, the N267 road cuts westwards though the hills to Aljezur (► 90). Forest fires have scarred part of the route, but this delightful road passes mainly through leafy woodland, past hillsides cut into terraces for vegetable cultivation, and fast-flowing streams. On the way, Caseis is worth a stop for its medieval church and the nearby ruins of what is claimed to be a Roman fort.

✚ 5E ✉ 25km (16 miles) north of Portimão ❚❚ Cafés and restaurants in Monchique and on the Fóia road

VILA SENHORA DA ROCHA

The sparkling white chapel standing on the cliff edge at Vila
Senhora da Rocha dates from at least the 13th century – a worn
capital in the triple-arched entrance porch is Visigothic in origin,
from the 6th century. The chapel has long been a place of
pilgrimage for Portuguese who come here to pray to the Virgin.
The once isolated chapel now nestles among apartment blocks
and hotels built along the sheltered beaches on this section of
coastline. Unfortunately there have been rock falls along the cliffs
here, so take advice on which beaches are safe.

🕂 7B ✉ 4km (2.5 miles) west of Armação da Pêra 🍴 Lord's Bar (€, Senhora
da Rocha, 8365 Armação de Pêra ☎ 282 315 764); more in Armação de Pêra

HOTELS

ALVOR

Pestana Delfim Hotel (€–€€)

In lush grounds above the Três Irmãos beach, the Pestana Delfim is a tower hotel, with golf and sports facilities nearby. Alvor is 10 minutes' walk away.

✉ Praia Três Irmãos, 8501-904 Alvor ☎ 282 400 800; www.pestana.com

CALDAS DE MONCHIQUE

Complexo Termal Monchique (€€)

A range of accommodation at the thermal spa from a four-star inn and three-star pension to self-catering apartments.

✉ Caldas de Monchique, 8550-232 Monchique ☎ 282 910 910; www.monchiquetermas.com

CARVOEIRO

Tivoli Almansor (€–€€€)

Close to a number of golf courses, the Almansor is on the clifftops above its own cove, sheltered by sandstone cliffs and reached by a path from the hotel. Facilities include a pool and shops.

✉ Apartado 1299, Vale do Coro, Praia do Carvoeiro, 8401-911 Carvoeiro, Lagoa ☎ 282 351 100; www.tivolihotels.com

FERRAGUDO

Casabela Hotel (€€–€€€)

Luxurious hotel in a picturesque setting above the Praia Grande beach that makes an excellent base for walking and water sports.

✉ Vale da Areia, Ferragudo, 8400 Lagoa, near Portimão ☎ 282 490 650; www.casabela.de

PORCHES

Vila Lara (€€€)

This luxurious, clifftop resort is set amid tranquil landscaped gardens. All rooms have a private terrace and its acclaimed Talasso-Therapy Spa centre offers more than 50 treatments.

✉ Praia das Gaivotas, Alporchinhos, Porches, 8400-450 Lagoa ☎ 282 320 000; www.vilalararesort.com

PORTIMÃO
Le Meridien Penina Golf and Resort (€€–€€€)
See page 78.

SILVES
Hotel Colina dos Mouros (€)
This modern, good-value hotel in Moorish style is across the river from Silves and has wonderful views over the town. Facilities include gardens, a pool, children's pool, bar and restaurant.
✉ Apartado 2, 8301-999 Silves ☎ 282 440 420; www.colinahotels.com

RESTAURANTS

ALGOZ
O João (€€)
In this restaurant you will be surrounded by local people who come to enjoy hearty Portuguese specialities. It's especially atmospheric at lunchtime, when the workers come in from surrounding towns.
✉ Rua Dra Ataide de Oliveira, Senhora do Pilar, 8365 Algoz ☎ 282 575 332
🕐 Lunch, dinner; closed Sun

ALVOR
Restinga
This wood and glass structure sits right on the beach at Alvor and offers both indoor and deck dining. It specializes in grilled fish and meat. Children's meals are available throughout the day.
✉ Praia de Alvor, 8500-000 Alvor, Portimão ☎ 282 459 434 🕐 Jun–Sep lunch, dinner; Oct–May lunch

CARVOEIRO
Grande Muralha (€€)
This Sino-Portuguese restaurant has familiar and not-so-familiar dishes on its menu. The not-so-familiar include curried squid and fried ice cream. For something more down-to-earth, try the delicious sizzling prawns.
✉ Estrada do Farol, B1 Farol–Lj5 R/C, Praia do Carvoeiro, 8400-505 Carvoeiro, Lagoa ☎ 282 357 380 🕐 Lunch, dinner

Tia Ilda (€€)

With over 100 items on the menu and 70 wines in stock there should be something for every member of the family, including *tapas*, Italian choices and Portuguese dishes. Good rooftop terrace.

✉ Rampa do Paraíso 18, 8400-522 Carvoeiro, Lagoa ☎ 282 357 830
🕐 Lunch, dinner; closed Mon

FERRAGUDO

Sueste (€€)

Fresh fish is a speciality of this restaurant, at the end of the fishing docks. Sit outside and look over the river estuary or eat in the dining room, with its 17th-century painted ceiling.

✉ Rua da Ribeira 91, 8400-256 Ferragudo ☎ 282 461 945 🕐 Lunch, dinner; closed Mon

MONCHIQUE

Jardim das Oliveiras (€€)

On the Monchique/Fóia road, Jardim das Oliveiras serves mountain cuisine. Try the pork loin stuffed with chestnuts or the wood-oven roasted kid with clams.

✉ Sitio do Porto Escuro, 8550-351 Monchique ☎ 282 912 875
🕐 Lunch, dinner

Quinta de São Bento (€€)

The views from this award-winning restaurant vie for attention with the grandeur of the building, located near the summit of Fóia, the Algarve's highest peak. The menu specializes in game and also offers wild boar.

✉ Estrada da Fóia, Sitio de Belém, Belém, 8550-218 Monchique ☎ 282 912 700 🕐 Lunch, dinner; Oct–May dinner only by reservation; closed Wed

PORTIMÃO

Dona Barca (€)

One of the best of Portimão's renowned fish restaurants, in a converted riverside warehouse. It serves fish straight off the boats and has live music in summer.

✉ Largo da Barca 9, 8500-527 Portimão ☎ 282 484 189 🕐 Lunch, dinner

Forte e Feio (€€)

Set in one of the old dockside warehouses, this restaurant with its bare stone walls and long wooden tables has a great selection of seafood and fresh fish. Try the *açorda de marisco* (bread-based dish with seafood).

✉ Largo da Barca 1, 8500-527 Portimão ☎ 282 413 809 🕐 Lunch, dinner

PRAIA DA ROCHA

Barrote (€€)

Although fish and seafood appear on the menu, Barrote is renowned for its meat dishes, a rarity in coastal Algarve. Try the *barroso* beef with oven-baked potatoes, or *chateaubriand* for two.

✉ Hotel Júpiter, Praia da Rocha, 8500-802 Portimão ☎ 282 415 041
🕐 Lunch, dinner

Casa de Rocha (€€)

With three terraces giving stunning views of the coastline, the Casa de Rocha makes a great place for a sunset meal. Traditional Portuguese dishes are served in this former summerhouse.

✉ Avenida Tomás Cabreira, Sítio dos Castelos, Praia da Rocha, 8500-000 Portimão ☎ 282 419 674 🕐 Lunch, dinner

SILVES

Café Inglês (€–€€)

Opposite the cathedral and alongside the castle entrance, this café is in an elegant 1920s house originally built as the residence of the mayor. Enjoy home-baked bread and cakes with afternoon tea or more substantial Portuguese and English snacks.

✉ Escadas do Castelo 11, 8300-144 Silves ☎ 282 442 585 🕐 Lunch, dinner; closed Mon and Sat lunch

Casa Velha de Silves (€€)

Overshadowed by the gates to the old Moorish city, the Casa Velha offers traditional Portuguese grilled fish, *cataplana* (fish stew) and *espetada* (kebabs). The restaurant holds regular concerts of *fado* and other folk music.

✉ Rua 25 de Abril 11, 8300-184 Silves ☎ 282 445 491 🕐 Lunch, dinner

SHOPPING

ANTIQUES
A Tralha
A vast warehouse of objects large and small. There are also shops at Almancil and Albufeira.
✉ Largo do Dique 15, 8500-531 Portimão ☎ 282 423 888 🕓 Mon–Sat 10–1, 3–7

ARTESANATO
Casa dos Arcos
Specializes in folding wooden chairs and tables, but also has good knitwear and rugs.
✉ Estrada Velha, 8550-242 Monchique ☎ 282 911 071 🕓 Apr–Sep daily 10–7; Oct–Mar Mon–Sat 10–6

Estudio Destra
Ceramic artist Kate Swift produces an excellent range of *azulejos* in modern styles and also undertakes commissions.
✉ Largo Jeronimo Osorio, 8300-113 Silves ☎ 282 442 933 🕓 Mon–Sat 10–12, 2–6

GIFTS
Montra D'Arte
Fascinating studio and gallery belonging to the artists Stella Barreto and Franco Charais, who both work in the modern genre.
✉ Rua da Hortinha 42 r/c Esq, 8500-596 Portimão ☎ 282 423 305; www.montradarte.com 🕓 Mon–Fri 3:30–7, Sat 11–1 or by appointment

LEATHER GOODS
Chic Shoes
As the name suggests, this shop specializes in chic handmade leather boots and shoes.
✉ Edificio Delmar, Loja 5, Rua Direita, 8500-624 Portimão ☎ 282 417 355 🕓 Mon–Sat 10–1, 3–8

Kostas Leather
Hand-crafted sandals and bespoke leather clothing.
✉ Centro Commercial E LeClerc, 8500-000 Portimão ☎ 282 088 555
🕐 Mon–Sat 9–8

PERMANENT MARKETS
Every town of any size has a permanent covered market, which opens every day except Sunday from 6:30am until around 1pm.

Silves
Everything under one roof, including delicious bread baked in a wood-fired oven.
✉ Rua J Estevão ☎ 282 312 531 🕐 Mon–Sat 8–1

STREET MARKETS
Alvor: second Tuesday of the month.
Monchique: second Friday of the month.
Portimão: first Monday of the month (next to the station).
Silves: third Monday of the month.

ACTIVITIES

BOAT TRIPS AND FISHING
MCR Centro Náutico
Offers inshore and offshore fishing opportunities aboard a charter boat from Portimão marina.
✉ Rua Eng José Bovar, 8500 Portimão ☎ 965 140 400

Dolphin Seafaris
Head out to sea to spot these intelligent mammals in the wild (also from Lagos and Alvor).
✉ Portimão marina, Kiosque Dolphin Seafaris, 8500 Portimão ☎ 282 799 209; www.dolphinseafaris.com

CINEMA
Cinemas Castello Lopes
✉ Centro Comercial Modelo, Qunita da Malata, Lote 1, 8500-000 Portimão
☎ 282 418 180

Cinemas Castello Lopes

✉ Centro Comercial Algarve Shopping-Guia, Estrada Nacional 125, 8200-417 Albufeira ☎ 289 560 351

FADO
O Cais

Fado performances on Thursday evenings at 9:30pm.

✉ Rua José Estêvão, 8300-Silves ☎ 282 445 202; www.ocais.net

🕐 Mon–Sat 11am–midnight; Sun 3pm–midnight

OUTDOOR PURSUITS
AlternativTour

Guided hiking, 'rapelling', cycle tours and mountain bike tours in the Algarve hinterland are among the activities this company has to offer.

✉ Sítio das Relvinhas-Apartado 122, 8550-909 Monchique ☎ 282 913 204; www.alternativtour.com

RIVER CRUISES
Arade River Cruise

This is one of many to choose from on the dockside.

✉ Arade Mar, Portimão harbour ☎ 966 143 483

SPA AND BEAUTY TREATMENTS
Vilalara Thalassa Resort

Vilalara offers a comprehensive list of treatments using sea water and other marine products such as sand and seaweed, in addition to extensive beauty treatments (► 61).

✉ Praia das Gaivotas, Alporchinhos, 8400-450 Porches, Lagoa ☎ 282 320 000; www.vilalararesort.com ☎ Daily 9–6

WATER SPORTS
Divers Cove Portugal

Training, certification and accompanied dives.

✉ Quinta do Paraíso, Praia de Carvoeiro, 8400-558 Carvoeiro, Lagoa ☎ 282 356 594; www.diverscove.de

Eastern Central Algarve

Between Albufeira (west) and Faro (east) lie most of the Algarve's big holiday resorts – Vilamoura, Quarteira, Vale do Lobo, Quinta do Lago and Albufeira itself – tempting visitors with their whitewashed villas set around manicured lawns, and huge sandy beaches stretching to the horizon.

Faro

Yet, unless you are staying in one of these resorts, you need never know of their existence: most lie to the south of the main road system, built on poor sandy soils on the marshy fringes of the Algarvian coast. If the fishermen have seen their coast transformed, the rich and fertile inland region has scarcely been changed by tourism at all, and prosperous cities – including the Algarvian capital, Faro, and the second city, Loulé – offer the chance to flow with the mainstream of everyday Portuguese life.

FARO

Visitors arriving at Faro airport could be forgiven for judging the Algarvian capital to be a dusty industrial town with nothing to offer. So it looks from the airport road, with its heavy traffic and jumble of seemingly unplanned tower blocks and light-industrial estates. Yet, at the centre of all this chaos, there is a quiet walled city of great historic character, as well as a lively shopping centre, where cosmopolitan Faroites meet for lunch in the outdoor cafés of the traffic-free streets, or stroll after work in the cool of the evening.

The port is the best area from where to begin a tour of the city. The 18th-century Alfândega (Customs House), with its elegant wrought-iron balcony, is to the north of the port basin, overlooking an obelisk commemorating Ferreira d'Almeida (1847–1910), former naval minister and citizen of Faro. From the adjacent Jardim

Manuel Bivar public gardens it is a short step to the impressive Arco da Vila (Town Gate, with the tourist information centre alongside). This imposing baroque archway, with its stork's nest and statue of St Thomas Aquinas, Faro's patron saint, serves as a stately entrance to the calm streets of the old walled city.

The 13th-century wall that protects the old city was solid enough to survive the 1755 earthquake, but the handsome stone palaces that line the streets, and the beautiful convent buildings of the main square, all date from the latter end of the 18th century. There is a great contrast between the huge cathedral and magnificent bishop's palace, and the more domestic streets to the south and east of the walled city, with their wrought-iron balconies and peeling facades draped with washing.

A few of those nearest to the Arco do Repouso have been converted to chic shops and restaurants. Nearby is a statue of King Afonso III, who in 1249 captured the city from the Moors and expelled them from the Algarve. He is said to have rested here after vanquishing the Moors, hence the name of the gate – the Arco do Repouso (Arch of Repose).

From the intimacy of the walled city, the arch leads out to the huge Largo de São Francisco, a square that is used for carnivals and feast days. Crossing the square, it is a short walk up Rua do Bocage and left into Rua de Portugal to the regional museum, and from there to Rua de Santo António, the shop- and café-lined pedestrian street that leads back to the harbour.

✠ 18G 🚂 Railway station on Avenida da República, at northern end 🚌 Bus terminus is on Avenida da República, by the port ☎ 289 899 760, with services to and from Albufeira, Armação de Pêra, Estói, Lagoa, Loulé, Monte Gordo, Olhão, Portimão, Quarteira, São Brás de Alportel, Tavira, Vilamoura, Vila Real de Santo António

ℹ Rua da Misericórdia 8–12, 8000-269 Faro ☎ 289 803 604

Capela dos Ossos

Best places to see, ► 44–45.

Museu Arqueológico

Faro's archaeological museum is in the Convento da Nossa Senhora da Assunção, whose elegant 16th-century, two-storey cloister survived the earthquake of 1755. The ground floor's collection includes Roman and medieval funerary monuments, Manueline window frames, a Moorish stela inscribed with Arabic characters, and finds from the Roman villa at Milreu (► 50–51). Upstairs the collection includes everything from dress uniforms and heavy Sino-Portuguese rosewood furniture, to art nouveau vases and kitsch ashtrays.

🚩 *Faro 2b* ✉ Largo Dom Afonso III 14, 8000-167 Faro ☎ 289 897 400 🕐 Jun–Sep, Tue–Fri 10–6:30, Sat–Sun 11:30–5:30; Oct–May, Tue–Fri 10–5:30, Sat–Sun 10:30–4:30
👐 Inexpensive

Museu Etnográfico Regional do Algarve

The grainy pictures and displays of saddlery, straw-weaving, salt-panning, net-weaving and lace-making in this museum give a picture of everyday life in the Algarve as it was until the mid-1970s, and still remains in the more remote rural regions. Among the museum's fascinating exhibits are reconstructions of typical village interiors and displays of ornamented chimneypots.

🚩 *Faro 3c* ✉ Praça da Liberdade 2, 8000-164 Faro ☎ 289 827 610
🕐 Mon–Fri 9–12:30, 2–5:30. Closed Sat, Sun and public hols
👐 Inexpensive

Museu Marítimo

Housed in the same building as the harbour authority, this museum contains model ships – from 15th-century caravels to modern naval gunships as well as a collection of colourful shells and models explaining the techniques of the fishing industry. In contrast with today's high-tech factory ships, with sonar devices and sweep nets, the sardine and tuna boats shown here seem charmingly antiquated.

🚩 *Faro 1c* 🖂 Capitania do Porto de Faro, 8000-308 Faro ☎ 289 894 990 🕐 Mon–Fri 2:30–4:30 🎟 Inexpensive

Sé (Cathedral)

Faro's cathedral stands on the site of the main mosque of the Moorish city, which itself replaced the remains of a Visigothic church built on the ruins of the Roman basilica. The 1755 earthquake demolished much of the original 13th-century cathedral, leaving only the truncated stump of the tower. The interior can be deliciously cool on a hot summer day. The Gothic chapel on the south side, with its rib vaults and bosses, survives from the 15th century, and the rest is typically 18th century, with gorgeous gilded woodwork and blue *azulejos*.

✚ *Faro 2b* ✉ Largo da Sé, 8000 Faro ✪ Mon–Fri 10–5:30, Sat 10–1; closed Sun and public hols ✋ Moderate

More to see in Eastern Central Algarve

ALBUFEIRA

Albufeira typifies the way that tourism has transformed the sleepy fishing towns of the Algarvian coast into today's bustling holiday resorts. Until the 1960s, only fishermen used the beach below the town. They still do, bringing in their daily catch every morning, but now they are surrounded by thousands of sun-bronzed bodies.

The narrow cobbled streets of the attractive old town now play host to boutiques, bars and restaurants, and the beach is reached by a tunnel. The streets are paved with black and white mosaics, a traditional form of paving originally invented as a way of using up the rubble from houses demolished by the 1755 earthquake.

However, Albufeira has grown so big that it takes in several adjacent bays, and a more modern centre of tourism has grown up 2km (1.2 miles) to the east centred on 'The Strip', a street lined with English-style pubs, bars and restaurants at Montechoro. To the west of the old town an impressive modern marina with multi-coloured buildings adds a new glamour to the established resort.

The coastline around Albufeira features several good bays where the beach areas have attracted hotel development, including Praia de Galé, 8km (5 miles) west, which offers excellent water-sports facilities.

➕ 8B ✉ 36km (22 miles) west of Faro 🍴 Cafés (€) in Rua 5 de Outubro; O Penedo (€€; ➤ 161) 🚌 Buses from Faro

ℹ Rua 5 de Outubro, 8200-109 Albufeira ☎ 289 585 279

ALMANCIL

Almancil has little traditional character but has grown rapidly in recent years, becoming a service centre for the resorts at Vale do Lobo and Quinta do Lago, and boasting some of the best galleries, shops and restaurants along the Algarve. One outstanding attraction draws visitors here – the church of São Lourenço dos Matos (St Lawrence of the Woods), beside the main N125 road east of the town (just before the start of the Almancil bypass). The interior of this domed, whitewashed church is covered in blue and white *azulejos*, dating from 1730. The gilded altarpiece, typical of those found on the Algarve, is known as *talha dourada*. Just below the church, the **Centro Cultural São Lourenço** displays modern art and hosts jazz and contemporary music concerts.

✚ 17G ✉ 13km (8 miles) northwest of Faro 🕐 Church open Mon 2:30–5, Tue–Sat 10–1, 2:30–5 ✋ Inexpensive 🍴 Café (€) in Centro Cultural

Centro Cultural São Lourenço
✉ Apartado 3079, 8136-901 Almancil ☎ 289 395 475; www.centroculturalsaolourenco.com 🕐 Tue–Sat 10–7

ALTE

Best places to see, ➤ 38–39.

THE BARROCAL

The Barrocal stretches from São Brás de Alportel in the east, across to Silves in the west, down to the N125 highway in the south and up to the Serra do Caldeirão hills in the north. Despite its stony appearance, this region is highly fertile, with deep, rich soils derived from eroded limestone. For centuries, local farmers have been clearing the boulders to create fields bounded by the massive drystone walls that are such a feature of the region. These walls, and the bare fields – known as *terra rossa* (red earth) – are rust red in colour, reflecting the large amounts of iron in the soil.

Once cleared, the fields are ploughed and planted with oranges, almonds, figs, carobs (for animal fodder) and vines.

The Barrocal is sparsely populated and villages are tranquil and unhurried. Wildlife flourishes; in spring or early summer, you will not have to look far to see bulbs and rare orchids in flower, and at night you will hear the sound of owls, bats and foxes.

To visit the Barrocal, take the road from Alte to Benafim Grande, then head south via Alto Fica, following signs for Loulé, or the road that runs further east, from Salir to Loulé and on to São Brás de Alportel.

✚ 16J 🍴 Cafés in Alte and Loulé

BOLIQUEIME

This small settlement, 1km (0.5 miles) north of the N125, seems almost bypassed by tourism. The few visitors who stop here do so because of the novels of Lídia Jorge, one of Portugal's best-known modern writers, born here in 1946. One of her most popular novels, *The Day of the Miracle* (1982), is set in a fictional Algarvian village called Vilamaninhos, loosely based on Boliqueime.

✚ 9C ✉ 12km (7.5 miles) northeast of Albufeira 🍴 Cafés (€) in the main street

ESTÓI

Best places to see, ➤ 48–49.

LOULÉ

Loulé is a city to savour at leisure, arriving early for the market and exploring the attractive streets and historic buildings before lunch. It combines bustling modernity – symbolized by the space-age church prominently sited on the hilltop to the west of the city – with narrow, cobbled alleys where tile- makers, metal-workers and seamstresses carry on age-old craft traditions.

Parking can be a problem, but spaces are often available around Largo de São Francisco. From here, pedestrianized Rua de 5 Outubro leads to Largo Dr Bernardo Lopes, at the foot of Praça da República, the city's main street. The first right turn (Rua de Paio Peres Correia) takes you to the **Museu Arqueológico** (Museum of Archaeology) and tourist office, which are built against the remaining walls of the town's medieval castle. The museum displays flint tools and pottery fragments from the many prehistoric grave sites in the area, as well as a number of Iron-Age stelae (incised grave markers).

Opposite is the Espirito Santo monastery, with its quiet, shady cloister. Part of the monastery has been turned into a Municipal Art Gallery, with exhibitions by contemporary artists. Heading downhill from here, cobbled Rua das Bicas Velhas ('The Street of the Old Spouts') is named after the spring-fed drinking fountains.

To the right of here, Praça Dom Alfonso III takes you outside the ancient city walls for a view back up to the surviving medieval towers, then the modern Rua da Mouraria follows the line of the ancient walls for a short distance until you find the steep alley called Calçada dos Sapateiros (Shoemakers' Alley).

The narrow alley opens out into the square that is dominated by Loulé's Gothic parish church, **São Clemente.** The tower survives from the 12th century,

originally built as the minaret, or prayer tower, of the city's Moorish mosque. Though now hung with bells, and given a short dome and steeple, the minaret is one of the few examples of Arabic architecture to survive in the Algarve. Inside are several splendid side chapels – notably the 16th-century São Brás chapel and the São Crispim chapel. To the west of the church is the palm-shaded Jardim dos Amuados. In the opposite direction, Rua Martim Farto leads to the Municipal Market, a vast Moorish-style building in the city centre. In the market and the surrounding streets are shops and stalls selling everything from animal feed and (sadly) caged songbirds to cheese, dried herbs, olives, honey and fruit. From the colourful market, with its facade decorated with art nouveau tiles, Praça da República runs downhill, back to Rua 5 de Outubro, lined with many cafés.

🚻 17H 🚌 Bus terminus in Rua Nossa Senhora de Fátima, with services to and from Albufeira, Almancil, Alte, Armação de Pêra, Faro, Lagoa, Messines, Portimão and Quarteira

🏢 Avenida 25 Abril 9, 8100-506 Loulé ☎ 289 463 900

Museu Arqueológico

✉ Rua de Paio Peres Correia 17, 8100-564 Loulé ☎ 289 400 624 🕐 Mon–Fri 9–5:30, Sat 10–2 👋 Inexpensive

São Clemente

✉ Largo da Matriz, 8100-549 Loulé 🕐 Sat 9–6, Mon–Fri open for Mass only 9–11 👋 Free

MILREU

Best places to see, ➤ 50–51.

OLHOS D'AGUA

The white-painted concrete hotels, apartments and bars of this fast-growing resort cascade down the hillside to a fine sand town beach making Olhos d'Agua the modern equivalent of the traditional Portuguese fishing village. Though nightlife may be low key, it's an easy journey by car to the bright lights of Albufeira 6km (4 miles) west or Vilamoura 6km (4 miles) east.

✚ 9B ✉ 6km (4 miles) east of Albufeira
🍴 Cafés (€) on the road leading to the beach

PADERNE

Paderne is an attractive village sitting on the western edge of the Barrocal (➤ 146–147). High-walled villas with beautiful cultivated gardens in the hills to the east indicate that this is a favourite retreat for wealthy Algarvians. For visitors, it is not the village that is of interest so much as the castle on its outskirts.

The castle is some way from the village, but is signposted 'Fonte de Paderne + Castelo' as you enter from the west (turn right just before the town cemetery). Another signposted right turn leads past a small municipal campsite before the asphalt road gives way to a dirt track. Leave the car here and walk up to the castle (1km/0.5 miles) or drive with care on the dirt road and park directly by the walls.

The castle's external walls survive to a good height, but it is not possible to explore the interior. Rubble fills the chapel that was built after the castle was conquered in 1249 in a fierce and bloody battle between the Moors and the Christian army of King Afonso III.

The ambience of the site is somewhat spoiled by the traffic noise from the nearby motorway, but you'll have panoramic views of the countryside and you'll probably have the site all to yourself.

✚ 9C ✉ 12km (7.5 miles) north of Albufeira 🕐 Castle open 24 hours
🍴 Cafés (€) near the parish church

QUARTEIRA

One of the first Algarvian resorts to be developed, Quarteira's utilitarian hotel blocks are a million miles away in spirit from the villas of later resorts, which mirror traditional Algarvian architecture in scale and colouring. Despite its lack of charm, however, the town has a long sandy beach and a seafront promenade lined with seafood restaurants and bars. In the old quarter, there is a lively fish and produce market, and the gypsy market, held on Wednesdays, is one of the best and biggest in the region.

➕ 16G ✉ 11km (7 miles) southwest of Loulé 🍽 Cafés (€) on Rua Abertura Mar; Sea Horse (€) Avenida Infante Sagres, Edifício Praiamar, Loja A/B, 8125-160 Quarteira ☎ 289 313 074; Pizzaria Mamma Mia (€) Avenida Infante Sagres 119, 8125-133 Quarteira ☎ 289 314 737 🚌 Bus station on Avenida Sá Carneiro ☎ 289 389 143 with services to and from Albufeira, Loulé and Vilamoura

ℹ Praça do Mar, 8125-156 Quartiera (☎ 289 389 209)

QUERENÇA

A modest, but atmospheric, farming village in the Barrocal region, Querença is a good spot to enjoy a leisurely lunch, with two well-regarded restaurants on the main square. Choose between pavement tables with views of the pretty, onion-domed tower of the parish church, or interior views stretching for miles over the Barrocal countryside.

As well as its carved and gilded baroque altar surrounds, the parish church has a small collection of painted wood statues dating from the 16th and 17th centuries.

🚩 17J ✉ 9km (5.5 miles) north of Loulé 🍽 Restaurante de Querença (€€; ➤ 163)

ROCHA DA PENA

The clifflike Rocha da Pena is a wall of limestone rising to a height of 479m (1,571ft) in the north of the Barrocal (➤ 146–147). The site is now classified because of its diversity of flora and fauna – information plaques offer drawings of birds of prey and small mammals but the text is only in Portuguese – and a 5km (3-mile) circuit has been well marked out, starting from the Bar das Grutas in the tiny settlement of Rocha (reached by car along a dirt road off the Penina/Pena road, or from east of Salir on a poor asphalt track).

✚ 16K ✉ 9km (95.5 miles) east of Alte 🍴 Bar das Grutas (€)

SALIR

Salir's huge 12th-century castle survives in the form of a cobbled rampart walk, which passes some huge bastions of concreted rubble, all that remains after villagers robbed the walls of their facing masonry in the past. From the western stretch of the ramparts there is a good view over the hillside olive groves and the patchwork of cultivated fields in the valley below to the Rocha da Pena.

The castle is one of the few Moorish structures to survive in the Algarve, and its scale is illustrated by the number of more recent houses that now fill the interior. Though heavily defended, the castle fell to Christian forces in 1249, towards the end of the campaign to drive the Moors from Portugal. The parish church occupies a high platform (shared with a huge water tower) with fine views over the Barrocal countryside. Inside, there is an unusual Last Judgement scene on the north wall.

✚ 17J ✉ 14km (9 miles) north of Loulé 🍴 Casa de Pasto Mouro Bar (€), Rua dos Muros do Castelo, 8100-202 Salir

VALE DO LOBO

Vale do Lobo ('Valley of the Wolves') is an attractive, luxurious holiday resort built among the dunes west of Faro and attractively landscaped with umbrella pines, lakes and manicured lawns. The developers have been careful to use traditional materials in the construction of the low-rise villas with whitewashed walls and orange roof tiles.

The sandy beaches of Vale do Lobo and nearby Vale do Garrão (also known as Paradise Beach) are lined with bars and fish restaurants, and there are watersports facilities here and at nearby Quinta do Lago. A great part of Vale do Lobo's appeal, however, is its proximity to some outstanding golf courses (➤ 76–77). There are many organizations offering cycling, horse-back riding and walking trips into the adjacent Parque Natural da Ria Formosa (➤ 52–53).

✚ 16G ✉ 12km (7.5 miles) south of Loulé 🍴 Several bars and restaurants (€–€€€) in Rua da República; good restaurants (€€–€€€) on the road between Vale do Lobo and Almancil

VILAMOURA

The purpose-built resort of Vilamoura has, as its focal point, a large marina ringed by shops, bars and restaurants. From here it is a short walk to the sandy beach, and there are further beaches nearby at Falésia. The region benefits from excellent golf courses, tennis centres, fitness centres, horse-riding schools and watersports facilities, all within walking distance. Though the current resort

dates back only to the 1970s, the site has a surprisingly interesting history.

The **Cerro da Vila Museu e Estação Arqueológica,** north of the waterfront, is a new archaeological park created at the site of a Roman settlement and later Moorish farm. Remains include the floor plan of a Roman villa, complete with bathhouse.

➕ 16H 🖂 11km (7 miles) southwest of Loulé 🍽 Restaurants (€–€€€) around the marina 🚌 From Faro and Quarteira

Cerro da Vila Museu e Estação Arqueológica
🖂 Avenida Cerro da Vila, 8125-403 Vilamoura, Loulé ☎ 289 312 153 ⏰ Nov–Apr daily 9:30–12:30, 2–6; May–Oct daily 10–1, 4–9 ✋ Moderate

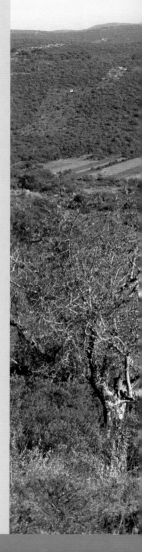

a drive around the central highlights

This drive takes in farming hamlets, river valleys, gnarled olive trees and scented orange groves. Consider stopping for a leisurely lunch in Alte or Querença.

From Loulé, head out west on the N270 road signposted to Boliqueime (➤ 147).

As you leave the town, a wide new road to the left leads up to the unusual modern church of Nossa Senhora da Piedade. It is worth driving up for the views from the terrace in front of the church and for the little 16th-century chapel alongside.

Continue to Boliqueime; take the road north (signed Lisbon) to Paderne (➤ 150–151).

Take the road north out of the town and go left to explore the well-preserved 12th-century castle above the River Quarteira.

Drive on through the village of Purgatório, continue to Portela de

Messines, then turn right for Alte.

Alte (➤ 38–39) is the Algarve's most attractive village. The church was built in the 13th century by the local overlord as a thankyou offering for his safe return from the Crusades, and has some fine statuary and tile-work. The river tumbles through the village, over a mini waterfall and past converted mill buildings. Continue eastwards, stopping to scale Rocha da Pena, if time allows, or to explore Salir castle (➤ 154–155).

From Salir take the road south to Vicentes, and turn left. After 2km (1.2 miles), the road crosses a bridge, turns sharp left in front of a mill, and then sharp right. Continue to Querença, then to the main road and turn right to return to Loulé.

Distance 74km (46 miles)
Time 7 hours
Start/end point Loulé ✚ 17H
Lunch Fonte Pequena restaurant/bar (€; ➤ 162)

HOTELS

ALBUFEIRA
Hotel Baltum (€)
A perfect budget location for sunbathing and partying, this no-frills hotel is 50m (55yds) from both the famed town beach and the restaurants and bars.

✉ 26 Avenida 25 Abril 26, 8200-014 Albufeira ☎ 289 589 102; www.hotelbaltum.com

Vila Joya (€€€)
Considered one of the most exclusive hotels in the Algarve and priced accordingly, each room is individually styled and equipped to a high standard. The hotel has the only two-star Michelin restaurant in Portugal.

✉ Praia da Galé, Apartado 120, 8201-902 Guia Albufeira ☎ 289 591 795; www.vilajoya.com

ALTE
Alte Hotel (€)
Many of the people who come here are walkers, taking advantage of the village's central location to explore the fascinating Barrocal countryside, with its limestone caves, cliffs and valleys and unspoiled Portuguese way of life. Rooms are simple but comfortable, and facilities include tennis courts and a swimming pool, plus a restaurant specializing in fresh fish, game and rural Portuguese dishes such as pigs' trotters.

✉ Estrada de Sta Margarida, Montino, Alte, 8100-012 Alte, Loulé ☎ 289 478 523; www.altehotel.com

LOULÉ
Loulé Jardim Hotel (€)
This renovated, early 20th-century town mansion makes an excellent inland base. Rooms are simply furnished but the roof terrace has a pool and bar (summer only).

✉ Praça Manuel de Arriaga, 8100-665 Loulé ☎ 289 413 094; www.loulejardimhotel.com

VALE DO LOBO
Le Meridien Dona Filipa (€€€)

Part of the manicured and prestigious Vale do Lobo estate, the Dona Filipa enjoys a privileged position beside the Atlantic, close to the beach and surrounded by golf courses – guests enjoy discounted green fees and an early start at the São Lourenço Club, rated one of the best in Europe. There are three floodlit tennis courts and a heated outdoor swimming pool to enjoy, as well as the tranquillity of this relatively small, elegant hotel. The two restaurants pride themselves on their wine lists.

✉ Vale do Lobo, 8135-901 Almancil ☎ 289 357 200; www.lemeridien.com

VILAMOURA
The Lake Resort (€€€)

Set in central Vilamoura, this luxury resort lies between the beach and the marina. Rooms are spacious and decorated in relaxing tones. The Blue and Green Spas offer a wide choice of hydrotherapy and massage treatments (➤ 60).

✉ Praia da Falésia, Apartado 811, 8126-910 Vilamoura ☎ 289 320 700; www.thelakeresort.com

RESTAURANTS

ALBUFEIRA
O Penedo (€€)

Delicious garlic clams are the speciality of this popular clifftop restaurant.

✉ Rua Latino Coelho 15, 8200-150 Albufeira ☎ 289 587 429 ⚙ Lunch, dinner; closed Wed

ALMANCIL
Casa de Portuguesa (€€)

One of the prettiest restaurants on the Algarve, with an interior of stucco and *azulejos*. Family-friendly and serving excellent local cuisine.

✉ Vale Formosa, Almancil, 8100-267 Loulé, (on the road to Areeiro) ☎ 289 393 301 ⚙ Lunch, dinner; closed Mon

Fuzio's (€€€)

An extensive selection of Italian cuisine in this beautifully renovated Portuguese house.

✉ Rua do Comércia 286, 8135-127 Almancil ☎ 289 399 019 🕓 Dinner; closed Wed

São Gabriel (€€€)

One of a cluster of fine restaurants in the Almancil area, São Gabriel has earned a Michelin star. Book ahead.

✉ Estrada Vale do Lobo, Quinta do Lago, 8135 Almancil ☎ 289 394 521; www.saogabriel.com 🕓 Dinner; closed Mon

ALTE
Fonte Pequena Restaurant/Bar (€)

Large restaurant with wood-panelled dining room and terraces overlooking the stream and springs. There is a log fire in winter. The menu includes hearty meat dishes and a range of snacks.

✉ Fonte Pequena, Estrada da Fonte, 8100-012 Alte ☎ 289 478 509; www.restaurantefontepequena.com 🕓 Lunch Tue–Sun, Wed dinner also

FARO
Aliança (€)

The food is unexciting at this traditional Portuguese café, one of the oldest in the country, but people come for the ambience of the dimly lit, wood-panelled 1920s interior, and to sit where statesmen and philosophers, including Simone de Beauvoir, once sat.

✉ Praça Francisco Gomes 6, 8000-306 Faro ☎ 289 801 621 🕓 Breakfast, lunch, dinner

LOULÉ
Avenida Velha (€€)

This distinguished old restaurant is famous for its home-made bread, and small savoury dishes, similar to Spanish *tapas*.

✉ Avenida José da Costa Mealha 40, first floor, 8100-501 Loulé ☎ 289 416 474 🕓 Lunch, dinner; closed Sun lunch

QUERENÇA
Restaurante de Querença (€€)
While away the long siesta hours in this restaurant, in the main square of a tiny hilltop village, or enjoy a dinner with accordion music at the weekend. Rabbit and wild boar appear on the menu, as well as fish kebabs and lamb dishes. Book at weekends.

✉ Largo da Igreja, 8100-129 Querença ☎ 289 422 540 🕐 Lunch, dinner; closed Wed

VALE DO LOBO
La Crêperie (€)
A perfect place for a light lunch or snack, just off the beach. Salads, wraps, sandwiches, crêpes and more.

✉ Vale do Lobo Praça, 8135 Almancil ☎ 289 353 429 🕐 Breakfast, lunch, dinner

SHOPPING

ANTIQUES
Seculo XIX
Interesting shop with cut glass, jewellery and china.

✉ Marina Plaza shop 32, 8125 Vilamoura ☎ 289 312 502 🕐 Summer 10–8; rest of year 10–1, 3–8

ARTESANATO
Café Regional
Café that doubles as a shop selling attractive hand-painted plates and basketry.

✉ Largo José Cavaco Vieira, 8100-012 Alte (just south of parish church, in Alte's main square) ☎ 289 478 105 🕐 Daily 9–8

Centro de Artesanato
Perhaps the best display in the Algarve: more unusual items include ornaments made from palm leaves and wood caravels.

✉ Rua da Barbacã 11–13, 8100-546 Loulé ☎ 289 412 190 🕐 Mon–Sat 9:30–7 (Nov–Apr 9:30–2 on Sat)

Galerias Ivette

Painted plates and realistic silk flowers are among the best buys in a huge shop full of every kind of souvenir.

✉ Largo da Igreja 6, 8100-012 Loulé ☎ 289 478 122 🕔 Daily 9–1, 3–7

O Pipote

Tiny shop selling quality ceramics, basketry and embroidery.

✉ Rua Joaquim Manuel Gouveia 15, 8200-000 Albufeira ☎ 289 513 814
🕔 Summer daily 10–8; rest of year Mon–Sat 10–1, 3–8

ACTIVITIES

BOAT TRIPS
Polvo

Offers boat trips from luxury motor yachts and small boat charter to dolphin-spotting excursions.

✉ Vilamoura Marina, 8125-409 Quarteira ☎ 289 301 884; www.marina-sports.com

CINEMAS
Algarve Shopping

✉ Estrada Nacional 125, 8200-417 Albufeira ☎ 289 560 351

Forum Algarve

✉ Estrada Nacional 125, Sitio das Figuras, 8000-800 Faro ☎ 282 887 210

OUTDOOR PURSUITS
Mega Sport

In addition to hiring out a full range of bicycles, Mega Sport can supply child trailers and seats. It can also provide guides.

✉ Estrada Nacional 125, Km89, Quatro Estradas, 8100-321 Loulé ☎ 289 393 044; www.megasport.pt 🕔 Daily 9–1, 3–7

Zebra

This well-established company offers adventure activities and guided day-trips exploring the lesser-known Algarve countryside.

✉ Edifício Arcadas de São João loja 10, 8201-911 Albufeira ☎ 289 583 300; www.zebraincentives-portugal.com

Eastern Algarve

Away from the coast, the countryside consists of a great, rolling succession of hills, covered in wild Mediterranean scrub, interspersed with cork oak trees. In the future, dense forests will make this landscape look very different.

The homogeneity of the central hilly region contrasts with the pleasing variety of the region's coastal and riverine scenery. The broad, flat valley of the River Guadiana, with its bird-filled shores and reed beds, is endlessly fascinating, and the town of Vila Real offers a gateway to the very different Spanish region of Andalucia. The coastal towns include the port of Olhão, the city of Tavira and the resort of Monte Gordo, with its glorious beach and holiday atmosphere.

TAVIRA

This distinctive town has a greater variety of architectural detail than most. Both banks of the River Gilão, which passes through the centre, are lined by noble houses with baroque window frames and balustraded parapets. Most have wrought-iron balconies, whose decoration is mirrored in the railings of the pedestrian bridge that links the two sides of the town. The hip-gabled roofs are highly distinctive, known as *tesouro* (treasure) roofs.

Wealth from the Portuguese colonies was lavished on Tavira's numerous churches, whose turrets and belfries add further interest to the skyline. The best place to view all this architectural diversity is from the walls of the castle (➤ opposite) on the south bank of the river. Cross the footbridge, take the first turn right, climbing uphill, past the tourist office, and pause to admire the

superb Renaissance doorcase to the
Church of Nossa Senhora da Misericórdia
(Our Lady of Mercy). Above the portal,
angels hold aside curtains to reveal the
figure of the praying Virgin. Turning left
takes you to the castle, and to the hilltop
church of Santa Maria do Castelo (➤ 168).

Heading north from the castle, turn
down Rua Detraz dos Muros to Rua dos
Pelames; this riverside street has some
rare 16th-century houses, distinguished by stone doorcases
which survived the 1755 earthquake. Crossing the footbridge
again takes you down Rua 5 de Outubro to São Paulo church
(➤ 168–169). Restaurants and bars line the square in front of the
church (Praça Dr Padinha), and the streets running to the south
and east. Look out for the latticed doors, made
of turned and woven strips of wood.

➕ 21H 🚇 Railway station is in Rua da Liberdade
🚌 Bus terminus is in Rua dos Pelames ☎ 281 322 546,
with services to and from Cabanas, Cacela, Faro, Monte
Gordo, Olhão, Pedras d'El Rei, Santa Luzia and Vila Real
de Santo António
ℹ️ Rua da Galeria 9, 8800-329 Tavira ☎ 281 322 511

Castelo

Tavira's Moorish castle was rebuilt after the
Christian Reconquest, and the present walls
date from the reign of King Dinis (1261–1325).
From the rampart walk there are superb views
over Tavira's ornate chimneys, rooftops and
church towers, and to the few short stretches of
the town's medieval walls that survived the
1755 earthquake.
✉️ Calçada de Paio Peres Correia ⏰ Daily 9–5 ✋ Free

Igreja de Santa Maria do Castelo

Standing alongside the castle, Tavira's parish church incorporates
the minaret of the town's Moorish mosque, remodelled to form
the clock tower. Inside are the fine 13th-century tombs of seven
knights of the crusading Order of St James, whose ambush and
murder prompted the Christian reconquest of the city. In addition
to the fine tilework and gilded altar surrounds, the sacristy has a
small museum displaying vestments and chalices.

✉ Calçada de Paio Peres Correia, Alto de Santa Maria, 8800 Tavira
🕐 Mon–Fri 9:30–12:30, 2–5:30, Sat–Sun times vary. Closed public hols
✋ Inexpensive

Igreja de São Paulo

Entered through a classical portico, more like a Greek temple than
a church, St Paul's is unusual for the heavy, dark woodwork of its
two side altars, ornately carved but not covered in gold. The fine

collection of religious statues includes a delicate 15th-century
Flemish *Virgin*.

✉ Praça Dr António Padinha, 8800-637 Tavira 🕓 Mon–Fri 9:30–12:30,
2–5:30, weekend times not fixed. Closed public hols. Note times can vary
✋ Free

Ilha de Tavira

This 10km-long (6-mile) island, with its sandy beaches and
sheltered bathing, is the most accessible of the barrier islands in
the Parque Natural da Ria Formosa (► 52–53). Ferries make the
short crossing from the Quatro Águas jetty, on the south bank
of the River Gilão. You can also walk to the island across the
footbridge from Santa Luzia, the seafront fishing village 3km
(2 miles) west of Tavira.

✉ Just offshore from Tavira 🕓 Ferries run daily 8am–10pm, May–Oct,
weather permitting ✋ Free 🍴 Cafes (€) at northeastern tip of island

More to see in Eastern Algarve

ALCOUTIM

Alcoutim has the atmosphere of a timeless town. Life here
moves at the pace of the horse-drawn ploughs that are still
used to till the surrounding fields. Ferrymen frequent the
O Soeiro café, just above the quay, and take passengers
across the river to Sanlúcar in Spain on request. There are
no border controls, so it is easy to slip across the river.

Both towns are dominated by their castle. Sanlúcar's is the
biggest – crowning the cone-shaped hill above the town – but
Alcoutim's is the oldest. The excavated remains of Roman
structures have been overlain by 11th-century Moorish remains,
in turn superseded by a 1304 fortress.

Besides Alcoutim's castle, the other good viewpoint in town
is the Ermida de Nossa Senhora da Conceição (Hermitage of
Our Lady of Conception). This whitewashed church, approached
via an 18th-century stone staircase, stands at the highest point
in the village and allows intimate views into the village gardens
and across the flat rooftops of the simple, cube-shaped houses.

➕ 23M ✉ 40km (25 miles) north of Vila Real de Santo António
🍴 O Soeiro café (€), Rua do Munícipio 4, 8970-066 Alcoutim ☎ 281 546
241 🕓 Mon–Fri
ℹ Rua 1º de Maio ☎ 281 546 179

BARRANCO DO VELHO

In the empty hills of the Serra da Caldeirão, Barranco do Velho is
one of the few settlements of any size, at a crossroads in an
elevated spot. Visitors come to refresh themselves at the cafés
lining the main street before heading on towards Lisbon or
south to the coast. The village is also popular with walkers and
mountain bikers, who follow the broad woodland tracks that
thread through the surrounding cork oak forests.

➕ 18J ✉ 32km (20 miles) north of Faro 🍴 Several cafés (€) on the main
street, including A Tia Bia (€€; ➤ 185)

CABANAS

Cabanas is a low-key resort just to the east of
Tavira. It has a broad, sandy beach facing a long
sandbank, with a warm and shallow lagoon
providing sheltered bathing conditions that attract
families with children.

A 5km (3-mile) stroll along the beach leads to
the fortified village of Cacela Velha, a tiny hamlet
consisting of a church and a few cottages
surrounded by massive walls. The perfectly
preserved fortress dates from the Peninsular War
of 1808–14, when Napoleonic troops invaded
Portugal. Cacela Velha can also be reached by car
signposted off the N125. Park on the approach
road as there is no room in the village itself.

✚ 21H ✉ 5km (3 miles) east of Tavira 🍴 Café (€) in
Cacela Velha 🚌 Buses from Tavira

CASTRO MARIM

At Castro Marim there are two huge castles
to explore, spreading across the two hills
that rise above the salt flats either side of
this fishing town.

The main castle, to the north of the
town, was built in 1319 as the headquarters
of the crusading Order of the Knights of
Christ, founded in 1119 as the Knights
Templar. The knights played a decisive role
in the Christian reconquest of Portugal. The
older medieval castle is now entirely
contained within the walls of its 17th-century successor, which is
six times larger.

A rampart walk allows visitors to walk all the way round
the castle, with great views down to the river and over the

fishermen's houses below, built with flat roofs for drying fish. Also within the castle walls are the offices of the Castro Marim Nature Reserve, from where walk leaflets are available.

The **São Sebastião fortress,** on the opposite hill, dates from the 17th century and is part of a much bigger complex of defensive walls that survive only in parts around the town. Like its medieval counterpart, the fortress served as a base from where to defend the entrance to the River Guadiana, bearing the brunt of hostilities between Portugal and Spain. Today, the two countries have abolished their common border and the modern suspension bridge, which crosses the river, carries the IP1 motorway, 2km (1.2 miles) northeast of the town.

🚆 23J 🖂 4km (2.5 miles) north of Vila Real de Santo António 🍴 Cafés (€) in Rua de São Sebastião 🚌 Buses from Vila Real de Santo António

ℹ️ Rua José Afonso Moreira 2–4, 8950-138 Castro Marim ☎ 281 531 232

Castelo and São Sebastiao fortress

🕐 Daily 9–5 🤚 Free

a drive around the eastern highlights

Explore the empty hills of the Serra do Caldeirão, with their abandoned windmills and scattered cork oaks, then follow the scenic Guadiana River.

From Tavira, head north on the N397 for 41km (26 miles) to Cachopo.

The countryside consists largely of shallow, acidic schistic soils that are not very fertile, though cork oaks thrive. In between the forests are hills covered in wild cistus and holly oak. Cachopo produces sheep's milk cheese and sweet, air-cured mountain hams.

Continue north on the N124 for 16km (10 miles) to Martimlongo, then south on the N506 for 7.5km (4.5 miles) to Vaqueiros.

Just north of Vaqueiros, visit the Cova dos Mouros mine, which was worked from the Copper Age (3500BC) onwards and is now an industrial museum (➤ 176–177).

Continue south, then turn left (east), signposted Melhedes/Soudes and

continue for 18km (11 miles) to the junction with the N122; head left (north) for 13km (8 miles) to the junction with the N124, then right (east) on the N124 for 6km (4 miles) to Alcoutim.

Stop for lunch in Alcoutim (➤ 170), then explore the castle.

Head south on the road that follows the River Guadiana.

In Guerreiros do Rio, visit the former school, now a small river museum. Further on look out for the Roman ruins lying by the roadside just as you enter Montinho das Laranjeiras, immediately before the bridge; the remains consist of a villa and an early Christian church, with apse and stone-lined graves.

When the river road meets the N122, turn left (south) and continue for 8km (5 miles) to Azinhal, noted for its lacework. Approaching Castro Marim (➤ 172–173), there are views to the left of the suspension bridge carrying the IP1 motorway across the River Guadiana to Seville. Join the motorway here and head west back to Tavira.

Distance 160km (100 miles)
Time 1 day
Start/end point Tavira ✚ 21H
Lunch O Soeiro (€) ✉ Rua do Município 4, 8970-066 Alcoutim ☎ 281 546 241 ◉ Mon–Fri

COVA DOS MOUROS PARQUE MINEIRO

The open-air mining park at Cova dos Mouros is on the N506 road as you drive south from Martimlongo, to Vaqueiros. Set in the empty, scrub-covered hills of the northeastern Algarve, this museum has been created around the spoil tips and shafts of an abandoned copper mine that has been in use for more than 5,000 years. The workings were rediscovered in 1865 and have since been developed into this unusual attraction – now designated an ecological park. The park centres on the reconstruction of a Chalcolithic village (2,500BC), which re-creates the lifestyle of the very first miners. Staff, dressed in animal skins, work the ground with copies of ancient tools.

After you have learned about the mining activities, Cova dos Mouros offers other ways to spend a pleasant few hours. The park is one of several across Spain and Portugal that works for the survival of the Iberian donkey. Once so numerous as beasts of burden, these gentle, hardy creatures have now almost disappeared throughout the peninsula. Children will enjoy the rides they give across the surrounding countryside.

If you prefer to use your own energy, there are posted walks where you can take in the upland flora and fauna. In spring copious wild flowers, including rare orchids, blanket the ground, and even in the height of summer butterflies and lizards provide interest as you stroll. Finally, you can enjoy a cooling dip in the natural pools of the Foupana River and you may catch a glimpse of a family of otters.

Note: The park is temporarily closed for renovation. Reopening may be delayed until 2009. Visitors should call first to confirm opening times.

➕ 20L ✉ 10km (6 miles) southeast of Martimlongo ☎ 289 999 229; www.minacovamouros.sitepac.pt ⏰ 2 Mar–Oct Tue–Sun 10:30–6; Nov–13

Dec Tue–Sun 10:30–4:30; 15 Jan–1 Mar Tue–Sun 10:30–4:30. Closed 14 Dec–14 Jan ✋ Expensive 🍴 Café on site

LUZ DA TAVIRA

Not to be confused with Luz in Western Algarve (➤ 93), Luz da Tavira has one of the few churches in the Algarve to survive the 1755 earthquake. Dating from the 16th century, it is dedicated to Nossa Senhora da Luz (Our Lady of Light), whose statue fills the niche above the large, Renaissance-style porch. To the side is another porch with the stone-rope mouldings typical of the Manueline style of the early 16th century, inspired by nautical themes. The altar surround is 16th century, as are the polychromatic *azulejos* on the steps and pavement.

The houses in Luz are worth a second glance: many have the distinctive traditional *platibanda* borders. Surrounding the doors and window frames, and sometimes running along the eaves and down the house corners, these ornate plasterwork bands are decorated with floral and geometrical motifs, often picked out in a colour that contrasts with that of the exterior walls. The chimneys are unusual, too: their filigree patterns reflect the art nouveau style popular in the early 20th century, when many of these houses were built.

➕ 20G ✉ 7km (4 miles) west of Tavira 🍴 Cafés (€) in the main street in nearby Tavira

MONCARAPACHO

This small, roadside town would be of little interest to visitors had not the local parish priest (who died in 1996) built up a remarkable small **museum** alongside the baroque Santo Cristo chapel (follow signs to 'Museu'). It is filled with a collection of curiosities that offer a profile of the history and archaeology of the whole region: there are coins, stones from an old olive press, shackles once used to imprison African slaves, Napoleonic cannon balls, and clay scoops from Moorish-style water wheels. Among the Roman masonry, there are soldier's tombstones and a milestone that once stood alongside the main road from Faro to Seville.

Upstairs, pride of place goes to a beautiful, 18th-century Neopolitan crib scene, with lively figures of shepherds and kings, made from wood and porcelain. Alongside the museum, the tiny 16th-century chapel is covered in 17th-century *azulejos*.

The main church in the town has an exceptional Renaissance facade carved with the Annunciation, St Peter and St Paul, and scenes from the Passion of Christ. Animated hunchbacked figures torment Christ as helmeted soldiers prepare to scourge him. The perfectly preserved Renaissance interior has classical columns, painted with swirling red and blue acanthus-leaf patterns.

🚩 19G ✉ 8km (5 miles) northeast of Olhão 🍴 Cafés (€) around the main square 🚌 Buses from Olhão

Museu

🕐 Mon–Fri 11–4 ☎ No phone. Call Junta de Freguesia (Town Hall) for information, 289 792 158 ✋ Moderate

MONTE GORDO

Separated from the beach by a wide, café-lined avenue, the hotels of Monte Gordo look down on one of the Algarve's finest beaches – a vast sweep of golden sand. Numerous seasonal seafood restaurants and cafés, housed in makeshift timber cabins, sit along the sands, offering fresh fish provided by the local fishermen.

With its warm waters, gentle offshore breezes and endless sands, Monte Gordo is a popular place for novice windsurfers to take their first tentative lessons, and there are plenty of beachside businesses offering watersports equipment and tuition. The nightlife is very lively and cosmopolitan, with folk dance evenings, a casino and all-night discos. Spain is a short drive away across the road bridge that crosses the River Guadiana, and local tour agents offer day-trips to Seville, about two hours' drive to the east.

✚ 23H ✉ 5km (3 miles) southwest of Vila Real de Santo António

🍴 Cafés (€) along Avenida Infante Dom Henrique 🚌 Buses from Vila Real de Santo António

ℹ️ Avenida Marginal, 8900 Monte Gordo ☎ 281 544 495

OLHÃO

Olhão is, along with Portimão, the biggest of the Algarve's fishing ports. The fish market along the seafront, with its patterned brick walls and corner turrets, has been modernized to meet EU health regulations, but has lost none of its vital character. Equally colourful is the fruit and vegetable market, its stalls piled high with dried figs, almonds, honey, herbs and local cheeses, as well as fresh fruits.

Across the seafront promenade Olhão has some of the Algarve's most attractive buildings. One fine group of buildings lines the same square that houses the tourist information centre, one block from the seafront, and there are more in the streets radiating north – look above the shop facades in the main commercial streets to take in the detail. A maze of cobbled pedestrian-only streets leads to the town's main church, Igreja Matriz, with its marvellously baroque facade. Inside, life-size angels flank the splendid, gilded altar. Behind the church, the **Museu da Cidade** holds temporary exhibitions and there is a small gallery displaying prehistoric and Roman finds.

✚ 19G ✉ 8km (5 miles) east of Faro 🍴 Cafés (€) near the market 🚌 Bus station on Avenida General Humberto Delgado ☎ 289 702 157. Buses to Cacela, Faro, Fuzeta, Moncarapacho, Monte Gordo, Tavira, Vila Real de Santo António

🛈 Largo Sebastião Martins Mestre 8A, 8700-349 Olhão ☎ 289 713 936

Museu da Cidade

✉ Edifício do Compromisso Marítimo, Largo da Restauração, 8700-350 Olhão
☎ 289 700 184 🕐 Tue–Fri 10–12:30, 2–5:30, Sat 10–1; closed Sun–Mon
🎫 Inexpensive

PARQUE NATURAL DA RIA FORMOSA

Best places to see, ➤ 52–53.

SÃO BRÁS DE ALPORTEL

São Brás lies sandwiched between the scenic Serra da Monte Figo region and the Serra do Caldeirão to the north. The area is renowned for its almond orchards. A good spot from where to view the fertile countryside is the tombstone-flagged terrace of the largely rebuilt 15th-century church, Igreja Matriz, which contains lively 18th-century paintings and statues of the Archangel Gabriel and St Euphemia. East of the church, the building that once served as the summer palace of the Bishops of Faro is fronted by an attractive domed pavilion, which shelters the eight-spouted Episcopal Fountain.

The Museu Etnográfico do Traje Algarvio (Algarvian Ethno-graphic Costume Museum) is in the former home of a wealthy 19th-century cork merchant. There are displays of clothing, furniture and domestic objects, and the farm buildings alongside house a collection of agricultural implements and old vehicles.

🚪 18H ✉ 13km (8 miles) east of Loulé 🍴 Cafés (€) around Largo do Igreja and Largo da Mercado 🚌 Buses from Faro

ℹ Largo São Sebastião 23, 8150-107 São Brás de Alportel ☎ 289 843 165

VILA REAL DE SANTO ANTÓNIO

Vila Real was founded by Royal Charter in 1773 and represents the town planning ideals of the Marquês de Pombal (1699–1782), Portugal's chief minister under King José I (1714–77). It was the Marquês, virtually exercising absolute power, who expelled the Jesuits from Portugal and swept away many church-based institutions. He planned this city to represent the rational ideals of the Enlightenment, in contrast to the Spanish city of Ayamonte on the opposite bank of the River Guadiana.

Ayamonte has prospered, as shown by its gleaming white tower blocks and modern port facilities, while charming Vila Real remains in a time warp. Vila Real's riverside embankment is lined by grand hotels and scores of restaurants and shops catering for the Spanish bargain hunters who come here to buy household goods.

One block inland from the river embankment, the legacy of the Marquês de Pombal is evident in the strict grid of streets and the geometrical precision of the elegant main square, Praça Marquês de Pombal, with its church, town hall and former infantry barracks.

In the centre of the square, the obelisk monument to King José I acts like the needle of a giant sundial, casting its shadow on the traditional black and white mosaic paving.

In 1991, a suspension bridge opened across the River Guadiana, linking Portugal to Spain, but the river ferry continues to do a brisk trade, plying the river at roughly half-hourly intervals, from 9 until 9. You do not need a passport to visit **Ayamonte** (Spain and Portugal have abolished their common borders) and this is a good way of seeing the different cultures. Don't forget that Spain is an hour ahead of Portugal, and that almost everything shuts for the siesta during the afternoon, from 1 to 4 (2–5 Spanish time).

By contrast with the monochrome Pombeline style of Vila Real, Ayamonte seems the more colourful town of the two, with its flower-filled streets and its lavishly tiled facades. It is also a town with many art galleries and studios displaying the work of contemporary artists, attracted by the lucid air and bold colours of the Costa del Luz (Coast of Light).

Ayamonte does not have the monopoly on modern art, however. Back in Vila Real, the Centro Cultural António Aleixo contains the **Museu Manuel Cabanas** with works by this renowned local painter and engraver, whose woodcuts of Algarvian life in the 1950s are fascinating.

✚ 23J ✉ At eastern edge of Algarve, 23km (14 miles) east of Tavira
🍴 Cafés (€) in Praça Marquês de Pombal and pedestrian streets north of the square 🚌 Bus station on Avenida da República ☎ 281 511 807 with services to and from Altura, Cacela, Castro Marim, Faro, Manta Rota, Monte Gordo, Olhão and Tavira

Ayamonte

✚ 23J ✉ In Spain, on opposite bank of River Guadiana to Vila Real
🍴 Cafés (€) and restaurants (€) in Plaza de la Coronación

Museu Manuel Cabanas

✉ Rua Dr Teófilo Braga 38, 8900-303 Vila Real de Santo António ☎ 281 510 049 🕐 Jul–Aug Mon–Fri 4–midnight, Sat–Sun 8–midnight; Sep–Jun 10–1, 3–7 🎫 Free

HOTELS

MONTE GORDO
Vasco da Gama (€–€€)

This modern three-star hotel is spotlessly clean. It has direct access to Monte Gordo's spectacular beach.

✉ Avenida Infante Dom Henrique, 8900-412 Monte Gordo ☎ 281 510 900; www.vascodagamahotel.com

SÃO BRÁS DE ALPORTEL
Pousada São Brás (€–€€)

Set in the peaceful foothills of São Brás de Alportel, this hotel is part of Portugal's *pousada* chain. The facilities include a swimming pool and tennis court.

✉ 8150-054 São Brás de Alportel ☎ 289 842 305; www.pousadas.pt

TAVIRA
Pousada de Tavira (€€–€€€)

Founded in the 16th century as a convent for the Cloistered Augustinian nuns, this sumptuous *pousada* still boasts fantastic architectural features.

✉ Rua Dom Paio Peres Correia, 8800-407 Tavira ☎ 281 329 040; www.pousadas.pt

VILA REAL DE SANTO ANTÓNIO
Hotel Guadiana (€)

This 1920s hotel with grand facade has period features and comfortable, though dated, accommodation. Its central location is ideal.

✉ Avenida da República 94, 8900-206 Vila Real de Santo António ☎ 281 511 482; www.hotelguadiana.com

RESTAURANTS

ALCOUTIM
Alcatiã (€€)

This simple eatery has great views across the river to Spain and serves hearty mountain meat dishes and freshwater fish.

✉ Bairro do Rossio, Mercado Municipal, 8970-052 Alcoutim ☎ 281 546 606
🕒 Lunch, dinner; closed Sun dinner and Mon

BARRANCO DO VELHO
A Tia Bia (€€)
Specializing in game dishes, wild boar is often on the menu, as well as partridge with cabbage, and pumpkin with rabbit.

✉ Barranco do Velho, 8100-159 Salir, Faro ☎ 289 846 425 🕓 Lunch, dinner

MONTE GORDO
Dourado (€€)
One of a group of timber shacks on the beach serving *cataplana* (fish stew), other traditional Portuguese dishes and pizzas.

✉ Avenida Infante Dom Henrique 9–10, 8900-412 Monte Gordo ☎ 281 512 202 🕓 Lunch, dinner

OLHÃO
O Bote (€€)
Across the street from the market, this restaurant serves delicious grilled meat and fish. Small terrace but large indoor dining area.

✉ Avenida 5 de Outubro 122, 8700-304 Olhão ☎ 289 721 183 🕓 Lunch, dinner; closed Sun

SÃO BRÁS DE ALPORTEL
Churrasqueira Paraiso 'Luís dos Frangos' (€)
Mouth-watering barbecued chicken, chips, salad and local wine.

✉ Rua Dr José Dias Sancho 132, 8150-142 São Bras de Alportel ☎ 289 842 635 🕓 Lunch, dinner; closed Mon

Pousada de São Brás (€€)
Elegant restaurant in one of the *Pousada* hotels with beautiful views over wooded hills. Try the *caldeirada de borrego* (lamb stew).

✉ 8150-054 São Brás de Alportel ☎ 289 842 205 🕓 Lunch, dinner

TAVIRA
Beira Rio (€€)
By the old bridge, this riverside restaurant has a range of vegetarian dishes and is noted for its baked turkey. Book ahead in summer.

✉ Rua Borda d'Água da Asseca 46–52, 8800-325 Tavira ☎ 281 323 165 🕓 Dinner. Closed last three weeks in Nov

Churrasqueira O Cota (€)

Dine on the roof terrace for views over the rooftops of Tavira.
Specializes in charcoal-grilled meats.

✉ Rua João Vaz Corte Real 38, 8800-351 Tavira ☎ 281 324 873 🕐 Lunch,
dinner; Jul–Aug closed Sat lunch, Sep–Jun closed Sun dinner

O Pátio (€€)

Try lobster or tiger prawns flambé, or sample something more
modestly priced, such as clams *cataplana*, couscous or fish kebab.

✉ Rua António Cabreira 30, 8800-344 Tavira ☎ 281 323 008 🕐 Lunch,
dinner; closed Sun

VILA REAL DE SANTO ANTÓNIO

Caves do Guadiana (€€)

In a lovely spot on the banks of the Guadiana River, this restaurant
specializes in Portuguese-style seafood and spicy African-style cod.

✉ Avenida da República 89, 8900-203 Vila Real de Santo António ☎ 281
544 498 🕐 Lunch, dinner; closed Thu dinner

O Coracão de Cidade (€–€€)

The vast menu caters for the tastes of many nationalities, from
English sandwiches to Spanish *tapas* by way of Andalucian
gazpacho and squid *Sevilhana*, plus pizzas and chicken *piri-piri*.

✉ Rua Dr Teófilo Braga 19/21, 8900-303 Vila Real de Santo António ☎ 281
543 303 🕐 Lunch, dinner

SHOPPING

ARTESANATO

Azulejo Azul

Good range of traditional *azulejos* and other Portuguese ceramics.

✉ Rua 1º Maio 11 r/c, 8800-360 Tavira 🕐 Mon–Fri 9–12:30, 3–7, Sat
9–12:30. Also open through lunch and on Sun Jul–Aug

Bazar Tânger

Lots of choice of souvenirs – a browser's dream.

✉ Rua Jose P Padinha 34, 8800-354 Tavira ☎ 281 323 207 🕐 Mon–Sat
10–1, 3–7

Sight Locator Index

This index relates to the maps on the covers. We have given map references to the main sights of interest in the book. Grid references in italics indicate sights featured on the town plans. Some sights within towns may not be plotted on the maps.

Index

Acknowledgements

The Automobile Association would like to thank the following photographers, companies and picture libraries for their assistance in the preparation of this book.

Abbreviations for the picture credits are as follows: - (t) top; (b) bottom; (l) left; (r) right; (AA) AA World Travel Library.

4l Praia de Rocha, AA/M Birkitt; **4c** Loule, AA/M Chaplow; **4r** Estoi, AA/M Birkitt; **5l** Algar Seco, AA/M Chaplow; **5c** Olhao market, AA/C Jones; **6/7** Praia de Rocha, AA/M Birkitt; **8/9** Farmers at work, AA/J Edmanson; **10l** Ponta da Piedade boat trip, AA/C Jones; **10r** Café, Praia Dona Ana, AA/C Jones; **10/1** Luz, AA/M Chaplow; **11** Serra de Monchique, AA/J Edmanson; **12l** Ameijoas na cataplana, AA/M Chaplow; **12r** Loule market, AA/C Jones; **12/3** Orange groves, Serra da Monchique, AA/M Chaplow; **13** Cheeses at market, AA/J Edmanson; **14t** Loule market, AA/C Jones; **14b** Cataplana dish in restaurant, Lagos, AA/C Jones; **15t** Vineyard, Lagao, AA/M Chaplow; **15c** Lagoa wine Co-operative, AA/C Jones; **15b** Port, Alvor, AA/C Jones; **16/7** Silves, AA/J Edmanson; **17t** Grilling sardines, Portimao, AA/M Birkitt; **17b** Cape St Vincent, AA/C Jones; **18** Valamoura golf course, AA/C Jones; **18/9t** Faro Marina, AA/C Jones; **18/9b** Praia de Rocha, AA/J Edmanson; **20/1** Loule, AA/M Chaplow; **25** Fado singers, AA/M Chaplow; **26/7** Ilha da Tavira ferry, AA/C Jones; **31** Caldas de Monchique, AA/J Edmanson; **32** Policeman, AA/M Chaplow; **34/5** Estoi, AA/M Birkitt; **36** Algar Seco coast, AA/C Jones; **36/7** Algar Seco rock formation, AA/C Jones; **38/9** Fonte Grande Springs, Alte, AA/M Chaplow; **39** Alte, AA/M Chaplow; **40/1t** Cabo de Sao Vicente, AA/M Chaplow; **40/1b** Cabo de Sao Vicente, AA/A Mockford & N Bonetti; **41** Cabo de Sao Vicente, market, AA/M Chaplow; **42** Caldas de Monchique, AA/A Kouprianoff; **42/3** Caldas de Monchique, AA/J Edmanson; **44** Capela dos Ossos, Faro, AA/A Kouprianoff; **44/5** Capela dos Ossos, Faro, AA/M Birkitt; **45** Capela dos Ossos, AA/A Kouprianoff; **46/7** Silves, AA/J Edmanson; **47** Castle, Silves, AA/M Birkitt; **48** Estoi, AA/M Birkitt; **48/9** Palacio de Estoi, AA/M Chaplow; **49** tilework, Palacio de Estoi, AA/M Chaplow; **50t** Milreu, AA/M Chaplow; **50c** Milreu, AA/M Birkitt; **51** mosaic detail Milreu, AA/M Birkitt; **52** Parque Natural da Ria Formosa, AA/M Chaplow; **52/3** Parque Natural da Ria Formosa, AA/M Chaplow; **53** symbol, Parque Natural da Ria Formosa, AA/A Mockford & N Bonetti; **54/5** Ponta de Piedade, AA/M Chaplow; **56/7** Carvoeiero, Algar Seco, AA/M Chaplow; **59** Albufeira, AA/A Kouprianoff; **60/1** Real Spa Thalasso at Grande Real Santa Eulália; **62** Monchique, AA/M Chaplow; **65** pottery, AA/J Edmanson; **66/7** Fishing, Praia de Faro, AA/C Jones; **68/9** Praia da Marinha AA/C Jones; **70/1** view from Mount Foia, AA/M Chaplow; **72** Aljezur, AA/M Chaplow; **72/3** Sagres, AA/Kouprianoff; **74/5** Zoomarine, AA/C Jones; **77** Ocean Golf Course, Vale do Lobo, AA/C Jones; **78** Hotel Oriental, Praia da Rocha, AA/C Jones; **80/1** Olhao market, AA/C Jones; **83** Praia do Dona Ana, AA/A Mockford & N Bonetti; **84/5** Forte Ponta da Bandaira, AA/J Edmanson; **85** Praca Gil Eanes, AA/C Jones; **86c** San Antonio, Lagos, AA/A Mockford & N Bonetti; **86/7** San Antonio, Lagos, AA/A Kouprianoff; **87** San Antonio, Lagos, AA/A Kouprianoff; **88/9** walkers, Luz, AA/ M Chaplow; **90/1** Burgau, AA/J Edmanson; **92** Luz AA/A Mockford & N Bonetti; **93** Gardens and Fortaleza, Luz, AA/A Mockford & N Bonetti; **94t** Sagres, AA/C Jones; **94b** Sagres, AA/J Edmanson; **95** Cabo Sao Vicente, AA/A Mockford & N Bonetti; **96/7** Salema AA/J Edmanson; **105** Silves, AA/M Chaplow; Silves, AA/M Birkitt; **106/7** sculpture, Silves AA/A Mockford & N Bonetti; **106** Statue, Silves, AA/M Birkitt; **108** Municipal Archaeology Museum, Silves, AA/M Chaplow; **109** Se de Santa Maria, AA/M Chaplow; **110/1** Alvor beach, AA/J Edmanson; **111** church, Alvor, AA/C Jones; **112** Armacao de Pera, AA/C Jones; **113** Carvoeiro, AA/C Jones; **114/5** Ferragudo, AA/M Chaplow; **115** Ferragudo, AA/M Chaplow; **116** Lagoa, Sao Jose Monastery, AA/M Chaplow; **116/7** Igreja Matriz, Lagoa, AA/M Chaplow; **117l** Lagoa, wine, AA/C Jones; **117r** Lagoa wine Co-operative, AA/C Jones; **118/9** Calda de Monchique, AA/M Chaplow; **118** Monchique, Igreja Matriz, AA/A Kouprianoff; **120/1** Calda de Monchique, AA/M Chaplow; **122** Road trip nr. Portimao, AA/C Jones; **122/3** fort across River Arade viewed from Portimao, AA/C Jones; **123** Portimao, boat, AA/C Jones; **124/5** Praia da Rocha, AA/ M Birkitt; **126/7** Serra de Monchique, AA/M Birkitt; **127** Caldas de Monchique, AA/A Kouprianoff; **128** Serra da Monchique, AA/M Chaplow; **128/9** Vila Senhora da Rocha, AA/M Chaplow; **137** Praia de Faro beach, AA/C Jones; **138/9** harbour, Faro, AA/A Kouprianoff; **139** Faro, AA/M Chaplow; **140** Archaeological Museum, Faro, AA/M Chaplow; **140/1** Archaeological Museum, Faro, AA/M Chaplow; **142** Cathedral, Faro, AA/J Edmanson; **142/3** Albufeira, AA/M Birkitt; **144** San Lourenco, Almancil, AA/J Edmanson; **145** San Lourenco, Almancil, AA/C Jones; **146/7** The Barrocal, AA/M Chaplow; **147** The Barrocal, AA/M Chaplow; **148** Loule, AA/C Jones; **148/9** Loule's Museum Municipal, AA/M Chaplow; **149** Largo, Gago Coutinho, Loule, AA/C Jones; **150/1** Paderne AA/M Chaplow; **152/3** Quarteira, AA/J Edmanson; **153** Quarteira, AA/C Jones; **154/5** Salir, AA/M Chaplow; **154** Salir castle, AA/M Chaplow; **156/7b** Cerro de Vila Museum, Vilamoura, AA/C Jones; **156/7t** Vilamoura, AA/J Edmanson; **158** Loule, Igreja de Nossa Senhora da Piedade, AA/M Chaplow; **158/9** The Barrocal, AA/M Chaplow; **165** Ilha da Tavira, AA/C Jones; **166/7** Tavira, AA/M Chaplow; **167**, Ilha da Tavira, AA/C Jones; **168/9** Ilha da Tavira, AA/C Jones; **170/1** View from Alcoutim to Sanlucar, AA/M Chaplow; **172/3** Castro Marim, AA/M Chaplow; **172** Castro Marim, AA/M Chaplow; **174** Tavira, AA/A Kouprianoff; **174/5** Parque Mineiro, AA/M Chaplow; **176** Parque Mineiro, AA/M Chaplow; **177** Luz da Tavira, AA/M Chaplow; **178** Moncarapacho, AA/M Chaplow; **178/9** Monte Gordo, AA/J Edmanson; **180** Olhao, AA/J Edmanson; **180/1** Sao Bras de Alportel, AA/C Jones; **182** Vila Real de Santo Antonio, AA/M Birkitt

Every effort has been made to trace the copyright holders, and we apologise in advance for any accidental errors. We would be happy to apply the corrections in the following edition of this publication.

Dear Reader

Your comments, opinions and recommendations are very important to us. Please help us to improve our travel guides by taking a few minutes to complete this simple questionnaire.

You do not need a stamp (unless posted outside the UK). If you do not want to cut this page from your guide, then photocopy it or write your answers on a plain sheet of paper.

> *Send to:* **The Editor, AA World Travel Guides,**
> **FREEPOST SCE 4598, Basingstoke RG21 4GY.**

Your recommendations...

We always encourage readers' recommendations for restaurants, nightlife or shopping – if your recommendation is used in the next edition of the guide, we will send you a **FREE AA Guide** of your choice from this series. Please state below the establishment name, location and your reasons for recommending it.

_____
_____
_____
_____
_____

Please send me **AA Guide** _____

About this guide...

Which title did you buy?

   AA _____

Where did you buy it? _____

When? m m / y y

Why did you choose this guide? _____

_____
_____
_____
_____

Did this guide meet your expectations?

Exceeded ☐   Met all ☐   Met most ☐   Fell below ☐

Were there any aspects of this guide that you particularly liked? _____

_____
_____
_____

continued on next page...

Is there anything we could have done better? _____

_____

_____

_____

About you...
Name (*Mr/Mrs/Ms*) _____

Address _____

_____ Postcode _____

Daytime tel nos _____

Email _____

Please only give us your mobile phone number or email if you wish to hear from us about
other products and services from the AA and partners by text or mms, or email.

Which age group are you in?
Under 25 ☐   25–34 ☐   35–44 ☐   45–54 ☐   55–64 ☐   65+ ☐

How many trips do you make a year?
Less than one ☐   One ☐   Two ☐   Three or more ☐

Are you an AA member? Yes ☐   No ☐

About your trip...
When did you book? m m / y y   When did you travel? m m / y y

How long did you stay? _____

Was it for business or leisure? _____

Did you buy any other travel guides for your trip? _____

If yes, which ones? _____

_____

_____

Thank you for taking the time to complete this questionnaire. Please send it to us as soon as
possible, and remember, you do not need a stamp (*unless posted outside the UK*).

AA Travel Insurance call 0800 072 4168 or visit www.theAA.com

---